99p

CW00350438

ANGLER'S DIRECTORY

ANGLER'S DIRECTORY

Brian Morland

TREASURE PRESS

Foreword

The aim of this book is to give details of a wide selection of day ticket and free fishing available throughout Great Britain and Northern Ireland and to provide enough information about those fisheries to enable a visiting angler to obtain easy access to each and, hopefully, catch some fish. Where facilities for disabled anglers exist, this has also been stated. Some water authority areas, notably the Severn Trent and Anglian, contain more entries than other areas. This is partly because the area they cover is greater and also because more day ticket water is available in some regions. It will also be noticed that there is more stillwater fishing than river fishing. Many of the river fisheries are too short and fragmented to include in this directory. Also, it is a sad fact that some clubs which do issue day tickets for a stretch of river do not want the fact advertised for fear of greatly increased numbers of visiting anglers. The rivers that are included, however, are major waterways with good fishing that is easily accessible. The number of entries for each region roughly mirrors the amount of public fishing in that region. Hopefully there will be some waters in this book to suit all tastes.

Acknowledgements

Photographs
Angling Photo Service i, ii (bottom), iii, iv (bottom), v, vi,
viii, x, xi; Biofotos vii; Brian Morland xii; Nature
Photographers Ltd iv (top), ix; Arthur Oglesby ii (top).

Maps and line drawings by Brin Edwards/Format Publishing Services

First published in Great Britain in 1985 by
The Hamlyn Publishing Group Ltd

This edition published in 1989 by
Treasure Press
Michelin House
81 Fulham Road
London SW3 6RB

Reprinted 1990

ISBN 1 85051 464 X

Printed in Portugal

Contents

Introduction   6
Rivers and canals   9
Stillwaters   16
Stillwater trout fisheries   21
Water authority regions   25
Scotland   27
North West Water Authority   45
Northumbrian Water Authority   58
Yorkshire Water Authority   66
Welsh Water Authority   86
Severn Trent Water Authority   98
Anglian Water Authority   122
Thames Water Authority   148
South West Water Authority   172
Wessex Water Authority   187
Southern Water Authority   195
Northern Ireland   204
Useful information   220
Index   222

Introduction

Most anglers are familiar with their own local waters. Indeed, some anglers will fish just one particular venue for a full season or even longer. And, if you want to be successful, it does pay to concentrate on one water. In this way you can learn a great deal about the fish which inhabit the water and under what conditions it yields the best results.

It is refreshing to have a change of venue occasionally, however, and perhaps even a complete change in the method of fishing. (Many coarse fishermen have tentatively tried fly fishing for trout during the coarse fishing close season and become 'addicted' to that branch of the sport.) Anglers visiting different parts of the country, whether on holiday or working away from home, often take their rods with them in the hope that they can try different venues – although finding the ideal spot to fish under these conditions has been up to now a rather hit-and-miss affair. Likewise, an angler might read about a good catch of fish in the angling press and would like more information to enable him or her to fish the venue at which the catch was made.

The *Angler's Directory* will help solve these problems, for it describes over 400 venues – rivers, canals, lakes, gravel-pits, reservoirs and lochs – where the angler can find good sport. The directory is not intended to be a comprehensive list of fisheries, but is a guide to some of the best fishing readily available in each water authority area. The fisheries have been listed under the appropriate water authority, so only one rod licence is needed for the waters in that section. Information is included which will give the angler an insight into the physical features of the site, the type of fishing, the seasons operated on the water and how to obtain permits. Methods and baits used successfully by local anglers are also listed. Addresses and telephone numbers of the individuals or organisations who administer the fishing on the waters are provided, too. Directions to each fishery are, where possible, given from the nearest large town or village. Sometimes the fishing is described as being available on either the left-hand or the right-hand bank. In all cases, these refer to the banks as they would appear to an angler who is facing *downstream*.

Follow some simple commonsense rules when making enquiries about fishing. Always contact fishing tackle shops or estate offices during working hours. You will get no help from a fishing tackle dealer if you telephone him the minute he puts his feet up in the evening after a hard day's work. Likewise, do not go knocking on the bailiff's door for a permit at half-past five in the morning! If you want an early start obtain your ticket in advance. If you send away for a permit, or just for information about a fishery, always enclose a SAE. Anglers who make polite enquiries to fisheries and landowners will usually find people more than helpful.

The biggest problem when compiling any angling directory is the inevitable time lapse between collecting the information and final publication. Waters can change hands, day ticket facilities can cease and local rules can change. For this reason, waters included in the *Angler's Directory* are those which are unlikely to change. It would, however, be prudent to make a short telephone call to check on the fishing beforehand.

Waters that are listed as free in England, Wales or Northern Ireland are those which do not require a permit. You will definitely still need a local water authority rod licence, however. A separate rod licence is needed for each water authority region. These can be obtained from most tackle shops or direct from the water authorities in question. Weekly rod licences are available for short-stay visitors. A full rod licence costs only a few pounds, however, and lasts for 12 months. No rod licence is needed in Scotland. The addresses of all the water authorities are listed in the book on page 220.

Fish handling and bankside etiquette

Coarse anglers return their catches to the water and it is essential, therefore, that care is taken to ensure that the fish are returned in good condition. Knotless keepnets and landing nets have assisted greatly in preventing scale loss and split fins occurring to fish that are retained in a net. Fish placed in a large, micromesh, knotless keepnet should not suffer any damage providing a few simple rules are followed. The net should be staked out fully, so that it does not fold up. In slack currents a bank stick can be inserted through the tag at the bottom of the net to support it and prevent collapse. The mouth of the net should be wide, and positioned as close to the water as possible. If the mouth of the net is several feet above the surface, the fish will lose scales as they slide down the mesh.

At the end of the day, simply lower the mouth of the net into the water and, lifting the bottom of the net, allow the fish to swim away. Large fish, such as carp, tench and barbel should not really be placed in nets with small fish, such as roach or dace. In fact, neither carp nor barbel should be retained in keepnets, and you will find that many fisheries insist that these two species are returned immediately. Very small fish should not be kept in keepnets, either, unless you are fishing in a competition. Tipping fish out of the net on to mud or gravel to take a photograph also damages them. If you want to take a picture of the fish, spread a large polythene sheet on the ground and set up all the camera equipment before placing the fish on the polythene.

Fish should be handled as little as possible, since scale loss can lead to fungal infections. The fact that a fish swims away when released is no guarantee that it is going to survive. Roach and bream are probably the fish most susceptible to damage by keepnets.

Barbless hooks have helped prevent damage to fish, and many anglers now use them for all their fishing. If you have to use a disgorger to remove a hook, use one of the slim varieties with a conical end on small fish. For the larger species of fish a pair of artery forceps is the ideal tool for removing the hook.

Any fish that are to be taken for eating should be killed quickly and cleanly with a blow from a heavy priest. In fact, every trout angler should own a priest, and some trout fisheries insist on this in their rules.

Unfortunately, there are some anglers who, like any cross-section of the public, leave litter. Also unfortunately, the waters where litter is the biggest problem are either free waters or those open to day ticket visitors. Some fisheries are actually closed to visitors because of the amount of litter left on the banks by thoughtless people. Litter of any description is unsightly, and some is extremely dangerous to wildlife; discarded fishing tackle is positively lethal to wild birds. There is no excuse for leaving anything on the river bank; even cigarette ends and matches should be taken home in your tackle box. All that an angler should leave behind at the end of the day is a pair of boot prints in the mud at the water's edge. Indeed, the country code should be observed in all respects, and anglers should guard against fire risk; close all gates; keep to footpaths were possible; not damage hedges, fences or walls; and leave livestock, crops and machinery alone.

Rivers and canals

Despite massive clean-up programmes, like those carried out on the Thames and Trent, it is a sad fact that the standard of fishing is declining generally on most of the rivers in mainland Britain. The causes of this decline are many and complex, but ultimately are the result of the pressures of 20th century living. For instance, farming practices have become so intensive, and the use of nitrogen-based fertilizers has increased to such an extent, that they are even causing problems with drinking water as well as to the ecology of rivers.

Land drainage is another very important factor affecting some rivers. Even the moors, where many rivers have their source, have been intensively drained. The result here is that rain water is channelled into the headwaters of a river almost immediately, instead of slowly permeating through the peat and sphagnum beds. (The peat and sphagnum beds act like an enormous sponge and, during wet weather, soak up the water and release it gradually.) Thus the rivers now react very quickly to downpours, even in summer, and can rise and fall rapidly even during very localised rainfall.

Another effect of upland drainage is that in dry weather the rivers soon start to lose their flow. Some areas are affected more than others by this; Yorkshire is one of the most seriously affected regions. Another damaging aspect of water management is the practice of some water authorities of removing bankside vegetation, such as trees and willow bushes. The argument for doing this is that the vegetation restricts the flow of the water and encourages flooding. In effect, removing riverside bushes increases the flow and causes a great deal of bank erosion. To prevent this many banks are mechanically straightened and artificially raised to stop floodwater spilling over on to adjoining farmland. The result, where this work has been carried out, is disastrous to wildlife dependent on the river. Even rabbits and voles have their holes poisoned as, according to the engineers, they pose erosion problems.

Another problem to fisheries is the increasing amount of boat traffic on rivers. Parts of the Norfolk Broads have been virtually destroyed by boats, and the fishing in these rivers is now very poor compared with what is was thirty years ago. The continual wash from the boats causes bankside erosion and discolours the water. With the water permanently coloured, weed growth disappears and with it fish, spawning sites and rich food sources. Add to all this the other problems, such as acid rain, the salt-polluted run-off water from motorways, inefficient sewage works and accidental chemical spillages, and the problems facing river fisheries soon become apparent.

Despite all the problems, there is still some good river fishing to be enjoyed. For instance, the River Trent is fishing tremendously well at the moment, both for chub and for barbel. It wasn't too many years ago when you could smell this river as you approached it! The lower reaches of the River Thames have also been cleaned up, and salmon introduced as fry are now able to swim up through the estuary and have been caught in the lower weir pools, such as at Teddington. The middle reaches of the Thames are also fishing well, despite the problems caused by the heavy boat traffic in summer.

The Hampshire Avon and the Dorset Stour are two rivers that have also had their problems in recent years, but they are still the best rivers to fish if you want to catch a double figure barbel. Generally, the fishing in rivers is not as reliable as it is in stillwaters, but if you pick your venue carefully and the conditions are right you can enjoy some good sport.

Fishing the upper reaches of a river

The fishing on the upper reaches of most rivers is usually for trout and grayling. Here the water is fast flowing and interspersed with deeper pools. In spate rivers, the bed is usually boulder strewn, with uneven rocky banks. One of the great attractions of fishing the upper reaches of a river is the scenery. The river banks are in a natural state, usually with plenty of bushes and trees, and there is very little evidence of bankside drainage work. Much of the fishing on the upper reaches of rivers is in private hands, and the number of anglers is restricted to prevent overdue pressure. On some rivers there are good opportunities for visitors to fish, however, especially those in Wales and the upper reaches of the Severn and its tributaries.

On most of these fisheries the fishing is restricted to fly, at least until the end of the trout season, and then bait fishing may be allowed to catch grayling right through the winter. Wild brown trout are rare these days, and most of the trout caught by anglers have started life in a hatchery. To catch real wild trout you must travel to some of the more remote areas of the British Isles where the fishing pressure is not so great.

Fly tackle used on the upper reaches of a river should be fairly light, as the trout caught are unlikely to run to a great size. A size 5 floating line and a matching rod about $8\frac{1}{2}$ ft (2.6 m) long will enable you to fish most upland rivers for trout and grayling. There is no need to use a sinking line as the water is seldom deeper than 6 ft (1.8 m), and you can fish wet flies at all depths by degreasing the leader with fuller's earth.

During March and early April, when the trout season opens, the best way to catch trout is with a team of two or three standard wet flies cast across the stream and allowed to pull round with the current. Don't always assume that, because the water is cold, the trout will be in the deeper pools. Some of the best swims to try are the fast, broken stickles that run into the head of a pool. (Stickles are the places where water running over shallows is broken into ripples.) Leaded flies are worth trying, such as Walker's Leaded Shrimp and a Pheasant Tail Nymph, with a little lead added. Spider patterns, such as Waterhen Bloa, Snipe and Purple, and Partridge and Orange will nearly always catch fish, and other wet patterns worth trying are Red Tag, Zulu and Butcher. As the water warms up, then dry fly fishing can be good, especially when casting with Small Olives. I have seldom found trout to be very fussy over the type of dry fly presented on an upland river. The size of the fly is usually more important than the pattern, and should be one with good hackles that floats well on the water.

The grayling, if they are present, will often take the same flies as those used for trout. Good grayling patterns are White Witch, Sturdy's Fancy, Green Insect and Grey Duster. The best combination for a grayling fly seems to be a peacock hurl body and a white or pale blue hackle. Grayling can be difficult to catch in clear water, and you may have to resort to a 2 lb (0.9 kg) breaking strain point and a very sparsely hackled fly to catch them. Grayling which repeatedly 'boil' and rise at a dry fly without actually taking it are termed 'coming short'. In gin-clear water conditions, if your tackle is not presented correctly or is too heavy, grayling will do this repeatedly, and it can be infuriating.

Bait fishing for grayling with light float tackle during the autumn and winter can be good fun. Using a 12–13 ft (3.6–3.9 m) float rod, the grayling put up quite a struggle, especially in fast water. A grayling's fight is unique, and the fish feels like a cross between a trout and an eel. A centre-pin reel is far better for grayling fishing than a fixed-spool reel, and a line strength of 3 lb (1.4 kg) breaking strain to a hook length of 1½ lb (0.7 kg) breaking strain will handle most grayling. Maggots and redworms are the two best grayling baits. During very low water temperatures, redworms are the best bait, as maggots tend to stiffen and elongate in very cold water. The best type of worm is the gilt tail, which can be found under damp sacking or around the edge of a compost heap.

On some rivers, such as the River Severn, dace and chub can also be caught right into the upper reaches, and the same tackle used for grayling will take these fish.

Fishing the middle reaches of a river

The middle reaches of a river are very often the most productive part of the system. The water is still fast flowing, at least in parts, but the volume of the river has increased greatly, with a number of tributaries joining the main river. The number of species has also increased dramatically, although trout and grayling may still be present.

The middle reaches of a river can vary greatly in character within a very short distance. Long, shallow glides will funnel into slow-flowing, deep sections lined by willows; the nature of the river bed can change suddenly from fine gravel or sand to hard clay and mud. The features of a spate river can vary from year to year, especially during wet or snowy winters when the river carries a lot of floodwater. Whole gravel-beds can move position, or trees can become undermined and fall into the water creating new swims. Many rivers have much weed growing in the middle reaches, and these weed beds are an additional fish-holding feature.

One of the most widespread fish is the chub and, on the middle reaches of most rivers, they are the predominant species. Chub are the most obliging of

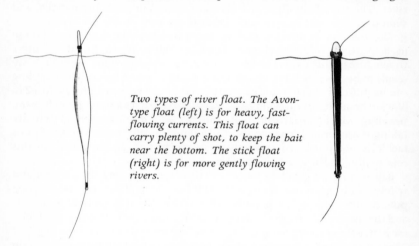

Two types of river float. The Avon-type float (left) is for heavy, fast-flowing currents. This float can carry plenty of shot, to keep the bait near the bottom. The stick float (right) is for more gently flowing rivers.

fish, as they can be caught right through the winter (unlike barbel) and can be taken by just about every method. In the deeper glides many anglers prefer to float fish for chub, using a stick float and small baits, such as maggots or casters. This is certainly a good way of catching a large number of chub, but will not lure the bigger fish. Casters are an excellent bait for chub, and loose feeding 'little and often' with casters can have the fish queuing up to take your bait.

Legered casters is also a good way of catching chub, especially during the winter when they are not so keen to take a moving bait. On the middle reaches of the Severn and Trent, anglers use open-ended swimfeeders packed with casters to get the bait in the right place. These rivers are swift flowing and a lot of lead must be fastened to the feeder to hold bottom. Some anglers are using feeders the size of ice cream cornets! The feeder is fastened to the main reel line with a link and then packed with casters. The ends of the feeder are plugged with groundbait so that, when this disintegrates in the water, the casters are washed out around the hook. During the summer months this will catch a lot of barbel as well as chub on the middle Severn and middle Trent. On other rivers, such as the Yorkshire rivers, the Thames and the Great Ouse, the same tactics can be used but with smaller feeders, since the chub and barbel are not present in such prolific numbers.

A rod with a built-in quiver tip is best used in conjunction with a reel line of 4–6 lb (1.8–2.7 kg) breaking strain. The hook length will be finer, but don't make the mistake of fishing too light, especially where barbel are likely to be caught. On some swims on the middle Severn the tackle will have to be stronger to keep hooked fish away from snags.

During summer, cheese paste takes some beating as a chub bait but, during the colder months of the year, it tends to harden around the hook and you will miss a lot of bites. In winter bread crust is much more effective. When using bread crust, stop the leger weight only 1 in (2.5 cm) away from the hook. Crust is a buoyant bait and it needs to be anchored close to the bed of the river. An excellent bait for chub and barbel, but one which isn't often used these days, is lobworm. Big roach will often take a lobworm, especially when the river is coloured and running above normal level.

Coping with these conditions is not easy, but fish can be caught even when the river is thick brown and running several feet above normal level. Providing the river is within its banks and the water authority have not removed all the natural features, such as willow bushes, there are always

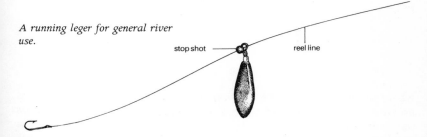

A running leger for general river use.

stop shot — reel line

slacks and backwaters where fish will congregate. 'Laying on' or legering are the best methods to use in these conditions. The two occasions when fishing a river is really a waste of time are when the river is rising fast and carrying a lot of debris, such as dead leaves, in suspension, and also when there is a lot of snow broth in the river, after a sudden thaw.

Fishing the lower reaches of a river

By the time most rivers have flowed towards their lower reaches, they are fairly slow and deep. There are a few exceptions, however, the Hampshire

Avon being one of them. This river is more like a big chalk stream, being exceptionally rich and swift flowing. Barbel and chub are the predominant species in the Avon right down to Christchurch.

In most other rivers, however, bream and roach start to dominate catches in the lower reaches. As the flow slows down and river bed gravel is replaced by mud and clay, barbel are less frequently encountered, if at all. Bream are great rovers, and locating them can be a problem. They will also move about a river with the changing seasons. The bream in the River Welland, for instance, tend to congregate in large numbers below Crowland Bridge during the winter. If the water in the river is clear and the bream are feeding they can be located by looking for cloudy areas where a big shoal has been rooting in the mud. There are some areas in rivers, however, that are well-known bream 'hot spots' and the shoals may be present for several months at a time.

In slow-flowing rivers, such as the Welland and lower Severn, many anglers prefer to fish for bream with waggler floats. In wide, deep rivers

A waggler float locked in position with two shot. This rig is ideal for stillwaters and slow-flowing rivers.

where the bream are a long way off, then legering is the only feasible proposition. A light quiver tip rod and swimfeeder tackle are used, in conjunction with maggots, casters or worm hookbait. Breadflake is another excellent bait for bream. Once, anglers fishing for bream in the Norfolk rivers, such as the lower Yare, used nothing but breadpaste but this bait is seldom used today, although it is still effective. Waggler fishing with maggots or casters is the most enjoyable method of fishing for roach and dace in the lower reaches of rivers. Big roach are also taken on leger.

Pike are a much neglected species in lowland rivers, yet the potential is good. Some rivers are capable of producing pike over 20 lb (9.1 kg), and a few have produced the occasional 30 lb (13.6 kg) pike.

Tackle for river pike should be strong. A 10–11 ft (3–3.3 m) carp rod, in conjunction with a line of not less than 10 lb (4.5 kg) breaking strain should be used, especially where snags or strong currents are present. One of the

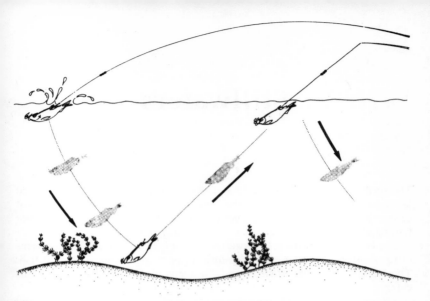

Retrieving a deadbait by the sink-and-draw method. This is an interesting and successful way to fish for pike.

most active and successful methods is to fish 'sink-and-draw' fashion with sprats or small coarse fish deadbaits. No weight is used, and the reel line is fastened directly on to the wire trace. Cast out and allow the bait to flutter down enticingly to the bottom.

Canals

Canals are not normally very prolific fisheries, although there are a few exceptions. The best canals to fish tend to be those where the boat traffic is light or has stopped altogether. Canals were designed for boat traffic and, although little freight is moved by barges along the canals these days, the number of pleasure craft using the canal networks across the country has increased greatly.

Much of the fishing in canals is for small specimens, and tackle must therefore be light. Tactics for float fishing are very similar to those used on stillwaters, but the tackle should be fine. Lines need be no more than 1½ lb (0.7 kg) breaking strain, and hook lengths can be scaled down to 12 oz (0.3 kg) breaking strain. Hooks need to be small, and sizes 18 to 20 will cover most needs. A very light, slim waggler float should be used. Never groundbait heavily on a canal; a few small balls of fine cloud groundbait with some loose hook samples is all that is needed.

In the more prolific canals where larger tench and carp are likely to be caught, the breaking strain should be increased to prevent breakages and standard stillwater tactics should be adopted.

Stillwaters

The term stillwater covers many fisheries, from large upland or lowland lakes and reservoirs to small tarns and ponds. Another very important category of stillwater is the gravel-pit; some of these are among the best fishing sites available, particularly when they have matured.

The large, high-altitude lakes and reservoirs are not usually rich in terms of natural food supplies, and therefore support only a few species of fish. The lakes of the Lake District and the lochs of Scotland come into this category.

The tactics used to fish these waters can be exactly the same as those used to fish gravel-pits, and are described in detail on the following pages. Lowland lakes often have a bed of soft mud or silt, and this can sometimes cause problems for the angler when trying to catch bottom-feeding fish such as tench, bream or carp. They are also generally shallower than upland lakes. If a bait is presented hard on the bottom it will often be obscured by the soft silt. When fishing over this type of lake bed, it is wise to set the float so that the bait is a few centimetres clear of the bottom. Fish feeding on a silty lake bed tend to disturb clouds of silt, and then swim about intercepting particles of food from among the suspended silt.

One advantage of a natural lake over a newly created gravel-pit is that fish holding areas, such as reed and rush beds, big submerged weed beds and other places, are easier to detect. Watercraft plays a more important part here in successfully locating feeding fish than it does on a large, featureless gravel-pit where fish location can sometimes only be achieved by trial and error.

Gravel-pits

Because large gravel-pits are so often rich in natural food, the fish are difficult to tempt with baits. The water is frequently very clear, so that tackle presentation has to be perfect or the fish will simply reject the bait. The water can also be very deep in places, even close to the bank, which makes float fishing more difficult. On really large pits, the bottom contours can be very irregular with gravel bars and steep shelves, so that presentation becomes a very hit and miss affair unless the depths are known.

For an angler to achieve the best results from a large gravel-pit, the water must be fished regularly over a period of time. Plumbing the depth in a swim is essential so that you know exactly by your float setting at what depth you are fishing. Make a note of the depth setting in a notebook for each area of a swim. This cuts out any guesswork and you can fish confidently, knowing exactly the depth at which your bait is being presented. There are times, especially in winter, when a slight adjustment of depth can mean the difference between plenty of fish and a blank day. I would say that finding the depths is one of the most important points when fishing a gravel-pit.

Fishing stillwaters

In depths greater than the depth of your rod, which is usually 12 to 13 ft (3.5 to 3.9 m) normal float fishing becomes impracticable. Legering or the use of a sliding float are the only ways of tackling the swim. At fairly close

plastic sleeve

Chemical lights which slip on to the top of the float have proved a boon to night fishermen.

range in deep water a swing tip is useless, however, as it will not function properly when the line enters the water at a steep angle, and a quiver tip must be used instead. Very few anglers use a sliding float; mainly, I believe, because they cannot master the technique. To hold the float at the required depth and stop it sliding back along the line, simply whip a stop knot on to the line at the required distance from the hook. A good idea is to use a different coloured nylon; this way you can see the stop knot easily. After casting out, allow the line to run through the bottom ring of the float and, after submerging the rod tip, tighten up so that the stop knot is hard against the float ring.

For roach fishing this is a far more sensitive method than legering. Another good use for a stop knot is when you are legering at long range in deep water. Groundbaiting and dropping your tackle back in the exact area

17

is nearly impossible unless you have some way of measuring your cast. Also, groundbaiting at long range in deep water by hand is very difficult to achieve accurately. Before fishing properly, tie a very big open-ended feeder on to the end of your line with no hook attached. Pack this with either groundbait, maggots or casters, and plug the ends with groundbait. Now take a good, hard look at the area you are intending to fish, and take a sighting line of an object in the distance, either a bush, tree or other fixed landmark. Cast along this sight line to the required area and then place the rod in the rest and tighten up to the fishing position. This is where your tackle must end up every time, so take a length of different coloured nylon and whip a stop knot on to the reel line immediately in front of the reel. Pull it tight so that there is no danger of it slipping. Once this is done you have a marker for the distance you are fishing and a sight line for the direction. Give the rod a sharp strike to empty the feeder, and then you can cast along the sight line repeatedly emptying the feeder to put a carpet of groundbait exactly where you want it. Once you have introduced sufficient groundbait, you can remove the big feeder and replace it with a Drennen feederlink to take a few maggots, tie on a hook, and begin fishing directly over your carpet of groundbait.

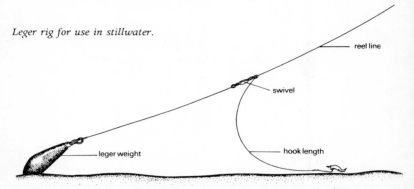

Leger rig for use in stillwater.

Most gravel-pits have a good firm bed, whether it is gravel or hard clay. This means that you can fish on the bottom without wondering if your bait is buried in soft mud. When roach fishing in winter use an antenna float, and set the depth so that the bait is just touching or just off the bottom, and shot the float so that just the tip is breaking surface. This way you have the most sensitive rig possible. The most universal float rig for a gravel-pit is a waggler or antenna float fixed through the bottom ring only and locked in position by a shot either side of the float ring. In really windy conditions, use a very long windbeater float and, in calm conditions, a slimbodied waggler. After casting out, place the rod at your side on two rests, angled so that the rod tip is submerged a few centimetres under the water. When you tighten up, this pulls the line under the surface.

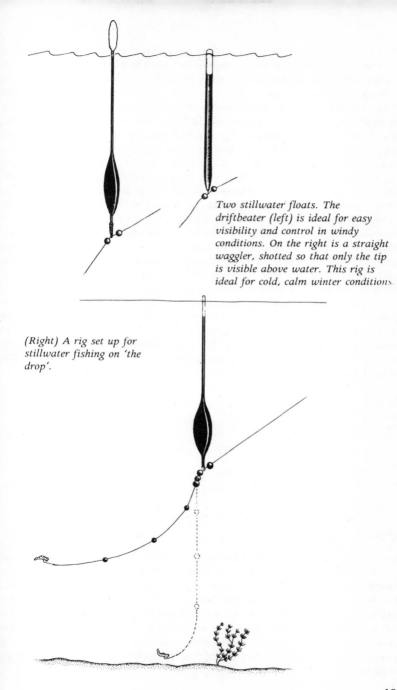

Two stillwater floats. The driftbeater (left) is ideal for easy visibility and control in windy conditions. On the right is a straight waggler, shotted so that only the tip is visible above water. This rig is ideal for cold, calm winter conditions.

(Right) A rig set up for stillwater fishing on 'the drop'.

19

A problem concerned with catching big fish is to present a bait in such a way that it avoids the attention of smaller fish. The choice of bait can often dictate what species you catch. A small bait is fine to use if the water you are fishing is not swarming with small roach or rudd. Generally large baits are better for big fish. Carp anglers have constantly developed new techniques in an effort to keep catching regularly fished for species. Carp learn fast, and a bait which catches fish consistently for a while begins to fail, and other baits have to be sought. Sweetcorn was, at one time, a superb carp bait but, where it has been used extensively, the carp have become wary. Some anglers have overcome this by dyeing the corn a different colour. Another method is to use a hair rig. This was devised after it was noticed that carp would pick up all the loose offerings lying on the bed of the lake, leaving only the bait attached to the hook. The hair rig is simply a short length of very fine nylon tied to the end of the hook. The grain, or grains of corn are threaded on to the fine nylon about 1 in (2.5 cm) away from the hook. When carp are sucking up all the loose samples of corn from the lake bed, they take the corn on the hair rig to be a 'free sample' and suck it into their mouths; the hook is then automatically pulled in with it.

Another problem found when carp sucked up loose particle baits such as sweetcorn was that the fish did not move very far after taking the bait. This meant that the fish either rejected the hookbait when they felt the tackle, or swallowed the hook before a bite was registered. Neither is very satisfactory for the angler. The only indication of this happening that the angler can detect is, at very best, a 'twitch' bite on the butt indicator. A

Specialist carp rigs. On the left is a bolt rig, and on the right a hair rig.

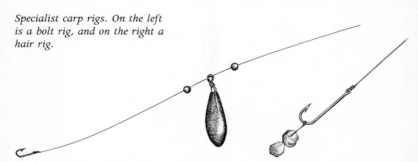

good bite is only indicated when the carp moves away with the bait. A bolt rig is now used by carp anglers to induce just this. A very heavy Arlesey bomb is locked in position close to the hook. As the carp sucks in the bait, the weight of the bomb pulls the hook into the carp's mouth and the fish bolts away. If you have to wait several hours for a bite, then this rig is the answer because the fish virtually hook themselves and run line off the open spool. The bolt rig is very useful for big fish on gravel-pits where long periods between bites are to be expected. It works for tench and bream, as well as carp.

Stillwater trout fisheries

During the last decade there has been a great increase in the demand for stillwater fly fishing. This demand was first met by the opening up of supply reservoirs for trout fishing, and then continued with the creation of literally hundreds of smaller stillwaters.

These smaller trout waters are some of the only true commercial fisheries in the country, where the owners actually earn their livelihood by selling sport. The standard of sport can vary widely, from poor to excellent. In between these two extremes there are some fine fisheries available to trout anglers. The cost of the fishing can vary, but generally the fishing on reservoirs is cheaper than on a small commercial fishery. This is partly because the catch rate is lower and partly because the water authorities do not have to make a profit. Small stillwaters with a high average catch rate of

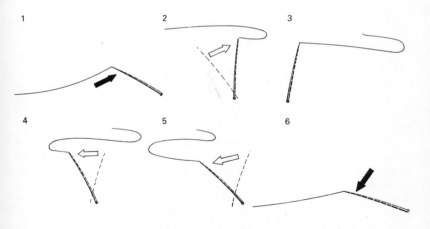

Fly casting technique. 1 – steadily lift the rod. 2 – at the 10 o'clock position pull the rod back to vertical position in a continuous action. 3 – wait while line straightens out behind you. 4 – power rod forward to 10 o'clock position. 5 – without pausing, let the rod drift down as the line alights on the water. 6 – final position of rod after cast is complete.

big rainbow trout can be fairly expensive but, generally, you get what you pay for and the more expensive the permit, the better the average size of the trout.

Small stillwater trout fisheries

Small is relative, but for the sake of this description, I class any stillwater under 20 acres (8 ha) as small. Most of these small trout fisheries are man-made (either gravel-pits, clay-pits or waters formed by damming a small stream in a shallow valley). The majority have been created with the sole purpose of running a trout fishery and do not contain many, if any, coarse fish. Another feature of these small trout fisheries is that most of them have good facilities, such as a surfaced car park, proper toilets (as opposed to buckets) and a fishing hut or club house. The number of anglers fishing on any one day is restricted, so that there is no overcrowding. The catch rate is carefully monitored to try and ensure that sport is constant throughout the season. Some of these small fisheries have been developed even further and have a small tackle shop and restaurant on site.

The tackle I would recommend for fishing a small trout fishery is an A.F.T.M. 6 to 7 rated carbon rod of around 10 ft (3 m) and two lines. One would be a size 6 double tapered floating line and the other a size 7 slow-sinking line. This combination will cover just about every eventuality. If the fishery stocks fish over 5 lb (2.2 kg) make sure there is plenty of backing available behind the fly line. Try to vary your style of casting and retrieving, as well as varying your lure. Great sport can be enjoyed fishing a small nymph or a buzzer on a floating line and a long leader. Retrieve very slowly and watch for a sign of the line twitching forward.

In a slight sideways ripple you can even let the surface drift do the retrieving for you. Simply retrieve line, figure-of-eight fashion, to keep in contact with the fly. Dry fly is also highly successful on small fisheries. Cast out a dry fly and leave it on the surface to just drift with the ripple. When you get a take to a dry fly, don't snatch, simply tighten up on the fish. To be effective, dry flies need to be really buoyant. Soak the fly thoroughly in Permafloat and make sure the hackles are really stiff. The only time I recommend fishing really fast is when the trout are chasing fry. Then a lure stripped back, just under the surface, can be really effective. It is very exciting when you see a big bow-wave 'lock on' to your fly. I recommend a slow-sinking line because it allows you to fish a lure on 'the drop'. It is surprising the number of takes you get as you are waiting for the line to sink down through the water. In a small water a fast-sinking line will simply drag the lure through the debris on the bed of the lake. If you retrieve faster to avoid this happening you will get fewer takes.

The most difficult period on a small stillwater is during July and August, especially if the weather is very hot and windless. Trout are a cold-water species and, as the water temperature approaches 70°F/21°C, they stop feeding properly. This is when fishing fast is virtually a waste of time. In really hot weather the trout are more interested in staying alive than feeding, especially if the water is not very deep. Some shallow lakes will lose trout through de-oxygenation in hot summers. In really adverse summer conditions find the deepest water and fish a buoyant lure (such as a Muddler) on a slow-sinking line. Give the line several minutes to sink down and take the fly with it. The line will eventually settle on the bed of the lake but the fly will be suspended above it because of its inbuilt buoyancy. This will prevent the fly becoming covered in debris, and will also make it more visible to the trout. Fish the fly back very slowly so that it just inches along the bottom. This will often produce fish, whereas anglers still stripping in lures mechanically will draw a blank. Trout will often pick up a static lure from the bed of the lake in hot weather. In hot, sunny or humid conditions in mid-summer, the trout in a small fishery are always going to be difficult, no matter how many new stock fish the owner has introduced to liven things up.

On some small stillwaters the water is very clear, so you have the opportunity to stalk and cast at individual fish. On some waters that stock big fish it has become standard practice to stalk specimen fish. Using polarised sunglasses you can find the fish you want to catch and then creep quietly into a casting position. Choose a leaded nymph and cast in front of the fish, using a floating line. Cast so that as the leaded nymph sinks it drops in front of the trout's nose. A deft upward lift of the rod should induce the trout to grab the nymph as it moves in front of it. This is exciting fishing if you can cast accurately and can see into the water.

One final point when fishing for trout; never leave your catch in the sun, especially wrapped in a polythene bag. I have seen lovely fish nearly turn to liquid after being left in the sun in a plastic bag for several hours. Even left in the shade on the bank your fish are likely to get fly blown. Treat yourself to a proper bass bag or, better still, a cooler box. This way your catch will still be edible when you get home.

Reservoir trout fishing

Much of the advice I have given for small stillwaters will hold good on reservoirs during the summer months. The obvious difference between small stillwaters and reservoirs is size, and the fly tackle needs to be stepped up accordingly. The rod needs to be able to cast out a number 8 line, or even a number 9, into a fresh breeze. Reservoirs can be quite choppy in even a moderate breeze, and distance casting is far more important than it is in small waters. A shooting head will also help you to cast further from the bank.

Lure fishing is more effective in a reservoir than in a small lake, and the trout are more ready to chase a lure stripped in quickly. The trout in a reservoir are seldom, if ever, spread around evenly and very often large concentrations of rainbow trout will shoal together in one area to feed. On a really large water locating the fish can be a problem, especially if the fish are feeding well down in the water and there is no visible sign of movement on the surface. Fish concentrating in small areas like this can sometimes lead to a lack of manners from anglers. There are some people, it seems, who just wait for an angler to start catching fish and then move in and begin casting over his shoulder. It can be quite dangerous when a group of anglers fishing alongside each other start casting out lures on heavy fly lines, especially in windy conditions. Hooks can get stuck in heads, ears or, even worse, eyes. (In fact, it is a very wise precaution to always wear polarised sunglasses when fly fishing.)

Trout are most difficult to locate when they are feeding at mid-water. To locate the exact depth at which they are feeding allow a slow-sinking line to sink for a count of ten, and then retrieve. Try this several times, using different rates of retrieve. If no takes are forthcoming, then try again, only this time allow the lure to sink for a count of 20. Repeat this, allowing the line to sink deeper every time until you are fishing along the bottom. If you still get no takes, try using a contrasting coloured lure; for instance, change from black to white or vice versa. Finding the depth and the speed of retrieve is very important, more so than the type of lure. Don't be frightened of casting into a strong wind because very often the best fishing will be had fishing directly into the wind. In a good chop the trout will often move in very close to the shore. If you are not proficient enough to master casting into a strong wind then choose an area of shoreline where the wind is blowing from left to right, parallel with the shore. Unless you are left handed the wind will be keeping the line from clipping you on the back of your head when you are casting.

Many upland supply reservoirs are slightly acidic, and hence rather poor in natural life. In fact, without stocking the waters, they would support very few trout indeed. The trout in these waters are often avid surface feeders because their main source of food is terrestrial insects blown on to the surface. Big, bushy dry flies can work well on these waters, especially during August and September. Muddlers and Daddy Long Legs are good patterns to use, especially the latter. Muddlers were designed to be fished through the waves with a fast retrieve and they work well this way but they also work well used like a dry fly. A big bushy Muddler, especially a white one floating on the surface in fairly calm conditions, looks rather incongruous but is extremely effective.

Many reservoirs have boats which can be hired by anglers and these give greater scope for locating fish. In mid-summer especially, they allow anglers to search the deeper water and catch fish when fishing from the bank is yielding very little. Also, if brown trout are present in the reservoir, then these are likely to be caught in the deeper water which can't be reached from the bank. A boat also enables you to fish in the traditional loch-style – on the drift – or troll.

Water authority regions

Scotland

Northumbrian

Northern
Ireland

North
West

Yorkshire

Severn Trent

Anglian

Welsh

Thames

Wessex

Southern

South
West

The areas controlled by the regional water authorities of the United Kingdom.

Scotland

Scotland is unique within the British Isles in that you do not need a rod licence to fish anywhere in the region. The country is blessed with thousands of lochs many of which, due to their remoteness and inaccessibility, may go unfished for years. Some of the hill lochs are full of small brown trout which can give a lot of pleasure on light fly tackle. What the fish may lack in size they more than make up for in numbers, and in some of the hill lochs it is quite possible to catch 20 or 30 trout in a day.

In Scotland many of the residents (and visitors) are interested solely in the splendid salmon fishing on such notable rivers as the Dee, Tay and Spey. The excellent fishing for wild brown trout tends to be ignored. There is very little coarse fishing in Scotland, except in Dumfries and Galloway. The main coarse fish are pike and perch, and north of the Great Glen even these species are rare. Some of the big Scottish lochs, such as Lomond and Ken, offer the chance of some really big pike. Visitors angling for this fish should note that the pike in these lochs are not like the slow-moving, plump specimens found in English waters. These pike are long and sleek and fight like demons, so stronger tackle than is normally required should be used.

Permits for trout fishing in Scotland are usually inexpensive and, on many waters, free fishing can be enjoyed simply by seeking the permission of the landowner. In many parts of Scotland, fishing is not allowed on Sundays (or the Sabbath) so it is worth enquiring before setting out.

Orkney trout fishing lochs (Orkney Isles) Scot 1

For those of you who like fishing for wild brown trout the lochs on mainland Orkney are an angler's dream. The scenery is wild and unspoilt and, not only are the brown trout plentiful, they grow big. Orkney is not the remote place that many people imagine. The road north from Inverness is now much improved and there are regular ferry sailings between John o'Groats and Burwic on South Ronaldsay during the summer. The sailing on this route is less then one hour's duration. The other ferry from Scrabster to Stromness is only two hour's duration. The mainland island is reached from South Ronaldsay by roads built across the wartime Churchill Barriers. Fishing on the six Orkney lochs listed here for brown trout is free.

Key	Page
1 Orkney trout fishing lochs	26
2 Loch Borralie	30
3 Loch Lanlish	30
4 Loch Hope	30
5 Loch Loyal	31
6 Loch Staink	31
7 Loch Naver	31
8 Loch Meadie	32
9 River Spey – Aberlour	32
10 Loch Lochindorb	33
11 Loch Ness	33
12 Loch Quoich	33
13 Loch Arkaig	34
14 Loch Lochy	34
15 River Don – Kintore	35
16 River Tilt – Blair Atholl	35
17 Loch Bhac	36
18 Loch Tummel	36
19 River Tummel – Pitlochry Dam	37
20 River Tummel – Pitlochry to Ballinluig	37
21 River Tay – Dalguise Fishery	38
32 Gladhouse Reservoir	43
33 Loch Skeen	43
34 Woodhall Loch	43
35 Loch Ken	44

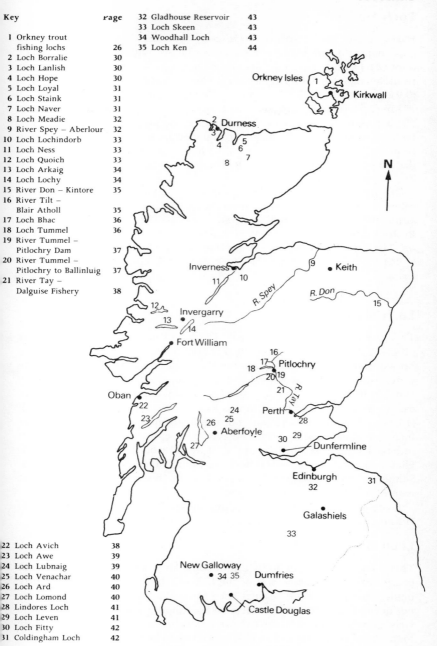

22 Loch Avich	38
23 Loch Awe	39
24 Loch Lubnaig	39
25 Loch Venachar	40
26 Loch Ard	40
27 Loch Lomond	40
28 Lindores Loch	41
29 Loch Leven	41
30 Loch Fitty	42
31 Coldingham Loch	42

27

SCOTLAND

Loch Harray

Harray is the largest area of fresh water in Orkney, covering 3000 acres (1210 ha). Although massive in size, it is shallow, with an average depth of only 12 ft (3.7 m). Harray is full of hard fighting, beautifully marked brown trout, averaging $\frac{3}{4}$ lb (0.3 kg). Every season a great many trout between 2 lb (0.9 kg) and 5 lb (2.3 kg) are caught. The record for the water is a fish of $17\frac{1}{2}$ lb (7.9 kg), taken in 1964. The loch is managed by the Orkney Trout Fishing Association, who stock the water. Good places to fish are the many bays along the banks, the feeder stream mouths and the rocky projections from the shoreline. The water is very clear, and when boat fishing on the drift one should keep an eye on the bottom so as not to damage the craft by drifting on to shallows.

The loch fishes very well in a good wave – which is just as well, as flat calms are not very common on Orkney. The bank fishing is excellent, although more water can be covered in a boat. Flies to use on Harray are Bushy Palmers, Loch Ordies, Whickham's Fancy, Invicta, Butcher and Kehe. The very best time for fishing Harray is in June and August.

Boats can be hired from the Merkister Hotel, Loch Harray, Mainland, Orkney

Loch Stenness

This is a magnificent loch to fish. The water is brackish although it is officially designated an extension of the sea and supports species including brown trout and sea trout. The shoreline in places is reed fringed, and the water is shallow. The average size of the brown trout is between $\frac{3}{4}$ lb (0.3 kg) and 2 lb (0.9 kg), but much larger fish are taken. The largest trout ever caught in Orkney was taken in this loch and weighed a staggering $29\frac{1}{4}$ lb (13.3 kg). Wading is successful, but can be hampered near the freshwater inlets by thick weed growth. The average size of the sea trout which run into the loch is $\frac{3}{4}$–5 lb (0.3–2.3 kg). There are also occasional runs of salmon. Flies that work well on Stenness are Zulu, Silver Cardinal, Alexandra, Soldier Palmer, Connemara Black and Invicta, in sizes 10 and 12. The best months are June, July and August.

Boats are hired from the Standing Stones Hotel, Stenness, Mainland, Orkney.

Loch Boardhouse

This is an excellent loch to fish, producing large numbers of brown trout every year. The average size of the fish is 1 lb (0.5 kg) which is slightly higher than in the more popular Loch Harray. Baskets of up to 12 fish are not uncommon. The only problem on Boardhouse is that there is a prolific weed growth in summer, and fish can be lost in the weed when fishing close to the weed beds. This loch is best fished from a boat as the margins are full of slippery stones making wading rather hazardous. Recommended flies are Loch Ordie, Black Pennel, Invicta, Alexandra, Ke-he, Soldier Palmer and Teal patterns in sizes 10 and 12. The best months are June, early July and late August.

Boats are hired from the Barony Hotel, Birsay, Mainland, Orkney

Loch Swannay

This loch has earned the reputation of being the best wild brown trout water in the United Kingdom. This is a very shallow loch with rocky outcrops and large boulders, so take care when boat fishing. Normally the water is clear, but in a strong wind the water may have colour stirred into it. The brown trout are superb, and 3 lb (1.4 kg) fish are common. The average size is well over 1 lb (0.5 kg).

The shore fishing from Swannay is good, especially on the southern end of the loch. Take care when wading because the stones in the bed of the loch are very slippery. Good flies for fishing Swannay are Zulu, Palmers, Coch-y-Bondhu, Wickham's Fancy, Black Pennel and small Muddlers in sizes 10 and 12. The best months are May to August, and the loch fishes well during cold spells in summer.

Boats can be hired from Mr W Sabiston, Louden Hill, Swannay, Birsay, Mainland, Orkney.

Loch Hundland

This is a smaller version of Loch Boardhouse, lying between Loch Swannay and Boardhouse. The water is stocked by the Orkney Trout Fishing Association, and the average weight of the trout is $\frac{3}{4}$ lb (0.3 kg). Larger fish are present, and 2 lb (0.9 kg) trout are occasionally taken. Wading is quite productive but the shoreline is rather boggy in places. Traditional drift fishing from a boat produces the best results.

Boats are hired from Mr L Hourston, Muckle Quay Farm, Birsay, Mainland Orkney.

Loch Kirbister

This is the only typical Highland loch in Orkney with lots of trout, although only small specimens are present. The average size is $\frac{1}{2}-\frac{3}{4}$ lb (0.2–0.3 kg), with few larger fish being caught. This is a 'hungry' water, and the small trout are fairly easy to catch. Wading is easy, especially along the southern shore. Any traditional loch fly will take Kirbister trout. The best months are June to August.

Boats can be hired from Mr G R Wishart, Barebrecks, Orphir, Mainland, Orkney.

Useful Addresses on Orkney

Merkister Hotel, Loch Harray, Orkney. Telephone: Harray 289.
Orkney Tourist Board: Information Centre, Kirkwall, Orkney. Telephone: Kirkwall 2856.
Secretary of Orkney Trout Fishing Association: Mr R Windwick, 17 Hermaness, Kirkwall, Orkney.
Standing Stones Hotel, Stenness, Orkney.

Loch Borralie (Durness, Highland region) Scot 2

This is a large limestone loch to the west of Durness. The water is crystal clear and the trout grow very large. The fishing is good all round the loch but an area worthy of special attention is in the vicinity of the island off the east shore. Some very large trout inhabit Borralie and fish in the 3–4 lb (1.4–1.8 kg) range are not uncommon.

SPECIES Brown trout and char.

TECHNIQUES AND BAITS Fly fishing only is allowed. Standard loch-style fishing will catch fish but in summer dry fly and nymph fishing is recommended.

SEASON 15th March to 6th October.

ACCESS The loch is reached via the A838 road near Durness. Permits are obtained from the Cape Wrath Hotel, Keoldale, Lairg, Highland.

Loch Lanlish (Durness, Highland region) Scot 3

This limestone loch is not easy to fish, yet it holds some very big brown trout. No boats are available so the fishing is only from the bank. A double figure brown trout is possible on this loch, and 5 lb (2.3 kg) fish are not uncommon. The water is very clear and a good ripple on the water is required to produce the best fishing.

SPECIES Brown trout.

TECHNIQUES AND BAITS Fly fishing. Dry fly fishing works well in summer. On wave-blown water, a large bushy sedge is worth trying.

SEASON 15th March to 6th October.

ACCESS Loch Lanlish lies to the north of the Cape Wrath Hotel at Keoldale, near Durness.

Permits are obtained from the Cape Wrath Hotel, Keoldale, Lairg, Highland region.

Loch Hope (Eriboll, Highland region) Scot 4

This beautiful loch, just north of Ben Hope, is long and narrow and primarily a sea trout fishery. Boats with outboard motors are not allowed on beats 1, 2 and 3 of the southern end of the loch but can be used on Middle Bay and the north end. Fishing is only from boats and is best during July, August and September.

SPECIES Sea trout, brown trout and salmon.

TECHNIQUES AND BAITS Fly fishing only. Fishing with a team of wet flies on the drop gives the best results with sea trout, and a few salmon can be taken in this way, too.

SEASON 1st April to 30th September.

ACCESS Loch Hope is south of the A838 road between Kyle of Tongue and Loch Eriboll.

Permits and boats are available from Mr A Finch, Altnaharra Hotel, Altnaharra, Highland region.

Loch Loyal (Tongue, Highland region) Scot 5

Loch Loyal is 5 miles (8 km) long and is very deep. Superb scenery and plenty of brown trout make this one of the best lochs in the area. Being very deep, the best fishing is in the shallow areas close to the shore. The trout average ¾ lb (0.3 kg) and up to 20 a day can be taken, if conditions are right. Boats are available (with outboard motors).

SPECIES Brown trout.

TECHNIQUES AND BAITS Fly fishing only. Most loch wet flies will catch fish.

SEASON 1st April to 30th September.

ACCESS Loch Loyal is north of Altnaharra on the right-hand side of the A838 road.

Permits and boats are available from Mr A Finch, Altnaharra Hotel, Altnaharra, Highland region.

Loch Staink (Altnaharra, Highland region) Scot 6

This is an easily accessible hill loch that is full of wild brown trout. Boats are available but the bank fishing is also good. The trout are not very big but they are very free rising, and provide excellent sport on light fly tackle. The scenery, as elsewhere in this region, is breathtaking

SPECIES Brown trout.

TECHNIQUES AND BAITS Light fly fishing with either wet or dry fly depending on the prevailing conditions.

SEASON 1st April to 30th September.

ACCESS The loch is close to the A836 road just north of Altnaharra.

Permits and boats arranged by Mr A Finch, Altnaharra Hotel, Altnaharra.

Loch Naver (Altnaharra, Highland region) Scot 7

This is one of the best salmon lochs in Scotland that is open to the public.

Loch Naver is 6 miles (9.7 km) long and ½ mile (0.8 km) wide and is mainly fished for salmon and sea trout, but brown trout can also be caught. The best salmon fishing is in March, April and May.

SPECIES Salmon, brown trout and sea trout.

TECHNIQUES AND BAITS Trolling is allowed during the period 12th January to 30th April. From 1st May to 30th September an area is reserved for fly fishing only.

SEASON 12th January to 30th September (salmon) and 15th March to 6th October (trout).

ACCESS Loch Naver lies beside the B873 road east of Altnaharra.

Permits and boats are available from Mr A Finch, Altnaharra Hotel, Altnaharra.

Loch Meadie (Altnaharra, Highland region) Scot 8

This is a superb brown trout water in the dramatic setting of Ben Hope. The loch is long and narrow and can be fished by boat or from the bank. There are many islands, and it is around these that boat anglers will find some 'hot spots'. If fishing from the shore, the southern end of the loch is usually the best area.

SPECIES Brown trout.

TECHNIQUES AND BAITS Traditional wet fly fishing from the shore or loch-style on the drift from boats.

SEASON 1st April to 30th September.

ACCESS The loch is next to the minor road that runs from Altnaharra to Loch Hope.

The fishing is controlled by the Altnaharra Hotel, Altnaharra

---

River Spey – Aberlour (Grampian) Scot 9

The Spey is arguably the best salmon river in Scotland. The river is 100 miles (roughly 160 km) long and flows along the northern edge of the Cairngorms. There are two beats at Aberlour. One stretch is from Low Burn to the suspension bridge and the other is from the suspension bridge to Milford. The river is wide and fast flowing. As well as salmon, there is a run of sea trout and the river is also stocked with brown trout.

SPECIES Salmon, grilse, sea trout and brown trout.

TECHNIQUES AND BAITS Fly fishing only at summer level. Prawn fishing is banned.

SEASON 11th February to 30th September.

ACCESS Aberlour is on the A95(T) road 23 miles (37 km) north-east of Grantown-on-Spey.

The Thames: there is still much good, free fishing to be had on this river.

(Above) Fly fishing below Aysgarth Falls on Yorkshire's River Ure (see page 69).

(see page 69)

(Below) A brown trout from an Irish lough; this specimen weighed 10 lb (4.5 kg).

Permits are obtained from Mr J A J Munro, 95 High Street, Aberlour.

Loch Lochindorb (Grantown-on-Spey, Highland region) Scot 10

This is a large shallow loch with an island on which are the ruins of a castle, reputedly the home of the Wolf of Badenoch. The fishing is for brown trout and from boats only. The trout average $\frac{1}{2}$ lb (0.2 kg) but there are plenty of them and they are hard fighting. There are a few bigger trout caught occasionally.

SPECIES Brown trout.

TECHNIQUES AND BAITS Fly fishing loch-style with a team of wet flies works best.

SEASON 1st April to 30th September.

ACCESS The loch is reached by a minor road off the Grantown-on-Spey A939 road to Nairn. Turn off the main road at the village of Bridgend.

Permits are obtained from Mr G Lilley, The Tackle Shop, 97b High Street, Forres, Grampian.

Loch Ness (Fort Augustus, Highland region) Scot 11

World famous because of the fabled monster, Loch Ness also gives some good trout fishing, with the chance of a salmon. The loch is about 26 miles (41.8 km) long and in a beautiful setting. Parts of it are very deep, but much of the best trout fishing can be enjoyed in the shallower bays and inlets or close to the shore. The trout in Loch Ness are a lovely deep gold colour and average 10 oz (0.3 kg).

SPECIES Brown trout and salmon (occasional).

TECHNIQUES AND BAITS Standard loch flies work well, especially if there is a good wave on the loch.

SEASON 1st April to 30th September.

ACCESS Virtually the full length of the north shore can be reached from the A82(T) Inverness road.

Permits are obtained from Glenmoriston Estate Office, Glenmoriston, Inverness, Highland

---

Loch Quoich (near Invergarry, Highland region) Scot 12

This is a wild and lonely place at the top of Glen Garry. In bad weather it can be windswept and inhospitable, but during the summer it is a glorious loch to fish. The loch is a mass of interesting bays and inlets and is the home of some really massive brown trout. The average size of the trout is $\frac{3}{4}$ lb (0.3 kg), but each year the loch produces double figure fish. The British record is a specimen of over 20 lb (9.1 kg) caught from Loch Quoich. A few boats can be hired, and a boat is really needed to troll for the largest trout. There is no bag limit. Free fishing is available from the shore.

SPECIES Brown trout.

TECHNIQUES AND BAITS There are no restrictions on methods, but most enjoyment will be gained from traditional loch fishing with a team of three flies. To catch the really big trout a mepps or spoon trolled from a boat in the deep water is best.

SEASON 15th March to 5th October.

ACCESS Take the A87(T) road west from Invergarry and then the minor road alongside Loch Garry, and follow this road along the Glen to Loch Quoich.

Permits are obtained from Tomdoun Hotel, Invergarry.

Loch Arkaig (near Fort William, Highland region) Scot 13

Loch Arkaig is 15 miles (24.1 km) long and, although it is surrounded by mountains and wooded banks, the shore is fairly accessible. The width of the loch is about $\frac{1}{2}$ mile (0.8 km). The loch is very deep in places, the deepest area being near Eilean a'Ghiubhaid, where the bottom drops away to 350 ft (107 m). Three or four boats are available and each boat can be used by two anglers. The boats must be booked in advance from the keeper. The average size of the trout in the loch is $\frac{3}{4}$ lb (0.3 kg) but recently a 14 lb (6.4 kg) cannibal trout was taken. The pike fishing potential is not really known, but with plenty of salmonoid food fish they will undoubtedly reach a large size. Salmon and sea trout are also occasionally encountered in the loch. No limit is placed on the number of trout killed.

SPECIES Brown trout, pike, salmon and sea trout.

TECHNIQUES AND BAITS Most trout are taken by traditional loch-style fishing with three flies. The really big trout are caught by trolling in the deep water. Any legitimate method can be used for the pike.

SEASON 15th March to 15th October (brown trout). No close season for pike.

ACCESS From Spean Bridge take the B8004 to Gairlochy and then the B8005 to Loch Arkaig.

Permits and enquiries to Mr McIntosh, The Keepers Cottage, Bunarkaig, near Gairlochy.

Loch Lochy (near Spean Bridge, Highland region) Scot 14

This loch is 10 miles (16.1 km) long and $\frac{3}{4}$ mile (1.2 km) wide, and is part of the Caledonian Canal System that runs across the Great Glen from Fort William to Inverness. The loch is well wooded along both shores, with a backdrop of mountains including Ben Nevis to the south. The loch is owned by British Waterways and the fishing is free, but local landowners' permission is required (usually readily given) to go on to the banks. Eight boats are available to fish the loch. This loch is grossly underfished and holds pike up to at least 30 lb (13.6 kg) as well as plenty of trout. Some trout up to 9 lb (4.1 kg) are caught by trolling in the deep water, although the average size is $\frac{3}{4}$ lb (0.3 kg). A few salmon and sea trout are also in the loch.

SPECIES Pike, brown trout, salmon and sea trout.

TECHNIQUES AND BAITS All legitimate methods of fishing can be used. Traditional loch-style fishing is most sporting for the smaller trout. The big trout and some pike are taken by trolling a mepps from a boat.

SEASON 15th March to 6th October (brown trout). No close season for pike.

ACCESS The A82(T) road runs alongside the southern shore of Loch Lochy.

The fishing is free but the landowner's consent is required. Motor boats can be hired from Mr Stevenson, Spean Bridge Garage, Spean Bridge.

River Don – Kintore (near Aberdeen, Grampian) Scot 15

The River Don is a good salmon river and rises at the top of Strathdon above Cock Bridge and then flows eastwards for 70 miles (113 km) to enter the sea at Bridge of Don just north of Aberdeen. The fishing at Kintore covers $3\frac{1}{2}$ miles (5.6 km) of the left bank and $2\frac{1}{2}$ miles (4 km) of the right bank. Some large salmon are taken on the Kintore beat and the Mill Stream stretch is most productive in lowish water. The brown trout fishing on this stretch of river can also be very rewarding.

SPECIES Salmon and brown trout.

TECHNIQUES AND BAITS Live minnow fishing is strictly prohibited at all times. Worm fishing is not allowed until 1st May. The brown trout are best fished for using standard river wet fly techniques. Fly fishing for the salmon is also very rewarding on this beat under low water conditions.

SEASON 15th March to 6th October (brown trout) and February to October (salmon) – exact dates vary, so please check.

ACCESS Kintore is 12 miles (19.3 km) north-west of Aberdeen on the A96(T) road.

Permits are obtained from the Kintore Arms Hotel, Kintore

River Tilt – Blair Atholl (Tayside) Scot 16

The River Tilt is a classic Highland spate river, where spawning takes place from fish that have run up the Tummel and Garry river systems. The Tilt flows into the River Garry at Blair Atholl. This is a late season river and salmon fishing before August is not really worthwhile. The best time for salmon on the Tilt is September and early October. An estate road runs the length of the river but some of the river bankings are very steep and care is needed. The riverside surroundings on the Tilt are superb.

SPECIES Salmon.

TECHNIQUES AND BAITS Mainly fly fishing only but spinning is permitted when the river is above summer level.

SEASON 15th January to 15th October.

ACCESS The river is reached by taking the A9(T) road to Blair Atholl and then the estate road alongside the river.

Permits can be booked through the Airdaniar Hotel, 160 Atholl Road, Pitlochry.

Loch Bhac (near Pitlochry, Tayside) Scot 17

This is a 20 acre (8 ha) hill loch, located close to the northern shore of Loch Tummel. The fishing on Loch Bhac (pronounced Vack) is controlled by the Pitlochry Angling Club, who have developed the water into a first-class fishery for both brown and rainbow trout. The loch is in an attractive setting with a large conifer plantation near one shore. Six boats are available for the use of anglers and there is a boathouse for shelter if the weather is bad. A good area to fish is in the south corners where feeder streams enter the loch. The trout are hard fighting fish, and the rainbow trout are stocked up to 8 lb (3.6 kg). No doubt some of these will eventually grow on to double figures.

SPECIES Brown trout, rainbow trout and brook trout.

TECHNIQUES AND BAITS Fly fishing only. The trout in the loch are free rising, and good sport can be enjoyed with dry fly, buzzer and nymph. When there are big waves on the water, a Muddler pulled across the surface works well.

SEASON 15th March to 6th October.

ACCESS From Pitlochry, take the A9(T) road to the north end of Loch Faskally and then turn left on to the B8019 road that runs along the northern shore of Loch Tummel. Turn off this road and on to the road to the Forest of Allean. Vehicles have to be left at the top of the Forestry Commission track and the short trip to the loch made on foot.

Permits are obtained before fishing from the Airdaniar Hotel, 160 Atholl Road, Pitlochry.

Loch Tummel (Tummel Bridge, Strathclyde) Scot 18

This famous loch is over 7 miles (11.3 km) long and 1 mile (1.6 km) wide. There is good access to the waterside all round the loch, since roads run along, or near to, both shores. The loch contains plenty of trout and, although the occasional fish to 3 lb (1.4 kg) is taken, the average size is 10 oz (0.3 kg). The predominant species are pike and perch. The pike potential of this loch has not really been explored fully, but early in 1984 some pike to 26 lb (11.7 kg) were netted out. Serious pike anglers travelling to Scotland should consider this loch as well as the usual pike waters, such as Lochs Lomond or Ken. The perch are plentiful and the average size is 10 oz (0.3 kg). Most of the loch can be fished, but there are one or two short lengths which are private. No boats are available at the moment.

SPECIES Perch, pike and brown trout.

TECHNIQUES AND BAITS Fly fishing only is allowed for the brown trout, but any legitimate method can be used for the coarse fish. The perch are best fished for with worm and spinner. All the traditional methods will take pike; perhaps the best is a perch livebait.

SEASON 15th March to 6th October (brown trout). There is no close season for the coarse fish, and they can be fished for all the year round.

ACCESS Permits are obtained from the Loch Tummel Hotel, Tummel Bridge, at the western end of the loch.

River Tummel – Pitlochry Dam (Pitlochry, Tayside)
Scot 19

The River Tummel immediately below Pitlochry Dam must be one of the best known salmon stretches in Scotland. The salmon pass at the dam has an observation window inside which attracts a lot of tourists who can actually watch the salmon making their way up the fish ladder. The pool immediately below the sluice gates at the dam is a sanctuary area for resting fish and cannot be fished. Immediately downstream is the Port-Na-Craig beat which is rated the best salmon beat on the River Tummel. The water is very popular and advance booking is advisable as the number of rods is limited. April and May are the best months for the fishing.

SPECIES Salmon.

TECHNIQUES AND BAITS Fly fishing, spinning and bait fishing are all permitted.

SEASON 15th January to 15th October.

ACCESS The fishery is at Pitlochry on the A9 road. Permits can be obtained from the Airdaniar Hotel, 160 Atholl Road, Pitlochry

---

River Tummel – Pitlochry to Ballinluig (Tayside)
Scot 20

Trout fishing is allowed on the River Tummel between Pitlochry and Ballinluig on both banks of the river, a distance of 5 miles (8 km). The River Tummel along this stretch is fast flowing with several deep pools and glides. The scenery is superb and the river is good for wading, although care needs to be taken on some of the rockier sections.

SPECIES Brown trout.

TECHNIQUES AND BAITS Fishing is restricted to fly only until 31st May and then worm fishing is allowed. Standard river wet fly tactics work best.

SEASON 15th March to 6th October.

ACCESS The river flows close to the A9(T) road south from Pitlochry and access is from this road or from the minor road which runs from Grandtully to Faskally along the western bank of the river.

Permits can be obtained from the Airdaniar Hotel, 160 Atholl Road, Pitlochry.

River Tay – Dalguise Fishery (Dunkeld, Tayside) Scot 21

The River Tay is a major Scottish salmon river and flows from Loch Tay first north-east and then south-east to enter the sea in the Firth of Tay near Perth. The Dalguise Fishery consists of $1\frac{1}{2}$ miles (2.4 km) of the Tay below its junction with the River Tummel. The fishing is usually let by the week but some day rods are available. A boat is available with a gillie. The best salmon runs are between April and July and again in September and October. Salmon to over 40 lb (18.1 kg) are caught on this beat of the river. Trout fishing on the river is readily available and is best during May, June and July.

SPECIES Salmon, grilse and brown trout.

TECHNIQUES AND BAITS Spinning is the best method for salmon in spring and autumn. During the summer, fly and worm fishing are the best methods. Fly fishing only is allowed for the trout, and standard wet fly fishing is best.

SEASON 15th January to 15th October (salmon) and 15th March to 6th October (brown trout).

ACCESS Dalguise is reached by taking the B898 road north from Dunkeld.

Permits are limited and should be booked in advance from Mr M C Smith, The Orchard, Dalguise, Dunkeld.

Loch Avich (Dalavich, Loch Awe, Strathclyde) Scot 22

This loch is on the western side of Loch Awe, and drains into the latter via the River Avich. At $3\frac{1}{2}$ miles (5.6 km) long, Loch Avich is quite large, even by Scottish standards. The loch is full of brown trout and, although the average size is only 10 oz (0.3 kg), the catch rate is high with a bag of a dozen fish being commonplace. Two boats are available for use by anglers and bank fishing is allowed from part of the shoreline.

SPECIES Brown trout.

TECHNIQUES AND BAITS Fly fishing only. Standard wet fly patterns are effective, and if conditions are right the fish will rise to a dry fly.

SEASON 15th March to 6th October.

ACCESS Take the B845 road south from Taynuilt to Kilchrenan and then the minor road south along the side of Loch Awe to the village of Dalavich. Loch Avich is then reached by a narrow road that runs along the northern shore of the loch.

Permits are obtained from the Chief Forester, Forest Office, Dalavich, Taynuilt.

Loch Awe (Dalmally, Strathclyde) Scot 23

This loch is 26 miles (41.8 km) long and very narrow. The loch is easily accessible, as the B840 road runs close to the southern shore and a minor road runs along the north shore. Loch Awe is famous for its big ferrox trout. There is an unofficial record of a trout caught from Loch Awe last century weighing 39 lb 8 oz (17.9 kg). As recently as 1980, a fish over 19 lb (8.6 kg) was taken in the loch. The average size of the ordinary brown trout is in the region of $\frac{3}{4}$ lb (0.3 kg), and the loch is full of these. The small fish are caught from the shore but in order to have a chance of catching the big ferrox trout a boat is required. The loch is very deep, in places down to 300 ft (91 m).
SPECIES Salmon, sea trout, pike, brown trout (including big ferrox trout), char and rainbow trout.
TECHNIQUES AND BAITS There are no restrictions on methods. Most sport with the smaller trout is with fly tackle and traditional wet flies. The big ferrox trout are taken trolling in the deep water from a boat.
SEASON 15th March to 6th October (trout).
ACCESS Dalmally, at the northern tip of Loch Awe, is reached by the A819 road from Invergarry along Glen Aray.

The fishing is free but boats can be hired from local hotels such as Carraig Thura Hotel, Loch Awe village, near Dalmally.

Loch Lubnaig (Callander, Central region) Scot 24

This is a long narrow loch. The best fishing area is the shallow northern end. The average size of the trout is around $\frac{1}{2}$ lb (0.2 kg) but, like many of the deep Scottish lochs, there are some really big fish present. Pike and perch are present in good numbers and during 1984 a 4 lb (1.8 kg) perch was caught on a spinner from this loch.
SPECIES Pike, perch and brown trout.
TECHNIQUES AND BAITS All legal methods are allowed but fly fishing is the most rewarding for the trout. Good flies are Blae and Black and Black Pennell.
SEASON 15th March to 6th October (trout) and all year for coarse fish.
ACCESS The loch is very accessible from the A84(T) road from Callander.

Permits are obtained from Mr J Bayne, (Tackle Shop), 76 Main Street, Callander.

Loch Venachar (near Callandar, Central region) Scot 25

This loch is in a beautiful setting with towering mountains as a backdrop. Venachar is 3 miles (4.8 km) long and 1 mile (1.6 km) wide. Ten boats are available for visitors, and most of the shoreline can be fished. The brown trout in the loch average $\frac{3}{4}$ lb (0.3 kg) although larger fish are encountered. The most popular area on the loch is at the western end where the Black Water enters. There are a few salmon and sea trout in the loch, and there are plenty of pike and perch as well, but these are something of an unknown quantity because few people fish seriously for them. The average depth of the loch is 20 ft (6.1 m), dropping away in places to 95 ft (29 m). The size limit for trout is 9 in (23 cm), and there is no bag limit.

SPECIES Brown trout, sea trout, salmon, pike and perch.

TECHNIQUES AND BAITS Spinning in deep water will be the best way of catching any big ferrox trout. Traditional loch-style fishing on the drift will take the most trout. After 1st May any legal method, including bait fishing, can be used.

SEASON 15th March to 6th October (brown trout). Fly fishing and spinning only until 1st May. No close season for coarse fish.

ACCESS Loch Venachar is just west of Callander on the A821 road.

Permits are obtained from Mr J Bayne (Tackle Shop), 76 Main Street, Callander.

Loch Ard (Aberfoyle, Central region) Scot 26

This is an attractive loch, set in Forestry Commission land, in an ideal family area with forest walks and picnic areas as well as some good trout fishing. The loch is 3 miles (4.8 km) long and is most easily accessible on the northern bank. The trout average $\frac{3}{4}$ lb (0.3 kg) and catches of up to ten fish are not uncommon.

SPECIES Brown trout.

TECHNIQUES AND BAITS Fly fishing only. Loch-style from the boats works best. Butcher, Black Pennell and Soldier Palmer are good flies.

SEASON 15th March to 6th October.

ACCESS The loch is alongside the B829 Pass of Aberfoyle road, 3 miles (4.8 km) west of Aberfoyle.

Permits and boats are obtained from the Forest Hills Hotel

Loch Lomond (near Dumbarton, Strathclyde) Scot 27

Loch Lomond has much to offer the visiting angler. The pike fishing is first class and so is the sea trout, salmon and brown trout fishing. The loch is massive – nearly 22 miles (35 km) long – and the scenery is splendid, with a backdrop of forests and mountains. Good areas for pike fishing are Ardlui and Balmaha, which are at the north and south extremities of the loch, respectively. The western shoreline is easily accessible, as the A82(T) road runs alongside the loch. Boats are available from several loch-side centres.

SPECIES Pike, perch, salmon, sea trout and brown trout.

TECHNIQUES AND BAITS Most of the pike are taken on deadbaits or livebaits, but spinning can produce some good sport. Bloody Butcher and Kingfisher Butcher are two good sea trout flies. Dapping from a boat is a good way to catch the sea trout. Brown trout will take just about every traditional wet fly fished from the bank or a boat.

SEASON 15th March to 6th October (brown trout). No close season for coarse fish.

ACCESS Permission to fish can be obtained from Ardlui Hotel, Loch Lomond, Arrochar, Strathclyde

Lindores Loch (Newburgh, Fife) Scot 28

This is a long, narrow loch, alongside the B937 road south of Newburgh. Fishing is for both brown and rainbow trout and is restricted to boats only. There are only seven boats for fishing, so advance booking is necessary. The average weight of the fish is a very high $1\frac{1}{2}$ lb (0.7 kg) and plenty of fish up to 5 lb (2.3 kg) are caught.

SPECIES Brown trout and rainbow trout.

TECHNIQUES AND BAITS Fly fishing from boats.

SEASON 15th March to 30th November.

ACCESS The loch is 3 miles (4.8 km) south-east of Newburgh at Lindores on the B937 road.

Permits are obtained from Mr F G Hamilton, 18 Strathview Place, Comrie, Tayside.

Loch Leven (Kinross, Tayside) Scot 29

Covering 4300 acres (1740 ha), Loch Leven is still the most famous trout fishery in Scotland but, sadly, the fishing, although still good, is not what it used to be. The loch is a beautiful place with seven islands scattered across its vast acreage. The fishing is from boats powered by outboards and advance booking is essential as the number of boats is restricted.

SPECIES Loch Leven brown trout.

TECHNIQUES AND BAITS Standard loch-style fly fishing is best. Occasionally some very good rises to dry fly are had.

SEASON 1st April to 30th September.

ACCESS Kinross can be reached via the M90 motorway.

Permits are obtained from the Manager, The Pier, Kinross.

Loch Fitty (near Dunfermline, Fife) Scot 30

This 160 acre (65 ha) lake is a shallow, water-filled, open-cast coal mining site, which has been developed into a splendid trout fishery. The banks are gently sloping grassland, making all the fishery accessible for fly fishing. The average size of the trout is a little over 1 lb (0.5 kg), but some big trout are caught each season. The record for the fishery taken in 1984 weighed 9 lb 1 oz (4.1 kg). There are 22 sturdy fishing boats available for anglers. The fishery is stocked at regular intervals throughout the season. The bag limit is five fish per rod. There are no clear 'hot spots', and the fishery management will advise on which area is producing on any particular day.
SPECIES Brown trout and rainbow trout.
TECHNIQUES AND BAITS Fly fishing only. Black lures work well early in the season, and during the summer the fish rise well for a dry fly.
SEASON 2nd March to 10th November.
ACCESS Loch Fitty is 3 miles (4.8 km) to the north of Dunfermline. The only road to the loch leads off Kelty Road.

Permits are obtained from the fishing lodge on site. Advance booking for boats at a weekend is advisable. For further information contact Game Fisheries Limited, Loch Fitty, Dunfermline.

Coldingham Loch (near Berwick-upon-Tweed, Northumberland) Scot 31

This loch is in an attractive situation near to the east coast at St Abbs Head. This is one of the best-known and best-managed trout lochs in Scotland. The water is very fertile, and covers just over 22 acres (9 ha). The depth of the loch varies, with shallows and deeper areas up to 45 ft (13.7 m). Five boats are available for anglers. The bank fishing is restricted to five rods a day, so plenty of space is guaranteed. Weed growth can be prolific in summer but the owners clear areas of it so that fishing is unhindered. The lock is regularly stocked with both brown and rainbow trout. Brown trout up to 7½ lb (3.4 kg) have been taken in recent years. Fish are stocked from 1¼ lb (0.6 kg) upwards. This is an excellent loch for trout fishing. The bag limit is five fish.
SPECIES Brown trout and rainbow trout.
TECHNIQUES AND BAITS Fly fishing only. All methods of fly fishing will take trout. The rainbow trout will chase lures, but also respond well to traditional loch-style, and also dry fly, fishing. There is no particular 'hot spot' on the lake.
SEASON 15th March to 6th October (brown trout), 15th March to 31st

October (rainbow trout).

ACCESS The loch is reached by taking the A1107 road to Coldingham and then turning east to the loch.

Permits are obtained from Dr E Wise, West Loch House, Coldingham, Borders region.

Gladhouse Reservoir (Eddleston, near Edinburgh, Lothian) Scot 32

This is a picturesque reservoir set in the Moorfoot Hills. The reservoir is irregularly shaped and covers 400 acres (162 ha). No bank fishing is allowed and the fishing is limited to four boats, one of which has been modified so that it can be used by a disabled angler. The reservoir is a nature reserve as well as a fishery and there are a lot of waterfowl.

SPECIES Brown trout.

TECHNIQUES AND BAITS Fly fishing only.

SEASON 1st April to 30th September.

ACCESS The reservoir is situated south of Edinburgh. Take the A703 road from Peebles north and turn right 3 miles (4.8 km) north of Eddleston on the minor road through the village of Westloch.

Permits are obtained in advance from Lothian Regional Council, Department of Water Supply Services, Comiston Springs, 55 Buckstone Terrace, Edinburgh.

Loch Skeen (near Moffat, Dumfries and Galloway) Scot 33

This is a good loch to fish if you like remote countryside. The loch can only be approached by foot up past the Grey Mares Tail Waterfall which is a spectacular 200 ft (61 m) cascade. The route past the side of the fall is steep but passable. For the less fit the loch can be reached by a slightly longer but less steep valley track. The loch is full of $\frac{1}{2}$ lb (0.2 kg) brown trout.

SPECIES Wild brown trout.

TECHNIQUES AND BAITS Fly fishing with small wet flies on light tackle works best. Dry fly works well if the conditions are right.

SEASON 15th March to 6th October.

ACCESS Take the A708 road north from Moffat for 6 miles (9.7 km) until the Grey Mares Tail waterfall is reached on the left-hand side of the road. Parking is on the roadside and the final ascent is on foot.

The fishing is free.

Woodhall Loch (near Castle Douglas, Dumfries and Galloway) Scot 34

This is a popular coarse fishing loch not far from the more famous Loch Ken.

Woodhall Loch is nearly 1 mile (1.6 km) long and, in places, nearly $\frac{1}{2}$ mile (0.8 km) wide. At the northern end a slow-flowing and fairly deep burn runs from the loch. The loch has plenty of perch, and also has a few good brown trout. The burn is reed fringed and has water-lily beds. The fishing in the loch is for pike, perch and roach. The roach and perch average $\frac{1}{2}$ lb (0.2 kg), but larger fish are present. The pike fishing is good, with specimens over 20 lb (9.1 kg) not uncommon. This is an attractive loch to fish and the access is easy. The area is teeming with wildlife, including deer at the wooded north end of the loch.

SPECIES Pike, perch, roach and a few trout.

TECHNIQUES AND BAITS There are no restrictions on baits or methods. Deadbaiting, livebaiting and spinning will all take pike. Perch and roach are best tackled with legered maggots in the lake itself or float-fished in the burn.

SEASON All the year round for coarse fish.

ACCESS Woodhall Loch is situated alongside the A762 road from Laurieston to New Galloway about 2 miles (3.2 km) from Laurieston.

Permits are obtained from the Post Office Shop, Mossdale, near Castle Douglas.

Loch Ken (New Galloway, Dumfries and Galloway) Scot 35

Lock Ken is over 10 miles (16.1 km) long but is a very narrow loch. The loch reaches from New Galloway in the north to Crossmichael in the south. This is a superb water for pike and roach fishing and is very popular with anglers from below the border during the statutory close season in England. Some anglers have organised small matches which have yielded over 30 lb (13.6 kg) of roach.

SPECIES Pike, roach, perch and brown trout.

TECHNIQUES AND BAITS Leger with an open-ended feeder using maggots or casters for the roach. They can sometimes be caught closer to the shore using a waggler float. The pike fall to spinning, deadbaiting and livebaiting.

SEASON 15th March to 6th October (brown trout). No close season for coarse fish.

ACCESS The loch is reached by the A713(T) road north-west from Castle Douglas.

The fishing is free but some landowners are now charging for access.

North West
Water Authority

This is a large area stretching from the Scottish border, north of Carlisle, down the Pennines to Glossop, Kidsgrove and Whitchurch, and then north again to the River Mersey. The region takes in some very contrasting scenery. In Cumbria, in the north of the region, there is the magnificence of the Lake District which is full of lakes and streams. There are also two major salmon rivers here, the Lune and the Eden. The centre of the region, around Manchester, Bolton and Rochdale, is heavily populated. In the south of the region the flatter area of Cheshire, near Crewe, has its rich bream-holding meres.

Although the Lake District is very popular and is full of visitors during the summer, it is always possible to find some quiet corner where you can fish undisturbed. For instance, the small hill tarns around Windermere and Coniston give you the chance to fish away from the crowds. Even on Windermere and Coniston themselves you can find a quiet corner if you move away from the popular towns of Ambleside and Hawkshead.

The only drawback to fishing in the Lake District is the lack of species. The species in the lakes tend to be restricted to trout, char, pike and perch, with a few migratory species for good measure. Nevertheless, the trout fishing is excellent, and in some of the lakes there are some very big pike. In recent years there has been a noticeable improvement in the canal fishing in the region. The Leeds–Liverpool Canal, for instance, is now fishing really well for tench. One of the largest perch caught in the country during 1984 came from the Leeds–Liverpool Canal, and weighed a staggering 4 lb 10 oz (2.1 kg).

Key	Page
1 River Eden – Carlisle	47
2 The Lough Trout Fishery	47
3 Abbot Moss Lake	47
4 Bassenthwaite Lake	48
5 Whins Pond	48
6 Crummock Water	49
7 Derwent Water	49
8 Watendlath Tarn	50
9 Red Tarn	50
10 Ullswater	51
11 Beacon Tarn	51
12 Blea Tarn	51
13 Blea Water	52
14 Burnmoor Tarn	52
15 High Dam	52
16 Esthwaite Water	52
17 Coniston Water	53
18 Ulverston Canal	53
19 Elliscales Ponds	53
20 Bank House Fly Fishery	54
21 River Ribble – Settle	54
22 River Ribble – Great Mitton	55
23 Sankey to St Helens Canal	56
24 River Weaver – Church Minshull	56
25 River Dane	57
26 Danebridge Fisheries	57

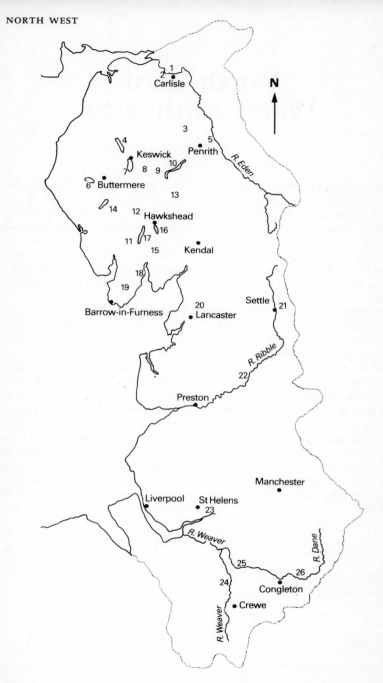

N

1
2 ● Carlisle

3
5
4
Keswick ● ● Penrith
7 8 9 10
6 ● Buttermere
13
14
12 Hawkshead
16
11 17
15 ● Kendal

18
19
Barrow-in-Furness ● 20 ● Lancaster Settle ● 21

22
Preston ●

Manchester ●

Liverpool ● St Helens ●
23
R. Weaver
R. Dane
25 26
24 ● Congleton
R. Weaver ● Crewe

R. Eden

R. Ribble

River Eden – Carlisle (Cumbria) NW 1

The Carlisle Angling Association control the fishing on the river for 7 miles (11.3 km) around Carlisle. The fishing is primarily for brown trout, salmon and sea trout but there are plenty of coarse fish which can be fished for, especially during the winter. The Eden is a spate river subject to fluctuating levels – especially early in the year when the salmon season begins. The best of the salmon fishing is in January, February and March and then again during September and October. During the winter the fishing for chub and dace can be excellent.

SPECIES Brown trout, salmon, sea trout, grayling, dace, and chub.

TECHNIQUES AND BAITS The dace and chub catches during the winter fall to float-fished maggots and casters. Most anglers fish for the trout on fly or worm. No spinning is allowed for the trout, and maggots are not to be used between 15th March and 15th June. Any legal method is allowed for the salmon.

SEASON 15th January to 14th October (salmon), 15th March to 30th September (trout) and 16th June to 14th March (coarse fish).

ACCESS The fishery is accessible from Carlisle town centre.

Permits can be obtained from McHardy Fishing Tackle, South Henry Street, Carlisle; R Raine & Co, 21 Warwick Road, Carlisle; or The Angling Centre, 105 Lowther Street, Carlisle. Separate permits are required for the salmon fishing.

The Lough Trout Fishery (Thurstonfield, near Carlisle, Cumbria) NW 2

This is a very beautiful 30 acre (12 ha) lake set among 50 acres (20 ha) of woodland. The area surrounding the lake is very rich in wildlife, making it an enchanting lake to fish. The lake is stream fed and well stocked with both brown and rainbow trout. The number of rods fishing the lake is restricted to 16 a day, and boats are available. The lake is fairly shallow with an average depth of 4 ft (1.2 m). The bag limit is six fish.

SPECIES Rainbow trout to 7 lb (3.2 kg) and brown trout to 3 lb (1.4 kg).

TECHNIQUES AND BAITS Fly fishing only. Loch-style fishing from the boats is the best technique.

SEASON 15th March to 30th September.

ACCESS The Lough is at Thurstonfield on the B5307 road, west of Carlisle. Advance booking is advisable from The Lough Trout Fishery, Thurstonfield, Carlisle.

Abbot Moss Lake (near Penrith, Cumbria) NW 3

This is a 3 acre (1.2 ha) lake managed as a trout fishery and regularly stocked. The water is stained a peaty brown colour, and consequently there is little weed growth. No wading is allowed, but there is one boat for anglers to use. A fishing hut is provided near to the lake, and has a table and benches where anglers can relax over lunch. The lake is surrounded by open grassland so there are no casting problems. The trout range in size from 10 oz (0.3 kg) to 5 lb (2.3 kg). The catch limit is five fish.

SPECIES Rainbow trout.

TECHNIQUES AND BAITS Fly fishing only.

SEASON Mid April to the end of October. The actual dates may vary, so please check.

ACCESS The number of anglers is restricted, so advance booking is advisable. For bookings and further information contact Mrs Potts, Castle Rig View, Calthwaite, near Penrith.

Bassenthwaite Lake (near Cockermouth, Cumbria) NW 4

Bassenthwaite is over 4 miles (6.4 km) long and is probably the most fruitful fishery among the larger lakes in the area. It is not as deep as the other lakes and has a maximum depth of 70 ft (21.3 m) with many shallower reed-fringed bays. The lake is connected to nearby Derwent Water by the River Derwent, which also flows out of the northern end of Bassenthwaite. Salmon run up the Derwent and into Bassenthwaite. The pike fishing in the lake is excellent, with a number of authenticated 20 lb (9.1 kg) fish. The average size of the pike is more like 8 lb (3.6 kg). The perch are also numerous and grow to $2\frac{1}{2}$ lb (1.1 kg). There are no boats for hire on the lake but you can launch your own if you obtain a special boat permit from the same source as the fishing permit.

SPECIES Pike, perch, brown trout, salmon (occasional) and eels.

TECHNIQUES AND BAITS Deadbaiting or livebaiting with small perch will catch pike, as will spinning. Some of the bigger perch are taken on legered lobworm in water up to 40 ft (12.2 m) deep.

SEASON 20th March to 14th September (brown trout) and 16th June to 14th March (coarse fish).

ACCESS The Keswick to Cockermouth A66(T) road runs alongside Bassenthwaite. The lake is under the control of the Lake District Special Planning Board. Most of the lake can be fished by a day permit but some of the eastern shoreline is privately owned. Permits are obtained from Temple's Sports Shop, Station Street, Keswick, Cumbria.

Whins Pond (near Penrith, Cumbria) NW 5

Despite the name 'pond', this is a fairly large water covering 28 acres (11 ha) which is managed as a trout fishery. The fishing is in a picturesque setting with two sides of the lake wooded, making the area secluded and sheltered. The water is stocked regularly throughout the season with fish up to 7 lb (3.2 kg). Wading is not allowed but boats are available. The bag limit is four fish for a full day. Half-day and evening permits are available.

A tranquil scene on the Grand Union Canal at Boxmoor.

(Above) The 'moonscape' of a newly dug gravel-pit.

(Below) Old Bury Hill Lake is a fine landscaped gravel-pit (see page 171).

SPECIES Rainbow trout.

TECHNIQUES AND BAITS Fly fishing only. Only legitimate flies and nymphs are allowed (not lures). Loch-style fishing from the boats works well.

SEASON 1st April to 30th September.

ACCESS Whins Pond is located close to Junction 40 on the M6 motorway. Take the main Alston A686 road to Edenhall.

Permits and information from Mrs E Siddle, Ewanway, Edenhall, Penrith.

Crummock Water (near Keswick, Cumbria) NW 6

Crummock Water lies between Buttermere and Loweswater, near Keswick. This lake has depths in excess of 100 ft (30 m). The lake contains brown trout, and some salmon and sea trout enter the lake when they come upriver to spawn. The perch are plentiful and there are also a few pike. In the deeper water there are also char, but fishing for them is not really worthwhile as they are not common.

SPECIES Brown trout, perch, sea trout, salmon, char and pike.

TECHNIQUES AND BAITS Most fish are taken by spinning or worm fishing.

SEASON 1st April to 31st October (salmon), 3rd April to 31st October (sea trout), 20th March to 14th September (brown trout) and 16th June to 14th March (coarse fish).

ACCESS Crummock Water lies alongside the B5289 Keswick to Cockermouth road.

Permits are obtained from Scale Hill Hotel, Loweswater, Cumbria.

Derwent Water (near Keswick, Cumbria) NW 7

This $3\frac{1}{2}$ mile (5.6 km) long water is connected to the southern end of Lake Bassenthwaite by the River Derwent. The lake is relatively shallow, with depths of less than 20 ft (6.1 m) within casting range of most of the shoreline. The deepest area drops away to 70 ft (21.3 m) and is just south of the four small islands in the lake. The lake is fairly rich in natural food, and subsequently the fish grow to a large size. The pike fishing can be very good and there is also a large population of perch. There are also brown trout and the occasional salmon which enters through the River Derwent. Another species in Derwent Water is the very rare vendace, a small silvery whitefish. The northern end of the lake gets crowded in the summer but the southern end is relatively peaceful.

SPECIES Pike, perch, brown trout, eels, vendace (rare) and salmon.

TECHNIQUES AND BAITS Most pike are taken on spinning tackle. The trout and perch are usually taken on worm baits.

SEASON 20th March to 14th September (trout) and 16th June to 14th March (coarse fish).

ACCESS The water is controlled by Keswick Angling Association and permits are obtained from Temple's Sports Shop, Station Street, Keswick. Boats can be hired from Keswick on the lake shore.

Watendlath Tarn (near Keswick, Cumbria) NW 8

This is a $6\frac{1}{2}$ acre (2.6 ha) natural lake which has been turned into a trout fishery. The lake is very deep and drops away quickly to over 50 ft (15.2 m). The banks are clear, allowing easy casting around the lake. Two boats are available for hiring by anglers. There are toilets on site and also a cafe. The lake is regularly stocked with both brown and rainbow trout. The bag limit is four fish.

SPECIES Brown trout to $1\frac{1}{2}$ lb (0.7 kg) and rainbow trout to $7\frac{1}{2}$ lb (3.4 kg).

TECHNIQUES AND BAITS Fly fishing only. This is a challenging fishery and the trout are not always easy to catch. The depth creates problems and there is also plenty of natural food. A sinking line is essential to lure any fish which happens to be lying deep, especially in hot weather.

SEASON 1st April to 31st October. Fishing from 9 am to 5 pm (day ticket) or 5 pm to dusk (evening ticket).

ACCESS Take the B5289 road from Keswick along the Borrowdale Valley. After 3 miles (4.8 km) turn off towards Watendlath village.

Permits are obtained from Mrs Richardson, Fold Head Farm, Watendlath, Keswick. For enquiries regarding the fishery contact Mr S Edmondson, Borrowdale Fisheries, Borrowdale, Keswick.

Red Tarn (near Ullswater, Cumbria) NW 9

This is among the most remote lakes in England and is only suitable for fit anglers who like some adventure with their fishing. The tarn is set in a natural amphitheatre nestling near the summit of Helvellyn 3000 ft (915 m) above sea-level. The tarn covers about 4 acres (1.6 ha) and can only be reached by a walk of several miles uphill all the way. There are plenty of brown trout in the tarn and also another of the rare whitefish family, the schelly. The fishing is good and you will never catch a wilder trout. It is virtually certain that you will have plenty of bank space at Red Tarn. However, one should never attempt to reach this remote hill tarn without proper clothing, and advising someone of your likely time of return.

SPECIES Brown trout and schelly.

TECHNIQUES AND BAITS Worm or fly fishing will catch fish, but fly tackle is easier to carry on the hike to the water.

SEASON 20th March to 14th September.

ACCESS The easiest route to Red Tarn is from Thirlspot on the western side of Helvellyn. The Tarn can also be approached from Glenridding. The fishing is free.

Ullswater (near Penrith, Cumbria) NW 10

A popular spot for holidaymakers, Ullswater is over 7 miles (11.3 km) long and, in places, the depth drops away to 200 ft (61 m). This is one of the few lakes to contain the very rare schelly, a silvery, herring-like fish. The small adipose fin near the tail points to it being a member of the trout family. The British record schelly was caught in Ullswater and weighed 1 lb 10 oz (0.7 kg). The predominant species are perch and brown trout, and the fishing for these is good. Salmon and sea trout enter the lake from the River Eamont at Pooley Bridge. Boats are available during the summer months from the boatyards at Glenridding and Pooley Bridge.

SPECIES Brown trout, char, perch, salmon, sea trout, schelly (rare) and eels.

TECHNIQUES AND BAITS Spinning and worm fishing take most fish.

SEASON 15th January to 14th October (salmon), 1st April to 14th October (sea trout), 20th March to 30th September (brown trout) and 16th June to 14th March (coarse fish).

ACCESS Ullswater lies alongside the A592 Penrith to Windermere road. The fishing is free.

Hill tarns (Cumbria)

There are many hill tarns in the Lake District which offer free fishing for brown trout and perch. The trout tend to be small but the perch are often numerous and sometimes big. These hill tarns vary in size and depth, but they seldom exceed 15 acres (6 ha) in area. The fishing in these tarns is unlikely to be scintillating but anglers who appreciate solitude and wide open spaces will enjoy the challenge they offer. The hill tarns have one thing in common, and that is they all require fell walking to reach them. The weather in the Lake District can close in very quickly so proper weather-protective clothing is essential. A large-scale map and compass are also worth taking, even in high summer.

Beacon Tarn (near Coniston) NW 11

This tarn is located high in the Blawith Fells to the west of Lake Coniston and covers 11 acres (4.5 ha). Take the A5084 road along the west bank of Coniston and at the southern end of the lake there is a turning off towards Water Yeat. Take this single-track road to Greenholme Farm. The tarn is a further $\frac{1}{4}$ mile (0.4 km) walk uphill along the public right of way towards Tarn Riggs. Free fishing is available.

Blea Tarn (near Boot) NW 12

Blea Tarn is situated 2 miles (3.2 km) west of the turning off towards the village of Boot on Eskdale Fell. A short steep climb is required to reach the water along the public right of way. Free fishing is available.

Blea Water (near Haweswater) NW 13

To reach this lake, follow the small stream which flows into the southern end of Haweswater and when the stream divides in two take the right-hand stream and follow it until Blea Water is reached. If you take the left-hand stream and follow its course you come to another small tarn also with free fishing.

Burnmoor Tarn (near Boot) NW 14

A 2 mile (3.2 km) walk north from the village of Boot leads to this tarn which is on Eskdale Fell. There are pike as well as perch and trout in this tarn. Free fishing.

High Dam (near Windermere) NW 15

Located near the southern tip of Lake Windermere, High Dam covers 10 acres (4 ha). The lake is near the village of Finsthwaite and it is well signposted. A car park is available near the lake but a stiff climb is needed to reach the actual water. Free fishing.

Esthwaite Water (near Windermere, Cumbria) NW 16

Esthwaite Water is 1¼ miles (2 km) long, covers 300 acres (121 ha) and is one of the most biologically rich lakes in the Lake District. It is one of the few Lakeland waters to support roach and rudd as well as the usual pike. The pike fishing is excellent, no doubt due to the good feed available, and a few sea trout also enter the lake each summer. Recently, the adjacent fish farm has been stocking the lake with rainbow trout, some of which are very large. During the summer months the lake receives a fresh stock every week. This lake is not greatly affected by the many tourists who descend on the popular nearby resorts of Windermere and Coniston Water each summer.

SPECIES Rainbow trout to 8 lb (3.6 kg), brown trout, roach, perch, rudd, pike to 20 lb (9.1 kg), eels and a few sea trout.

TECHNIQUES AND BAITS The fish respond to legering with maggot or worm baits in the shallower areas up to 20 ft (6 m). Spinning will take pike, perch and trout. There are no restrictions on methods and, to derive the greatest satisfaction, fly fishing ought to be undertaken for the rainbow trout.

SEASON No close season.

ACCESS Esthwaite lies alongside the B5285 road between Windermere and Hawkshead.

Day permits are obtained from The Trout Farm, Esthwaite; B & C Raistrick Ltd; The Post Office, Hawkshead; or Gills Cycles, Ambleside. For further details, contact Mr Woodhouse at The Trout Farm.

Coniston Water (Coniston, Cumbria) NW 17

Famous for Sir Donald Campbell's attempts at the world water speed record, Coniston is also well known among anglers for its char fishing. It is a very long, narrow lake with depths to over 200 ft (61 m). The char is not a very large fish, and the usual size is $\frac{3}{4}$ lb (0.3 kg). The close season for char has been lengthened recently in an effort to stop the decline in numbers (much damage has been done in the past by anglers removing far too many char from the water). Normally the char live in the very deep water and are not easy to catch, but at spawning time they venture into shallower water in large numbers. There are also plenty of trout and perch in Coniston, together with a few pike. A few boats can be hired from the boatyard in Coniston. No power boats are allowed on Coniston. Like most of the lakes in the area the bottom swarms with eels.

SPECIES Char, brown trout, pike, perch and eels.

TECHNIQUES AND BAITS Most char are taken on legered maggot or worm bait at long range. Worm fishing catches the perch and brown trout.

SEASON 1st May to 30th September (char), 20th March to 14th September (trout) and 16th June to 14th March (coarse fish).

ACCESS Coniston is near the town of Hawkshead, and the A5084 road runs close to the southern bank. The fishing is mostly free.

Ulverston Canal (Ulverston, Cumbria) NW 18

This canal is $1\frac{1}{4}$ miles (2 km) long and stretches from the town of Ulverston to Morecambe Bay. This is a coarse fishery which holds a good head of roach, bream, tench and carp. The depth is fairly even at 8 ft (2.4 m) throughout the length, but is shallower in the area of the low railway bridge half-way along the canal. Visiting anglers should be aware that match fishing takes place on the canal, especially at weekends. A notice informing anglers which lengths are being match fished is usually posted at the start of the road leading to the fishery.

SPECIES Roach, bream, perch, pike, tench and carp. There are also a few chub in the canal.

TECHNIQUES AND BAITS Canal float fishing tactics should be used. Fish very fine using small baits for the best results.

SEASON 16th June to 14th March.

ACCESS The start of the canal is located directly behind the Canal Tavern on the A590(T) road into Ulverston. A small single-track road runs along the entire length of the canal.

Permits may be obtained in advance from the fishing tackle shop in Ulverston or from the bailiff who will come and collect the fee on the bank.

Elliscales Ponds (Dalton-in-Furness, Cumbria) NW 19

Elliscales Ponds are five deep, flooded mine shafts which provide some first-class coarse fishing in an area where most waters contain only game fish. The perch and the rudd fishing is particularly good, with perch to $3\frac{1}{2}$ lb (1.6 kg) being caught in recent years. Another species caught to a large size is tench, and fish over 4 lb (1.8 kg) have been taken. One of the lakes also holds a number of pike.

SPECIES Tench, perch, roach, rudd, pike and a few bream.

TECHNIQUES AND BAITS Most methods of coarse fishing will catch the fish. Baits to try are maggots, casters, sweetcorn and worms.

SEASON 16th June to 14th March. Night fishing is allowed on these lakes by arrangement with the owner.

ACCESS Elliscales Ponds lie on the edge of Dalton-in-Furness on the A595 Askam road.

Permits to fish are obtained from the owner, Mr W Rigg, Elliscales Farm, Dalton-in-Furness.

Bank House Fly Fishery (Caton, near Lancaster, Lancashire) NW 20

Bank House is situated in the picturesque Lune Valley at the edge of the village of Caton. The water is 2 acres (0.8 ha) in extent, and is the only remaining mill lodge of a series of four which used to provide the mills of Caton with water power. The lake has been thoughtfully landscaped, with several islands to provide interest and seclusion for fishing. There are six casting jetties giving excellent access to the water. The well-appointed club house for anglers at the edge of the water has both toilet and cooking facilities and hot and cold water. The lake is stocked at least twice a week throughout the season. Six anglers a day are allowed to fish. The limit is four fish and once this limit is reached the angler must stop fishing or buy another permit.

SPECIES Brown trout, and rainbow trout to $10\frac{1}{2}$ lb (4.8 kg).

TECHNIQUES AND BAITS Fly fishing only. No long-shanked hooks or hooks larger than a size 10 may be used. Lures are not allowed on this fishery and only traditional nymphs, wet and dry flies are allowed. This is the type of water which the skilled nymph angler will enjoy. The water is clear and individual fish can be covered and tempted.

SEASON 1st March to 31st October. Fishing from 9 am to dusk.

ACCESS Caton is near Lancaster and can be reached by turning off the M6 at Junction 34 on to the A683.

Advance booking is advisable from Mr D J Dobson, Bank House Fly Fishery, Low Mill, Caton, near Lancaster.

River Ribble – Settle (North Yorkshire) NW 21

The River Ribble rises on Cam Fell very near the source of Yorkshire's River Wharfe but the Ribble flows down the western slopes of the Pennines, to enter the sea in a big estuary at Preston. In the upper reaches around Settle, the river is very much the typical upland trout river. The water cascades over rocks and boulders and then flows into deep smooth glides. The margins of the river are fringed with gravel beds and sand beds. The river reacts quickly to heavy rain and from running low and clear it can change to a brown frothing torrent in a few hours. The stretch at Settle covers 4 miles (6.4 km) of the river from the village of Stainforth 2 miles (3.2 km) upstream from Settle to Rathmell Beck 2 miles (3.2 km) downstream from Settle.

SPECIES Brown trout.

TECHNIQUES AND BAITS Fly fishing only. Wet fly fishing works best in the faster, broken water using standard spider patterns such as Waterhen Bloa. Dry fly will work well in the smoother glides and the tail end of pools.

SEASON 1st April to 31st October.

ACCESS Settle is on the A65(T) road running almost along the boundary between North Yorkshire and Lancashire.

Permits are obtained from the Royal Oak Inn at Settle.

The water is controlled by Settle Angling Club.

River Ribble – Great Mitton (near Clitheroe, Lancashire)
NW 22

This stretch of the Ribble includes the confluences of two major tributaries, the Hodder which is a game fish river and the Calder, which is a coarse fish river. The fishery covers the Ribble from Mitton Beck to Calder Foot, a distance of 1 mile (1.6 km). The fishing is divided into different sections. A permit can be obtained to fly fish for trout from Mitton Beck downstream to the confluence with the Hodder, a distance of $\frac{1}{2}$ mile (0.8 km). A permit to fish the whole stretch for salmon, brown trout and sea trout is also available. Another permit is also available to fish 656 ft (200 m) of the River Calder for coarse fish. When the trout season has closed permits are issued for coarse fishing on the entire stretch. The number of permits issued on any one day is restricted so advance booking is essential.

SPECIES Brown trout, sea trout, salmon, roach, chub, dace and barbel.

TECHNIQUES AND BAITS Fly fishing only is allowed for the brown trout. Spinning, fly fishing and worming are allowed for the salmon. During the winter, when coarse fishing is allowed, leger with a feeder for the chub. Float fishing with a stick float will take the chub, roach and dace; with maggots, bread or casters as bait.

SEASON April to October for game fish (the exact dates can change, so please check). 16th June to 14th March (coarse fish in the Calder). After the end of the trout season coarse fishing allowed in the Ribble. Fishing is from 8am to 12pm.

ACCESS Great Mitton is reached by taking the B6246 road off the A59 at Whalley south of Clitheroe.

Permits and information are available from Mrs M M Hayles, Mitton Hall Farm, Great Mitton, near Clitheroe, Lancashire.

Sankey to St Helens Canal (near Warrington, Cheshire) NW 23

This stretch of canal is unusual in that there are no boats to cause problems for anglers. The fishery, which centres around the Sankey Bridges, is controlled by Lymm Angling Club, who have created a very impressive fishery. The section between the Sankey Bridges and Ferry Inn is especially good. The canal has depths up to 7 ft (2.1 m) here, and is fringed with reedmace and rushes. The canal supports a variety of coarse fish, including some big carp. The main sport is with carp, tench, and roach. The tench fishing is especially good. Keepnets are banned.

SPECIES Roach, bream, rudd, golden rudd, crucian carp, carp, tench, chub, dace, perch, eels, pike and gudgeon.

TECHNIQUES AND BAITS The water is very clear so tackle needs to be fine. Float fishing with a slim-bodied waggler float is the best method. Use maggots or casters as bait and loose feed very sparingly.

SEASON 16th June to 14th March.

ACCESS The water at Sankey Bridges is reached via the A57(T) road, just west of Warrington.

Permits are obtained on the bank from bailiffs. Information regarding the fishery can be obtained from Mr P James.

River Weaver – Church Minshull (near Winsford, Cheshire) NW 24

The River Weaver rises near Audlem in Cheshire and flows north and then west to join the Mersey near Frodsham. This fishery covers 6 miles (9.7 km) of the river between Newbridge and Church Minshull, near Winsford. For most of the length, the fishing is on both banks but there are a few short lengths of single-bank fishing which are signposted. The river is slow flowing and fairly deep and the banks are fairly open with little bankside vegetation. The predominant species are bream with some large carp.

SPECIES Bream, carp, chub and roach.

TECHNIQUES AND BAITS Float fishing using a waggler float brings good results. The best baits are maggots, casters or bread. Sometimes light legering with a swing tip rod produces better results than the float.

SEASON 16th June to 14th March.

ACCESS Access to the river is from the B5074 road near Church Minshull.

Permits are obtained from bailiffs on the bank. The fishing is controlled by Winsford and District Angling Association whose Secretary is Mr J Bailey, 22 Plover Avenue, Winsford, Cheshire.

River Dane (near Middlewich, Cheshire) NW 25

The River Dane is a tributary of the River Weaver and rises just west of Buxton from where it flows south and then west to join the Weaver near Hartford. This fishery includes both banks at Croxton just outside Middlewich. The fishery is 1 mile (1.6 km) long and the river is small and fast flowing and fairly shallow. Dace and chub are the predominant species but there are also a number of barbel in the river.

SPECIES Chub, dace, roach, perch and barbel.

TECHNIQUES AND BAITS Float fishing using a stick float with maggots or casters as bait is the best technique for the most fish. The bigger chub and some barbel are taken on leger tackle, using maggot, cheese and bread as bait.

SEASON 16th June to 14th March.

ACCESS The river is reached from the A54 close to Middlewich.

Permits are obtained from bailiffs on the bank. The fishery is controlled by Winsford and District Angling Association whose Secretary is Mr J Bailey, 22 Plover Avenue, Winsford, Cheshire.

Danebridge Fisheries (near Macclesfield, Cheshire) NW 26

This is a 2 acre (0.8 ha) lake in a beautiful setting by the River Dane, which is managed as a trout fishery. The lake is stocked with rainbow trout from the trout farm which is part of the site. The average depth of the water is 8 ft (2.4 m) and the fishing is restricted to 12 anglers a day. The bag limit is three fish per day for a full permit. Five-hour session tickets are available which allow a two fish limit. The size of the trout is mostly in the 2–4 lb (0.9–1.8 kg) range but a few really massive rainbow trout are stocked each year.

SPECIES Rainbow trout – record: 16 lb 2 oz (7.3 kg).

TECHNIQUES AND BAITS Fly fishing only with wet or dry flies. Nymphs, such as Damselfly, Mayfly and Pheasant Tail are all effective. Dry fly fishing works best in July and August.

SEASON The season opens 1st March. The closing date varies.

ACCESS The fishery is on the A54 Buxton to Congleton road.

Permits are obtained from Mr D C Chadwick, Pingle Cottage, Danebridge, Wincle, near Macclesfield, Cheshire.

Northumbrian Water Authority

The Northumbrian Water Authority covers an area from just north of Berwick-on-Tweed, across to Kielder Water and down the Pennines to Barnard Castle, and then to the North Sea coast in Cleveland taking in Lockwood Beck Reservoir. This area covers the counties of Northumberland, Durham and Cleveland – the last of which used to be part of North Yorkshire. Scenically the region takes in some wild and magnificent countryside. The north and west of the region is hill country, with vast forested areas. The eastern strip of the region, from Newcastle down to Middlesborough, is heavily industrialised and includes the great ICI chemical complexes at Billingham and Wilton.

The rivers in the region are mostly for game fishing, and any coarse fishing is confined to the lower reaches of the rivers. Also, many of the best coarse fisheries are in private hands with no day ticket facilities for visitors. The lower Tees is probably the best coarse fishing river in the region with some good chub, dace and roach catches to be had.

The most important fishery in the region is the massive Kielder Water. This is a magnificent lake surrounded by forests and, although the fishing is not in the same class as that of Rutland or Grafham Reservoirs, it is well worth a visit. The upland reservoirs are not the places to visit if you want to catch very large fish, but they offer the chance of catching some good brown or rainbow trout among superb scenery. These supply reservoirs also provide the visitor with fairly inexpensive fishing, with additional facilities for visitors' families such as nature trails and forest walks.

Key	Page
1 Bakethin Reservoir	59
2 Kielder Water	60
3 Fontburn Reservoir	61
4 Burnhope Reservoir	61
5 Tunstall Reservoir	61
6 Cow Green Reservoir	62
7 Selset Reservoir	62
8 Grassholme Reservoir	63
9 Balderhead Reservoir	63
10 Blackton Reservoir	64
11 Hury Reservoir	64
12 Lockwood Beck Reservoir	64
13 Scaling Reservoir	65

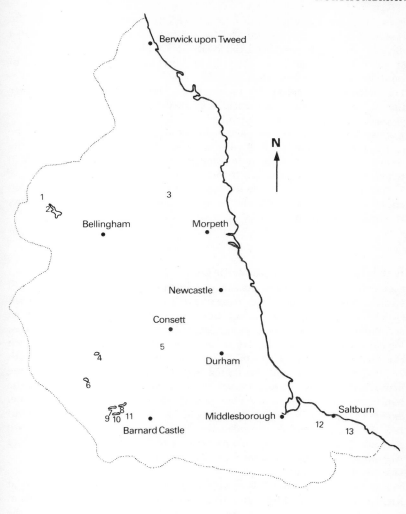

Bakethin Reservoir (near Kielder, Northumberland) N 1

Bakethin Reservoir is part of the Kielder Water Scheme and forms the tail of the 7 mile (11.3 km) long Kielder Water. Bakethin covers 138 acres (56 ha) and is used as a header tank to prevent large expanses of mudflats appearing in conditions of drawdown. The whole reservoir and adjoining land has been classed as a conservation area, and the southern shore of the reservoir is out of bounds. The growth rate of the fish in Bakethin Reservoir

59

is excellent, and already trout over 6 lb (2.7 kg) have been recorded. The reservoir is regularly stocked and the fishing is restricted to 50 anglers a day. No wading is permitted but boats are available.

SPECIES Brown trout to 6 lb 2 oz (2.8 kg), brook trout to 3 lb (1.4 kg), and rainbow trout to 5 lb (2.3 kg).

TECHNIQUES AND BAITS Fly fishing only. Most methods work, but lure fishing with sinking lines seems to produce the best fish.

SEASON 1st May to 30th September.

ACCESS The fisherman's car park, fishing lodge and the north shore can be reached via the unclassified road to Butteryhaugh at the head of the reservoir. The reservoir is signposted from the North Tyne Road (C200) which runs alongside the south shore of Kielder Water.

Permits are on a self-service basis from the fishing lodge. Written enquiries to the Kielder Water Operations Centre, Yarrow Moor, Falstone, Hexham, Northumberland.

Kielder Water (near Bellingham, Northumberland) N 2

Kielder Water is the largest man-made lake in western Europe, and is set in western Europe's largest man-made forest. The reservoir covers 2,684 acres (1,086 ha), and because of its huge area it is being developed to accommodate many types of water recreation. Caravan and camping sites, log cabins and outdoor activity centres are also being developed to match the provision of water sports. The fishery was originally stocked with 250,000 brown trout and it is hoped that they will breed naturally in the many feeder burns to create a natural brown trout fishery. Fishing from the bank can be undertaken anywhere along the 26 mile (41.8 km) shoreline, except in the clearly marked sanctuary areas. Wading is not permitted but boat fishing is allowed, provided the boats are manned by at least two persons. Boats may be reserved by writing to The Operations Centre (see Access details). The bag limit for trout is eight fish.

SPECIES Brown trout.

TECHNIQUES AND BAITS Worm fishing and fly fishing are allowed at Kielder, and both methods catch trout. Fly fishing works best from a boat, and traditional wet fly fishing with a team of three flies fished across the waves works well.

SEASON 1st June to 30th September inclusive.

ACCESS Kielder is located about 2 miles (3.2 km) from the Scottish border on the edge of the Northumberland National Park. The nearest town is Bellingham, and to reach Kielder from there take the North Tyne Road (clearly signposted) through the border forest.

Fishing permits must be bought before fishing from the Matthews Linn Fishing Centre at the Kielder end of the reservoir. Written enquiries regarding Kielder Water should be made to the Kielder Water Operations

Centre, Yarrow Moor, Falstone, Hexham, Northumberland.

Fontburn Reservoir (Rothbury, Northumberland) N 3

Fontburn Reservoir occupies an attractive site beneath the Simonside Hills, and is bordered on one side by shelter belts and on the other by agricultural land. The reservoir is not stocked and contains a large head of native brown trout. The average weight of the fish caught is 1 lb (0.5 kg). The western end of the reservoir is designated as a nature reserve and access is prohibited. Wading is not permitted. Anglers should note that water-skiing is allowed on Wednesday, Saturday and Sunday in a designated part of the reservoir. The reservoir covers 87 acres (35 ha), and there is no bag limit on trout caught.

SPECIES Brown trout.

TECHNIQUES AND BAITS Fly fishing, spinning and worm fishing are all allowed.

SEASON 22nd March to 30th September.

ACCESS The reservoir is situated 5 miles (8 km) south of Rothbury on the B6342 Rothbury to Scots Gap Road. Access is signposted along the private road. The fishing lodge, toilet and car park are situated to the south of the dam.

A self-service ticket system operates from the fishing lodge.

Burnhope Reservoir (Wearhead, County Durham) N 4

Burnhope covers 408 acres (165 ha), and is located in a natural wilderness that has been tamed by the conifer plantations which have been planted down the slopes of the valley leading to the water's edge. This reservoir is used as a compensation reservoir for the River Wear. The fishing rights are controlled by a private club but ten permits a day are available for non-members.

SPECIES Brown trout and rainbow trout.

TECHNIQUES AND BAITS Fly fishing and worm fishing are allowed.

SEASON 22nd March to 30th September (brown trout) and 22nd March to 31st October (rainbow trout).

ACCESS Access is from Ireshopeburn, Wearhead and Cowshill.

Tickets are obtained from the small fishing lodge at the north end of the dam where cars may be parked.

Tunstall Reservoir (near Wolsingham, County Durham) N 5

Tunstall Reservoir lies in the valley of the Waskerley Beck, some 3 miles (4.8 km) north of Wolsingham in Weardale, and covers 112 acres (45 ha). The reservoir is surrounded by mature woodland and well-tended fields, and is a most attractive place to visit. The reservoir is stocked with brown and rainbow trout. Boats can be hired for a full day or evening only.

SPECIES Rainbow trout and brown trout.

TECHNIQUES AND BAITS Fly fishing only. All standard methods of fly fishing will catch fish.

SEASON 22nd March to 30th September (brown trout) and 22nd March to 31st October (rainbow trout).

ACCESS The reservoir is approached via the dead-end road to Tunstall House, which leaves Wolsingham at the west end of the village.

Tickets are obtained by self-service from the fishing lodge at the west bank car park.

Cow Green Reservoir (Upper Teesdale, County Durham) N 6

Cow Green Reservoir covers 780 acres (315 ha) and is the highest of the Northumbrian Water Authority's waters. Because of its unique geographical situation, high in the Pennines in an area well known for its botanical and geological interest, it attracts many visitors. Below the dam lie two of Upper Teesdale's major scenic attractions: the foaming cataract of Cauldron Snout and the dramatic confluence of Maize Beck with the infant Tees below the crags of Falcon Clints. The fishing is for the native brown trout which exceed 2 lb (0.9 kg). Due to its high location, Cow Green is subject to severe weather conditions and anglers should always come prepared for sudden rain squalls.

SPECIES Brown trout.

TECHNIQUES AND BAITS Fly and worm fishing are allowed.

SEASON 22nd March to 30th September.

ACCESS The reservoir is best approached via the unclassified but signposted road running west from Langdon Beck Hotel on the B6277 Alston to Middleton-in-Teesdale road. A car park and toilets (including those for the disabled) are provided at the reservoir.

Permits are obtained from a self-service system at the boathouse building next to the car park.

Selset Reservoir (Middleton-in-Teesdale, County Durham) N 7

Selset Reservoir covers 625 acres (253 ha), and the water is used for river regulation and supply purposes on Teesside. The reservoir is also open to the public for birdwatching, fishing and sailing. It holds a good head of native brown trout and has been stocked with rainbow trout. Fishing is from the bank only.

SPECIES Brown trout and rainbow trout.

TECHNIQUES AND BAITS Fly fishing only. All methods of fly fishing will catch the trout.

SEASON 22nd March to 30th September.

ACCESS Selset is situated south of the B6276 Middleton-in-Teesdale to Brough road, 5 miles (8 km) from Middleton-in-Teesdale. Access to the reservoir is by the main entrance from the B6276 at the reservoir's eastern end. A car park is located at the waterside.

Tickets are obtained by a self-service system at the fishing lodge.

Grassholme Reservoir (near Mickleton, County Durham)
N 8

Grassholme is the lower of the two reservoirs in Lunedale and covers 250 acres (101 ha). The reservoir is long and narrow and is crossed at the southern end by the Pennine Way. In common with other upland reservoirs, Grassholme maintains a good head of native brown trout, and since 1972 there has been a continual stocking policy both with brown and rainbow trout. Boats can be hired for fishing. The catch limit is eight fish.
SPECIES Brown trout and rainbow trout.
TECHNIQUES AND BAITS Fly and worm fishing are allowed.
SEASON 22nd March to 30th September (brown trout), 22nd March to 31st October (rainbow trout).
ACCESS Grassholme Reservoir is situated between the B6276 Brough to Middleton-in-Teesdale road, and the unclassified road running from Mickleton to Kelton. Access is gained via the main gate on the Mickleton to Kelton road from where a tarmac track leads down to the dam and car park.

A self-service ticket system operates at the fishing lodge near the dam. Boats can be booked in advance from The Warden, Grassholme Reservoir, near Mickleton, Middleton-in-Teesdale, County Durham.

Balderhead Reservoir (near Cotherstone, County Durham)
N 9

Balderhead is the highest of the three Baldersdale reservoirs and covers 576 acres (233 ha). It is very similar in character to neighbouring Selset Reservoir in Lunedale, being in a wild moorland setting. The western end of the reservoir is a favourite resting place for migrating wildfowl. The fishing is leased to a private angling club but ten permits a day are available to visitors. Fishing is for the native brown trout, and returns can be very rewarding. There is no catch limit.
SPECIES Brown trout.
TECHNIQUES AND BAITS Fly fishing and worm fishing are allowed.
SEASON 22nd March to 30th September.
ACCESS The reservoir is approached from the northern side via the C class road running from Romaldkirk through Hunderthwaite village.

Tickets are issued on a self-service basis from the fishing lodge.

Blackton Reservoir (near Cotherstone, County Durham) N 10

Blackton is the middle of the three reservoirs in the Baldersdale Valley, and covers 110 acres (44 ha). The fishing rights on this reservoir are leased to an angling club but ten permits a day are available for visiting anglers. The fishing is for native brown trout and the reservoir is not stocked. The Pennine Way, Britain's first long distance footpath, crosses Baldersdale via the bridge at the head of the reservoir.

SPECIES Native brown trout.

TECHNIQUES AND BAITS Fly and worm fishing are allowed.

SEASON 22nd March to 30th September.

ACCESS Access by car is via the unclassified road from Cotherstone to the western end of Hury Reservoir. Here a stout iron gate on the right gives access to the unsurfaced road that leads to the parking area above the subsidiary dam.

Tickets are obtained from a self-service system at the fishing lodge near the car park.

Hury Reservoir (near Cotherstone, County Durham) N 11

Hury Reservoir covers 204 acres (83 ha) and is one of the oldest reservoirs in the area. There is a by-pass channel which runs along the south shore which takes water from a subsidiary dam at the head of the reservoir, and there is also a fish ladder for migrating fish. The surroundings of this reservoir are more pastoral than others in the area. The reservoir holds a good head of native brown trout and, since 1979, has been stocked with brown and rainbow trout. There are also some perch present in this reservoir. Hury Reservoir is being developed as a site where disabled members of the public can fish and relax, and special facilities have been built. These include toilets for the disabled, ramped pathways for access to the water's edge and fishing platforms over the water. Special permits at a cheaper rate are available to the disabled. Boats can be hired to fish the reservoir and may be booked in advance. The catch limit is eight trout.

SPECIES Rainbow trout, brown trout and perch.

TECHNIQUES AND BAITS Fly fishing and worm fishing are allowed.

SEASON 22nd March to 30th September (brown trout) and 22nd March to 31st October (rainbow trout).

ACCESS Access to the reservoir is at either end of the dam via either the C class road from Hunderthwaite along the north side of the valley or via the unclassified road from Cotherstone along the south side of the valley leading to the main car park at Hury House.

Tickets from the fishing lodge are obtained by a self-service system.

Lockwood Beck Reservoir (near Whitby, North Yorkshire) N 12

Lockwood Beck covers 60 acres (24 ha), and is an attractive reservoir set among mature plantations and farmland. It is regularly stocked with both brown and rainbow trout. Boats are available for hire and enquiries for boat bookings should be made to the site warden.

SPECIES Brown trout and rainbow trout.

TECHNIQUES AND BAITS Fly fishing only. All fly fishing tactics work on Lockwood Beck, and there are some good evening rises on this water. Small black dry flies work well, especially in a flat calm.

SEASON 22nd March to 30th September (brown trout) and 22nd March to 31st October (rainbow trout).

ACCESS The reservoir is just off the A171 Guisborough to Whitby road. Entry is via a narrow road over a cattle grid at the north-east corner of the reservoir which leads to the car park.

A self-service ticket system operates at the fishing lodge. Enquiries to the Northumbrian Water Authority, Tees Division office.

Scaling Reservoir (near Whitby, North Yorkshire) N 13

This reservoir covers 105 acres (42 ha), and is close to Lockwood Beck Reservoir. It lies within the North Yorkshire Moors National Park and is a popular area for recreation and birdwatching. The reservoir is valuable to wildfowl, and a nature reserve has been created at the south-west corner of the reservoir. The reservoir is stocked annually with brown trout and rainbow trout.

SPECIES Rainbow trout and brown trout.

TECHNIQUES AND BAITS Fly fishing and worm fishing are allowed.

SEASON 25th March to 30th September (brown trout) and 25th March to 31st October (rainbow trout).

ACCESS Scaling Reservoir is close to the A171 Guisborough to Whitby road.

Tickets are obtained from the fishing lodge located beneath the sailing club room verandah. A self-service system operates. Enquiries to the Northumbrian Water Authority, Tees Division office.

Yorkshire
Water Authority

The Yorkshire Water Authority controls an area from Sheffield and Doncaster in the south to Teesside in the north, and from the Pennines to the North Sea coast.

The Yorkshire Ouse river system is one of the largest in the country and virtually all of the rivers in the system flow from the Pennines towards the North Sea, where they converge to form the Humber Estuary. The quality of the rivers varies tremendously. Some of the rivers in the industrial south of the county are little more than open sewers, whereas most of the Dales rivers are clean, and flow through some of the most beautiful scnery in the British Isles.

The principal river of the system is the River Ouse, into which all the other rivers flow. The Ouse is really a continuation of the River Ure which changes its name when the Ouse Beck enters the river near Aldwark Bridge.

The middle and upper reaches of the rivers are fairly fast flowing and offer trout and grayling fishing, as well as some first-class coarse fishing. The middle and lower reaches of the rivers, and the Ouse itself, are coarse fisheries with big chub and barbel the predominant fish. A common feature of Yorkshire rivers is the fact that they are all spate rivers: heavy rain falling on to the Pennines runs straight into the rivers. The rivers can rise very rapidly and care should always be taken when fishing from islands or stretches with steep banks. It is possible for the Ure and Swale to rise several feet in an hour, especially during heavy summer thunderstorms.

The Yorkshire Water Authority area has few places where stillwater fishing can be enjoyed, but there are one or two notable exceptions. Hornsea Mere once held the national roach record with a 3 lb 10 oz (1.6 kg) specimen taken in 1917 by Wilf Cutting. Another stillwater worth visiting is Semerwater, which must be one of the most elevated bream fisheries in the country, set in a natural amphitheatre of Pennine peaks. Supply reservoirs in the region offer some fairly inexpensive trout fishing in pleasant surroundings, but the fishing on these reservoirs has not been as well developed as in other regions.

The Yorkshire Water Authority rod licence covers trout, coarse and salmon fishing in all the rivers in the region, with the exception of the River Esk.

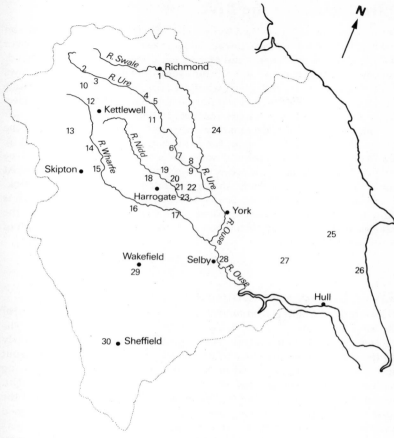

Key

Page

1 River Swale –
Richmond   68

2 River Ure –
Hawes   69

3 River Ure –
Bainbridge   69

4 River Ure –
Middleham   70

5 River Ure –
Spennithorne   70

6 River Ure – Ripon   71

7 River Ure –
Newby Hall   71

8 River Ure –
Boroughbridge   72

9 River Ure –
Boroughbridge   72

10 Semer Water   73

11 Leighton Reservoir   73

12 Greenfield Lake
and Beck   74

13 Malham Tarn   74

14 River Wharfe –
Grassington to
Appletreewick   75

15 River Wharfe –
Bolton Abbey   76

16 River Wharfe –
Pool-in-Wharfedale   76

17 River Wharfe –
Wetherby   77

18 Washburn Valley
Reservoirs   77

19 Farmire Fishery   78

20 Hay-A-Park   79

21 River Nidd –
Knaresborough   80

22 River Nidd – The
Lido, Knaresborough   80

23 River Nidd –
Little Ribston   81

24 Elm Hag Lake   81

25 Driffield Canal and
Frodingham Beck   82

26 Hornsea Mere   83

27 Market Weighton
Canal   83

28 Three Lakes   84

29 Nostell Priory
Fisheries   84

30 Damflask Reservoir   85

Introduction to the River Swale

The River Swale originates as a series of becks, high up in the Pennines on Birkdale Common. It quickly cascades down the valley through the villages of Muker, Gunnerside, Reeth and Marske to the market town of Richmond. This stretch of the river provides fishing for trout and grayling. As it flows down Swaledale the Swale is fed by hundreds of tiny becks and, by the time it reaches Richmond, the river is quite sizeable. The pace of the river slows down at Richmond as it reaches the Vale of York.

From Richmond downstream coarse fish predominate. At Topcliffe the weir pool on the Swale is famous for its big barbel. The fishing at Topcliffe has declined, but there are still some specimen barbel and chub to be caught. The Swale also produces some very big roach in these reaches. At Topcliffe the Swale is joined by the large tributary known as the Cod Beck, which flows through Thirsk. Below Topcliffe is Cundall Lodge, which is another stretch noted for its big barbel. The Swale then flows through the villages of Helperby and Myton before flowing into the Ure just south of Boroughbridge.

River Swale – Richmond (North Yorkshire) Y 1

The Richmond Angling Club control the fishing on over 8 miles (12.9 km) of the River Swale from Marske Bridge through Richmond to Brompton. The fishing is on both banks except for certain short lengths which are clearly signposted. Between Marske and Richmond there is some excellent trout and grayling fishing. Downstream from Richmond there are barbel during the summer and, in certain swims, large numbers of this fish can be caught. In general, the barbel around Richmond are not as big as lower down the river but fish up to 8 lb (3.6 kg) are caught. The dace fishing is very good and there are plenty of chub. The ticket for this stretch of river also covers the River Tees at Barnard Castle and three carp ponds in the Scorton area.

SPECIES Dace, chub, pike, grayling, brown trout and barbel.

TECHNIQUES AND BAITS Spinning and livebaiting are not allowed but anglers can use any other legitimate method of fishing. Most anglers float fish maggots, but legering is better for chub and barbel.

SEASON 25th March to 30th September (brown trout) and 1st June to 27th February (coarse fish).

ACCESS See above.

Day permits can be obtained from the following shops: Langstaff's Tackle Shop, Darlington; Metcalfe's Sports and Tackle, Richmond; or Angler's Corner, Middlesborough. Further details from Mr D Hutchinson, the Honorary Secretary, Richmond District Angling Society, Crosslanes, Richmond.

Introduction to the River Ure

The River Ure rises some 2000 ft (610 m) above sea-level on Lunds Fell, and flows south and east across the Vale of York. In the upper reaches, between Hawes and Wensley, the river holds plenty of trout and grayling. The grayling become more numerous towards Wensley. At Bainbridge the River Bain, which flows from Lake Semer Water, joins the Ure. This reach of the river varies in character between long shallow glides, deep pools and spectacular cascading falls. More impressive waterfalls occur at Aysgarth and Redmire, and Redmire Falls marks the upper limit of most species of coarse fish. Below the Falls, dace, chub, barbel and even pike can be found.

At Middleham the river changes character again for several miles. Between Middleham and Cover Bridge the river runs fairly slow and deep. Grayling are less numerous here and some big roach and perch can be caught. From Cover Bridge to Ripon most of the fishing is in private hands and the fishing is generally managed for trout, but some good-quality coarse fish abound in this length of the river.

At Ripon Racecourse the river deepens and the point where the canal joins the river marks the upstream limit of the navigable river. Below Ripon coarse fish predominate and there are plenty of opportunities for the visiting angler to fish. The River Swale flows into the Ure below Boroughbridge, and at Aldwark the Ure changes its name to the Ouse.

River Ure – Hawes (North Yorkshire) Y 2

This fishery covers 15 miles (24.1 km) of the upper Ure from its headwaters above the Moorcock Inn right down to the notice board 2 miles (3.2 km) above Bainbridge. The fishing is for grayling only, as tickets are not issued during the trout season. Both banks may be fished. Also included in the ticket is the fishing on all the tributaries to the Ure, including Hardrow Beck, famous for its 100 ft (30 m) waterfall. The grayling fishing can be very good especially in the lower part of the fishery.
SPECIES Grayling.

TECHNIQUES AND BAITS Fly fishing with wet flies such as Snipe and Purple, Waterhen Bloa and Partridge and Orange will take the grayling. Trotting the deeper glides with float maggot or redworm will also catch a lot of fish, especially in cold weather. There is no restriction on baits.
SEASON 1st October to 27th February. No Sunday fishing is allowed.
ACCESS Permits can be obtained from Mr A Barnes, Merridene, Gayle, Hawes.

River Ure – Bainbridge (North Yorkshire) Y 3

This fishery covers about 6 miles (9.7 km) of river from 3 miles (4.8 km) above Yorebridge to 1 mile (1.6 km) below the village of Worton. The fishing is mostly from both banks but there are short private stretches near Worton which are clearly signposted. The river is interesting at Bainbridge as it twists and turns, creating some good holding pools.

SPECIES Brown trout and grayling.

TECHNIQUES AND BAITS Fly fishing and worm fishing are allowed. Traditional wet flies work equally well for the trout and the grayling. A good grayling fly is Sturdy's Fancy. In spate conditions float-fished worm will catch a lot of fish. Maggots are not allowed.

SEASON 25th March to 30th September (trout) and 1st June to 27th February (grayling).

ACCESS For permits and enquiries contact the Secretary of Wensleydale Angling Association, Mr H G Leyland, Millgarth, Bainbridge, near Leyburn.

River Ure – Middleham (North Yorkshire) Y 4

The river starts to run deep at this point, with some big barbel and chub on the top section. The left bank for one field above the iron bridge and two fields below the bridge has good spots for chub and barbel. There are also a lot of quality dace and grayling above the bridge. On the right-hand bank downstream of the iron bridge, the first field can be fished, as can the stretch of about $\frac{1}{2}$ mile (800 m) to the notice board near the riding school. In between is a big riverside meadow where the fishing is strictly reserved for residents of Middleham.

SPECIES Barbel, roach, dace, chub, grayling, perch and some big pike. There are also a few brown trout.

TECHNIQUES AND BAITS Most anglers float fish maggots for the smaller fish. Legered lobworm will catch barbel, chub and the large perch.

SEASON 1st June to 27th February.

ACCESS Parking is on the land at the downstream end of the big meadow and on the grass margins on the Leyburn side of the iron bridge.

Day permits should be obtained before fishing from the Old Horn Inn, Spennithorne, North Yorkshire.

River Ure – Spennithorne (North Yorkshire) Y 5

The river here is fairly slow flowing, and has the advantage that it can take quite an amount of floodwater before making fishing impossible. The fishing is on the left bank from the signpost at the wall end to the notice board below Beggar's Mouth Beck. Only anglers are allowed on this water (i.e. no family picnics). This is not an easy water in which to catch fish, although it holds a good head of large fish, especially perch. In recent seasons a lot of perch over 2 lb (0.9 kg) have been caught.

SPECIES Dace, roach, perch, pike and a few chub.

TECHNIQUES AND BAITS Lobworm seems to be the best bait for perch. Float fished maggots are the best bait for the other species.

SEASON 1st June to 27th February inclusive.

ACCESS Day permits are obtained from the Old Horn Inn, Spennithorne, and must be bought before fishing.

River Ure – Ripon (North Yorkshire) Y 6

This stretch of several miles of fishing from the confluence of Hutton Beck downstream through Fishergreen to the Yacht Club near the racecourse includes some superb coarse fishing for chub, barbel and dace. In the winter some very large dace and grayling catches are taken in the deeper water upstream of North Bridge. In the bottom section below Hewick Bridge sizeable roach and perch are showing in catches.

SPECIES Chub, barbel, dace, roach, perch, grayling, brown trout, eels and pike.

TECHNIQUES AND BAITS Float-fished maggots in the glides are best for dace, chub and grayling. Leger cheese and bread for the better chub. In the deep water, leger caster and bread flake for the big roach. Fly and worm fishing only are allowed for the trout.

SEASON 1st June to 27th February (coarse fish) and 25th March to 31st May (trout).

ACCESS Permits can be obtained from Mr R C Hodgson, The Tackle and Gun Shop, 7 Queen Street, Ripon.

River Ure – Newby Hall (North Yorkshire) Y 7

Newby Hall Estate lies between Ripon and Boroughbridge and the house and grounds are open to the public. In the estate the river flows over a weir and there is also a canal which by-passes the weir. Fishing is available on the estate for visiting anglers. The roach fishing is very good and there are also some very large perch. Chub, dace and barbel are also plentiful at Newby. The weir pool is a natural holding pool for the few salmon that run up the Ure.

SPECIES Roach, perch, dace, chub, pike, barbel and brown trout.

TECHNIQUES AND BAITS All general methods of coarse fishing will catch the coarse fish. Legered caster is a good chub and roach bait.

SEASON 1st June to 27th February (coarse fish) and 25th March to 30th September (brown trout). Access to the estate from 1 hour after sunrise to 1 hour after sunset.

ACCESS The entrance to Newby Hall is at Skelton, between Langthorpe and Bridge Hewick.

Permits are obtained from the Estate Office at Newby Hall, No. 28 The

Lodges, Skelton (i.e. the Lodge Gate); or Mr J Steel, Crossways, Bishop Monkton, North Yorkshire. For further details contact the Estate Office, Newby Hall.

River Ure – Boroughbridge (North Yorkshire) Y 8

The Harrogate and Claro Angling Association own this stretch of the river and the upper limit is the old A1 road bridge in the town. The left-hand bank can be fished downstream from the bridge as far as the canal mouth at Milby. The canal can also be fished from Milby up to the notice board over the gravel workings. On the same permit, another short stretch can be fished from the weir upstream and round the point to the notice board in the canal. The big bay at Milby Lock where the canal enters the river is a pike 'hot spot'. Most bream are caught on the point above the weir. The canal holds mostly small fish and is best fished if the river is in flood.

SPECIES Chub, barbel, roach, perch, dace, bream and pike.

TECHNIQUES AND BAITS The stretch has a lot of willow bushes and legering under these will catch plenty of chub and barbel. Trotting with maggot or caster will take most species. The larger roach fall to legered caster which is also a good method for chub in winter.

SEASON 1st June to 27th February inclusive.

ACCESS Tickets must be obtained before fishing from M H and C Johnson (Fishing Tackle), Briggate, Knaresborough, North Yorkshire.

River Ure – Boroughbridge (North Yorkshire) Y 9

This stretch of fishing covers the right-hand bank downstream from the old cricket field to Hall Arms Lane. The first part of the fishery to Milby Lock is not used by boats. From opposite Milby Lock downstream to Hall Arms Lane the river is used by a few boats but the traffic is not very great, especially in winter. This is a good chub fishery with some big barbel also present. There are also some big pike to be caught. No day tickets are issued for Sundays on this length. The fishery covers $1\frac{1}{2}$ miles (2.4 km) of river.

SPECIES Chub, pike, barbel, roach, perch, bream, dace, eels and gudgeon.

TECHNIQUES AND BAITS Legered cheese is a deadly bait for the chub, and during the summer the barbel respond to legered worm or swimfeeder maggot.

SEASON 1st June to 27th February inclusive.

ACCESS The river is approached by the lane to the old cricket field beyond the Market Square, and also down Hall Arms Lane, where cars can be parked at the end of the lane.

Permits should be obtained before fishing from Tophams Post Office, Boroughbridge.

Semer Water (near Bainbridge, North Yorkshire) Y 10

Semer Water, a large shallow lake at the top of Wensleydale, is fed by the
River Bain. It normally covers 100 acres (40 ha) but in winter it can flood to a
far greater size. Located in a natural amphitheatre of rolling hills, it is in a
beautiful setting.

The lake has a gravelly sandy bed with very little bankside vegetation.
However, big beds of rushes and reeds do grow on the northern shore. The
water teems with bream and, although they do not grow much larger than
4 lb (1.8 kg), some very big catches (up to 100 lb/45 kg) are made. Roach and
perch are also abundant and there are a few wild brown trout.

SPECIES Bream, roach, perch and brown trout.

TECHNIQUES AND BAITS Because the lake is shallow, long-range legering
with a feeder and quiver or swing tip is the most successful method of
catching the bream. Maggot and worm cocktail baits seem very popular,
and casters will catch the bigger roach. Because the lake is so open, the
surface becomes very choppy in a wind, and in these conditions a quiver tip
works best. If you use a keepnet please take the trouble to stake it out in
deeper water as a lot of bream have died on this water by anglers cramming
many fish into nets tossed out into shallow water.

SEASON 25th March to 30th September (trout) and 1st June to 27th
February (coarse fish).

ACCESS Semer Water is reached by driving up Wensleydale to Bainbridge
and then taking the road to Countersett.

The fishing is controlled by two different clubs but tickets for both can
be obtained from Mr C Metcalfe at Low Bleam Farm, which is next to the
lake.

Leighton Reservoir (near Masham, North Yorkshire) Y 11

Leighton is a water supply reservoir of 100 acres (40 ha). The sporting rights
have been retained by the Swinton Estate and the fishery is managed as a
trout water. Leighton is an upland reservoir, and the water is slightly acidic
and, at times, a brackish colour. The reservoir is very deep and, being a
supply reservoir, the level can vary considerably in summer. The Swinton
Estate has its own trout hatchery and the reservoir is always well stocked
on a regular basis. Large numbers of small brown trout are stocked
periodically to try and produce a natural head of these fish to spawn in the
feeder streams. Anglers are well catered for with a large car park and
several toilets. No other water sports take place on the reservoir.

SPECIES Rainbow trout to 10 lb (4.5 kg) and brown trout to 5 lb (2.3 kg).

TECHNIQUES AND BAITS Fly fishing only is allowed and there is a bag limit
of six fish, but trout can be returned. Because of the acidity of the water, the
reservoir is not over-abundant in food and much of the trouts' diet
comprises land-borne insects. This is good for the angler as most fish are
taken on or near the surface. Muddlers, Daddy Long Legs and Sedges catch

a great many fish. One of the features of the reservoir is the free rising nature of the trout. Bank fishing only is allowed, and the dam wall corners are favourite 'hot spots'.

SEASON The first Saturday in April to the second Sunday in October. The actual date may vary from year to year.

ACCESS The reservoir is reached by taking the road from Masham through the villages of Fearby and Healey. The reservoir is about 2 miles (3.2 km) from Healey.

Tickets are obtained from the fishing hut in the reservoir car park. For details of the reservoir contact, The Estate Office, Swinton, Masham, Ripon, North Yorkshire.

Greenfield Lake and Beck (Buckden, near Skipton, North Yorkshire) Y 12

This attractive $2\frac{1}{2}$ acre (1 ha) lake, high up in the Yorkshire Dales, was formed by the damming of Greenfield Beck. Brown trout live in the beck and 2 miles (3.2 km) of this are included in the fishery. The lake is also stocked with rainbow trout up to 5 lb (2.3 kg). The average depth of the lake is 5 ft (1.5 m) but it is deeper near the dam. The number of rods is limited to six each day so advance booking is advisable.

SPECIES Brown trout and rainbow trout.

TECHNIQUES AND BAITS Dry or wet fly only. To obtain the most enjoyment here heavy reservoir tactics are not necessary. A good pattern to use is a Black and Peacock Spider.

SEASON 1st April to end of October (rainbow trout only after 30th September). Fishing is from dawn to dusk.

ACCESS The lake is near the village of Buckden at the head of Wharfedale.

Bookings to Mr A Sedgley, Greenfield Lake, Low Greenfield, Buckden, Skipton.

Malham Tarn (near Settle, North Yorkshire) Y 13

Malham Tarn is situated high up in the Pennines and, at first glance, appears to be a large barren sheet of water at the edge of open moorland. In fact, the tarn is very alkaline, and the water is extremely rich. Although the tarn is not deep, it supports a lot of invertebrate life which, in turn, feeds the native trout and perch. The brown trout in the lake are mostly wild fish which breed in the feeder streams, although a few fish are stocked by the water authority. The perch are good sized fish with plenty over 1 lb (0.5 kg). The limit for trout is six fish. There are four boats on the tarn and anglers must fish from these as no bank fishing is allowed. Three anglers are allowed to fish from each of the boats. Malham Tarn is used as a field centre for naturalists and the surrounding land is a nature reserve.

SPECIES Brown trout to 5 lb (2.3 kg) and perch to 3 lb (1.4 kg).

TECHNIQUES AND BAITS Fly fishing and worm fishing are the only two methods allowed at Malham. Most trout are caught using traditional wet flies, such as Mallard and Claret, and Peter Ross, on floating lines. Lures will also catch trout but they tend to take a lot of perch.

SEASON 1st May to 30th September inclusive. Fishing from 9 am to 9 pm or sunset (whichever is earlier).

ACCESS Malham is reached by taking the A65(T) Skipton to Settle road and turning off to Malham village near Gargrave.

Tickets are obtained from The Field Centre, Malham Tarn, Malham, North Yorkshire.

Introduction to the River Wharfe

The River Wharfe rises on Cam Fell, high in the Pennines, and flows south and east to join the River Ouse just above the town of Cawood. In the upper reaches the Wharfe flows through limestone and the water is very rich and clear. Trout and grayling abound in the upper reaches; the Wharfe is probably the most famous grayling river in Yorkshire.

Between Kettlewell and Bolton Abbey the river contains mainly trout and grayling with just a few dace. At Bolton Abbey the river flows through a very narrow gorge, known as the 'Strid'. The river is deceptively narrow and deep as it flows between two outcrops of rock. At one point it looks narrow enough to leap across, but several peoople have died attempting to do so.

Between Bolton Abbey and Pool-in-Wharfedale coarse fish become more numerous, although there are still plenty of trout. Dace and chub are plentiful around Otley, and below Harewood, perch, barbel and roach appear, together with some good pike. Below Wetherby the river is predominantly a coarse fish river but grayling are found right down to Boston Spa.

At Ulleskelf the river is tidal and some big barbel and bream feature in catches. The river at this point also swarms with eels, and a few flounders are caught.

River Wharfe – Grassington to Appletreewick
(North Yorkshire) Y 14

There are several stretches along this length of river than can be fished on a day ticket. Barden, Burnsall and Appletreewick Angling Club own one stretch and Bradford City Angling Association control another. Each section is clearly signposted. The fishing is for trout and grayling. The river alternates between wide shallow glides and deeper pools, and the river bed is mostly gravel and hard bedrock. The grayling run to a good size and provide sport right through the winter.

SPECIES Brown trout and grayling.

TECHNIQUES AND BAITS Part of this stretch is fly fishing only and traditional wet flies will catch both trout and grayling. There are no restrictions on the Bradford City Angling Association length and bait fishing is allowed.

SEASON 25th March to 30th September (trout) and 1st June to 27th February (grayling).

ACCESS Different clubs control the fishing on this part of the Wharfe. 'K' Tackle, 9 Water Street, Skipton, sell the day permits for all the separate waters on this length of the Wharfe and will give up to date advice on the best angling. They will also give up to date information on what is being caught and the river conditions.

River Wharfe – Bolton Abbey (North Yorkshire) Y 15

The Bolton Abbey Estate controls 5 miles (8 km) of fishing from Barden Bridge to Bolton Bridge, on both banks. The fishing is for trout and grayling. The Estate has its own hatchery and regular stocking with sizeable brown trout takes place throughout the season. The catch limit for brown trout is four fish but there is no limit on the number of grayling that can be taken. The river at Bolton Abbey is particularly beautiful, especially in the autumn when the grayling fishing is also at its best. A slight problem for anglers is that Bolton Abbey is a very popular tourist attraction in summer and the riverside near the Abbey gets rather crowded.

SPECIES Brown trout and grayling.

TECHNIQUES AND BAITS Fly fishing only. Spider patterns fished wet are the most successful.

SEASON 25th March to 30th September (brown trout) and 1st June to 31st December (grayling).

ACCESS Bolton Abbey is on the A59, 5 miles (8 km) east of Skipton.

Permits must be obtained in advance from The Estate Office, Bolton Abbey.

River Wharfe – Pool-in-Wharfedale (West Yorkshire) Y 16

This fishery is controlled by Leeds Amalgamation and extends for 5 miles (8 km) from the River Washburn to Castley Beck, $1\frac{1}{2}$ miles (2.4 km) below Arthington Viaduct on the left-hand bank, and on the right-hand bank for one field above the bridge and from the Sewerage field down to Arthington Viaduct. The fishing is for trout and coarse fish. No wading is allowed between 25th March and 31st May. This sensible measure is enforced to protect spawning coarse fish on the gravelly shallows. The catch limit for trout is three fish. This stretch of the Wharfe receives a lot of angling pressure at the start of the trout season, but later in the year it is well worth fishing for the grayling, dace and chub.

SPECIES Dace, chub, grayling, brown trout and also a few perch.

TECHNIQUES AND BAITS Bait or fly fishing is allowed and most anglers fish bait. Trotting with maggots is the most successful method.

SEASON 25th March to 30th September (brown trout) and 1st June to 27th February (coarse fish).

ACCESS Permits are obtained from Main Street Stores, Pool-in-Wharfedale, and all Leeds tackle shops.

NB Vehicles must not be parked on the Pool-in-Wharfedale to Harrogate road on its approaches to the bridge in either direction.

River Wharfe – Wetherby (West Yorkshire) Y 17

This stretch consist of 2 miles (3.2 km) of fishing controlled by Wetherby Angling Club. The fishing extends from the newly restored weir near the town road bridge upstream to Linton bridge. The stretch above the weir has produced some good catches of roach and dace in recent years. Towards Linton there are some grayling and a few barbel and chub in the streamier reaches. Perch have also increased in numbers in recent years. In the interests of conservation, the club are recommending that all visitors use barbless hooks, except for legitimate pike fishing on pike tackle.

SPECIES Chub, dace, roach, grayling, perch, pike, eels and brown trout.

TECHNIQUES AND BAITS There are no restrictions on baits or tackle, and most of the dace catches are taken on float tackle using a stick float.

SEASON 25th March to 30th September (trout) and 1st June to 27th February (coarse fish).

ACCESS Maps showing the extent of the fishing and approach routes to the river are posted on the garage door at the George and Dragon public house in Wetherby High Street.

Permits available from the George and Dragon pub.

Washburn Valley Reservoirs (Blubberhouses, near Harrogate, North Yorkshire) Y 18

Fewston

Fewston is a 156 acre (63 ha) reservoir stocked with trout by the Yorkshire Water Authority. No boats are provided and fishing is from the bank only, except on the south-west side between Blubberhouses Bridge and Thackray Beck, where the sporting rights are in private hands. The scenery at Fewston is beautiful with a lot of surrounding mixed woodland.

Swinsty

This reservoir is almost the same size as Fewston and is adjacent to that reservoir. In fact, the overspill from Fewston flows into Swinsty. The road to Fewston cuts across a small section of Swinsty Reservoir and the area where the feeder stream flows in (known as Swinsty Lagoon), is often a 'hot spot'.

Thruscross

This is the uppermost reservoir in the Washburn Valley and covers 142 acres (57 ha). It is very much deeper than the other two reservoirs and the view from the road across the dam wall is quite spectacular. This is the only one of the reservoirs where bait fishing is allowed.

SPECIES Brown trout and rainbow trout.

TECHNIQUES AND BAITS On Fewston and Swinsty only fly fishing from the bank is allowed. Most traditional methods of fly fishing will catch fish. On Thruscross, minnow, worm, maggots, spinning and fly can be used. Most trout on this reservoir are caught by float fishing with maggots or worm. The trout average 12 oz (0.3 kg) and the limit is four fish, but trout can be caught and returned.

SEASON 25th March to 30th September (brown trout) and 25th March to 31st October (rainbow trout). Fishing from 8 am to 1 hour after sunset.

ACCESS Fewston and Swinsty are reached by turning off the A59 Harrogate to Skipton road at Blubberhouses. Thruscross is reached by turning off the A59 to West End.

Permits are obtained from the vending machines at the Swinsty Moor Plantation Fishing Office. Each reservoir is covered by a separate permit and they are not interchangeable. For further details contact The Amenity, Fisheries and Recreation Department, Yorkshire Water Authority, 21 Park Square South, Leeds.

Farmire Fishery (near Knaresborough, North Yorkshire) Y 19

Farmire Fishery is a 5 acre (2 ha) gravel-pit set in a 14 acre (5.6 ha) nature reserve. The fishery is roughly rectangular in shape with depths up to 30 ft (9.1 m). Anglers must fish from the specially constructed fishing spots which are gravelled and have bench seats. Gravel paths around the fishery prevent the banks getting muddy and help to preserve rare orchids on the site. The deepest water is on the north bank nearest the car park. No fishing is allowed from the west bank. A fishing hut overlooking the water is on the east bank and toilet facilities are provided at the owner's house near the car park. The emphasis on this fishery is sport and, although the bag limit is two fish, trout can be caught and returned. Twelve anglers a day are allowed to fish. The record catch here is 98 trout, with the largest at 6 lb 8 oz (2.9 kg).

SPECIES Rainbow trout (record: 12 lb 14 oz/5.8 kg), brown trout (record: 11 lb 7 oz/5.2 kg) and brook trout (record: 4 lb 1 oz/1.8 kg).

TECHNIQUES AND BAITS Fly fishing only is allowed and all flies must be barbless. All methods of fly fishing will catch fish, but the trout are extremely free rising and large catches can be made on dry fly. In really hot weather, the north and east banks fish best with sinking lines and lures fished slowly in the deep water.

SEASON 1st April to 3rd November with some limited winter fishing.

ACCESS The entrance to the fishery is between Farnham village and Scotton, just outside Knaresborough. An angler's car park is on the site.

Tickets must be booked in advance. For details and bookings contact Mr B Morland, Farmire House, Farmire Fishery, Farnham, Knaresborough.

Hay-A-Park (Knaresborough, North Yorkshire) Y 20

This is a large mature gravel-pit of over 60 acres (24 ha). In some areas it is over 20 ft (6.1 m) deep but there are extensive shallows. The water is generally gin clear and there is prolific marginal weed growth. There are a couple of large bays and this gravel-pit has a very irregular shape. The banks are open with very few trees, although some waterside willow bushes are growing on one bank. At present this gravel-pit does not have a large population of small fish and it is of more interest to the specialist big fish angler than someone who is hoping for lots of small fish in a mixed bag. The potential is relatively unexplored but some very big fish have been caught here. The water holds double figure bream, and carp up to 30 lb (13.6 kg).

SPECIES Bream to 9 lb (4.1 kg), roach to $1\frac{1}{2}$ lb (0.7 kg), rudd to 2 lb (0.9 kg), tench to 7 lb (3.2 kg), pike to 24 lb (10.9 kg), carp to 25 lb (11.3 kg) and perch.

TECHNIQUES AND BAITS Legering using big fish tactics is the way to get the best results at this gravel-pit.

SEASON 1st June to 27th February. Night fishing is allowed.

ACCESS The lake is reached via Chain Lane on the outskirts of Knaresborough and parking is provided near the lake.

Tickets must be obtained prior to fishing from M H and C Johnson (Fishing Tackle), Briggate, Knaresborough.

Introduction to the River Nidd

The River Nidd has its source on the slopes of Great Whernside near Kettlewell. Two supply reservoirs, Angram and Scar House, have been made by damming the infant Nidd. The Nidd is still a small river as it flows through Middlesmoor and Ramsgill into Gouthwaite Reservoir, and these upper reaches hold only trout and grayling.

From Pately Bridge the Nidd flows through Nidderdale to the town of

Knaresborough. This section of the river is mainly for trout and grayling also, but a number of coarse fish start to appear at Ripley. These include chub, dace and, in recent years, a number of perch. At Knaresborough the river is much wider and slower because of a series of dams and weirs built across the river.

Below Goldsborough Weir the river seems to shrink again and is predominantly coarse fishing. The lower Nidd twists and turns as it flows between willow-lined high flood banks to join the River Ouse at Nun Monkton. These lower reaches abound with shoals of chub and barbel. The Nidd is unusual in that grayling can be caught along its entire length, which is an indication of the high quality of the water in the river's lower reaches.

River Nidd – Knaresborough (North Yorkshire) Y 21

Free fishing is available between the High Bridge in Knaresborough upstream on the right-hand bank of the river only for one field above the Conyngham Hall footbridge. The lower part of this stretch is used for boating in summer, and fishing is difficult to impossible during the day. The pool immediately below Conyngham Hall footbridge and the fast glides between the islands are free from boating. Chub and dace are the main species together with a few grayling and perch. This part of the river also teems with gudgeon and minnows.

SPECIES Chub, perch, dace, gudgeon, grayling and eels. Also a few trout.

TECHNIQUES AND BAITS Float fishing with maggots or casters is best for the dace and chub. In the evening, when the boats have finished for the day, the chub respond to legered bread.

SEASON 25th March to 30th September (trout) and 1st June to 27th February (coarse fish).

ACCESS Cars may be parked in the Conyngham Hall car park for a fee. Cross the road bridge and proceed to the riverside by the path at the side of the pub.

The fishing is free.

River Nidd – The Lido, Knaresborough (North Yorkshire) Y 22

On the outskirts of Knaresborough, the River Nidd forms a huge pool between two weirs across the river. The fishing is controlled by the owners of the Lido Caravan and Camping Site. This pool is stocked with rainbow trout and also has a natural head of brown trout, dace and chub. A lot of dace can be caught in the fast water flowing into the pool over the top weir.

SPECIES Rainbow trout, brown trout, dace, chub, and gudgeon.

TECHNIQUES AND BAITS Float fishing, fly fishing and spinning will all catch the rainbow trout. Float fishing with maggot is best for the dace and chub.

SEASON 25th March to 30th September (trout) and 1st June to 27th

(Above) Boat fishing from Slapton Ley, a shallow lowland lake.

(Below) Bala Lake – one of the best mixed fisheries in Wales (see page 89).

Several waters described in this book include superb match fishing venues.

February (coarse fish).

ACCESS The Lido is reached by taking the B6164 (Wetherby Road) out of Knaresborough and turning right into the Lido over the Grimbald road bridge.

Tickets on sale from Mr Harper, The Lido, Wetherby Road, Knaresborough.

River Nidd – Little Ribston (North Yorkshire) Y 23

The river at this point is narrow, and twists and bends as it flows from Goldsborough to Ribston. This is a good water for coarse fish, notably chub, and fish to 6 lb (2.7 kg) have been caught in recent years. Barbel are also present but they do not reach a great size. The river also teems with dace and small to medium sized grayling. The fishing is on the right-hand bank only.

SPECIES Chub, barbel, grayling, dace, roach, perch, pike and a few brown trout.

TECHNIQUES AND BAITS The largest chub and barbel are caught by legering under the willow bushes or among the streamer weed. Cheese paste is a very good bait for these species. Float fishing will produce plenty of small chub, dace and grayling.

SEASON 25th March to 30th September (trout) and 1st June to 27th February (coarse fish).

ACCESS The river is alongside the B6164 Knaresborough to Wetherby road, and parking is in a lay-by at the side of the road.

Permits must be obtained before fishing from M H and C Johnson (Fishing Tackle), Briggate, Knaresborough, North Yorkshire.

Elm Hag Lake (near Kilburn, North Yorkshire) Y 24

Elm Hag Lake is situated at the bottom of a heavily wooded valley in the North Yorkshire National Park. The lake is about 3 acres (1 ha) in extent and has a promontory which almost cuts the lake in two. The lake is stream fed. The water is normally very clear and there is a prolific weed growth. The shallowest part of the lake is where the stream flows out of the lake. The lake is extremely rich in fly life, with exceptional sedge and buzzer hatches. The average size of trout caught is $1\frac{1}{2}$ lb (0.7 kg) but much larger fish are present. The bag limit is two fish and fish can be carefully returned to the lake.

SPECIES Brown trout, rainbow trout and brook trout.

TECHNIQUES AND BAITS Fly fishing only is allowed and barbless hooks must be used. This lake responds well to skilful anglers using nymphs and buzzers on floating lines. Lures fished carefully will catch plenty of fish but this is not a water for stripping lures in at high speed on sinking lines.

SEASON 25th March to 30th September (approximately).

ACCESS This is not an easy lake to find. Take the A19(T) from Thirsk towards York and just south of Thirsk turn left through the village of Bagby, to Kilburn. From Kilburn take the road to the hamlet of Oldstead and the car park to the fishery will be found just beyond the village pub.

Tickets must be obtained in advance and are limited to 12 a day. For bookings and enquiries contact Mr P Bradley, Woolaway, Oldstead, Coxwold, York.

Driffield Canal and Frodingham Beck (near Driffield, Humberside) Y 25

This is a clear, steadily flowing water controlled by the Yorkshire Water Authority. The fishing is separated into four different sections.

Section A – Driffield to Whinhill Lock

This section is well stocked with brown and rainbow trout and is restricted to fly fishing only.

Section B – Whinhill to Wansford Lock

Although this section is stocked with trout, the best fishing is for large grayling, roach, perch and chub. Bait or fly fishing is permitted in this section but spinning and groundbaiting are not allowed.

Section C – Wansford to Snakeholme Lock

Mixed fishing for trout and grayling and other coarse fish is available here. This is a good stretch for roach. Fly or bait fishing is allowed but not spinning or groundbaiting.

Section D – Snakeholme to Hempholme Lock and Frodingham Beck to Frodingham road bridge

This section provides mixed fishing for trout and coarse fish, including pike, perch and eels.

SPECIES Trout, grayling, roach, dace, chub, pike, perch and eels.

TECHNIQUES AND BAITS On the fly only stretch (Section A) small traditional wet flies, such as Snipe and Purple, work well for the trout and the grayling. On the other stretches, delicate float tackle using small hooks and baits works best.

SEASON 25th March to 30th September (trout) and 1st June to 27th February (coarse fish).

ACCESS On Sections A, B and C a permit must be purchased before fishing from The Post Office, Wansford, Great Driffield, North Humberside. On Section D, the fishing is free to holders of a Yorkshire Water Authority rod licence.

NB A special facility to allow paraplegic anglers to enjoy the use of the fishery has been constructed at Wansford. Reserved car parking, adjacent to the public highway, surfaced access ways and individual fishing stations have been provided. Able-bodied anglers are asked not to park vehicles in the spaces marked for use by disabled anglers.

Hornsea Mere (Hornsea, Humberside) Y 26

Hornsea Mere is the largest stillwater in Yorkshire and extends to 480 acres (194 ha). It was at Hornsea Mere that Wilf Cutting caught his 3 lb 10 oz (1.6 kg) roach which held the British record for over ten years. Some big roach still exist in the mere. Part of the mere is out of bounds to anglers, as it is kept as a nature reserve. Only limited bank fishing is available near the boat house. Ten boats are available and it is from these that most of the larger fish are caught. The mere is not very deep and in many places there are extensive shallows with rushes extending right out into the lake.

SPECIES Pike to 25 lb (11.3 kg), roach to 2 lb (0.9 kg) and perch to 3 lb (1.4 kg).

TECHNIQUES AND BAITS The smaller roach and perch can be caught quite easily using float-fished maggots and worm from the bank and landing-stages near the boat house. The larger fish are rather more difficult to locate. It pays to anchor the boat in a deeper area and persevere in one spot. Some big perch catches have been taken on float-fished lobworms. For the bigger roach, bread flake is probably best. Freelined deadbaits catch a lot of pike, with sprats and smelts being a favourite bait. Spinning will also take the pike and will often produce some good perch.

SEASON 1st June to 27th February. Fishing from 9 am to 8 pm.

ACCESS The mere is not difficult to locate being the focal point of Hornsea.

Tickets can be obtained from Mr G Hood, The Boat Yard, Hornsea Mere, Hornsea.

Market Weighton Canal (near Market Weighton, Humberside) Y 27

This 6 mile (9.7 km) long section of canal is between 25 and 45 ft (7.6 and 13.7 m) wide. The canal is normally slow flowing or still, depending on the level of the River Humber at Weighton Lock. During very low tides in the Humber, the flow may increase considerably. Some permanent pegs have been installed along the bank between the lock and Newport Bridge for match fishing. Above Newport Bridge, the right-hand bank is pegged to the confluence of the River Foulness.

SPECIES Bream, roach, dace, chub, pike, carp, rudd, eels and flounders.

TECHNIQUES AND BAITS The most successful tactics are to fish with light waggler floats, and to set the depth so that the bait is just touching or just above the bottom. Small hooks and baits are best. Caster will take plenty of roach and rudd, with maggots and bread taking the bream. There are a lot of small pike along the canal and some good sport can be enjoyed using sink-and-draw tactics with sprat deadbaits.

SEASON 1st June to 27th February inclusive.

ACCESS Market Weighton can be reached from junction 38 of the M62, on the B1230.

The water is free to holders of a Yorkshire Water Authority rod licence. Applications from clubs to book fishing matches should be made to The Amenities, Recreation and Estates Officer, Yorkshire Water Authority, North and East Division, 32/34 Monkgate, York.

Three Lakes (Selby, North Yorkshire) Y 28

These lakes are 5 acres (2 ha) each in area and are matured clay-pits. The water is 20 ft (6.1 m) deep in places and the margins are fringed with rush and reed beds. The clear water has a few weed beds growing at its edges. The lakes contain some very big carp up to 35 lb (15.9 kg). The banks of the lakes are accessible all round.

SPECIES Carp, roach, bream, tench and trout.

TECHNIQUES AND BAITS Specialist tactics are needed for the carp. High-protein paste baits are worth trying either freelined or on leger tackle. For the other species, a waggler float fished with bread, maggots or casters as bait is best.

SEASON 25th March to 30th September (trout) and 1st June to 27th February (coarse fish). Fishing from dawn to dusk.

Permits are obtained from the bungalow at the lake. For information contact Mr Standish, Three Lakes, Bawtry Road, Selby.

Nostell Priory Fisheries (near Wakefield, West Yorkshire) Y 29

This fishery consists of three lakes totalling 40 acres (16 ha) on the Nostell Estate. The upper lake is the largest at 26 acres (11 ha) and is tree and reed lined. This lake is famous for its early season tench catches and in winter some very large pike (up to 28 lb/12.7 kg) are caught. The middle lake is $7\frac{1}{2}$ acres (3 ha) and was created in 1730 when the priory gardens were laid down. Caravans and camping facilities are available near this lake. The 6 acre (2 ha) lower lake is particularly beautiful, being surrounded by mature hardwood trees and rhododendrons. This lake was formerly a trout lake but in 1980–81 it was stocked with carp to create a specimen carp and tench water. At Foulby Lodge there is a fully equipped fisheries shop selling tackle and a large selection of baits. The shop is open seven days a week during the coarse fishing season.

SPECIES *Upper Lake*: tench, carp, pike, bream, roach, perch and eels.

Middle Lake: tench, bream, carp, roach, perch and pike.
Lower Lake: Specimen carp and tench, perch and roach.

TECHNIQUES AND BAITS Early season tench catches are taken on float-fished sweetcorn, maggot and worm. Fishing next to the weed beds is most effective for the tench. The best bream catches are taken by long-range legering in the deep water with swimfeeders and maggots. Livebaiting and deadbaiting are equally effective for the pike.

SEASON 1st June to 27th February inclusive. Fishing from dawn to dusk.

ACCESS Nostell Priory is 5 miles (8 km) from Wakefield on the A638 Wakefield to Doncaster road. Access is through Foulby Lodge where parking is available.

Permits should be bought prior to fishing from Mr J Austerfield, Head Bailiff, Foulby Lodge, Foulby, Wakefield.

Damflask Reservoir (near Sheffield, South Yorkshire) Y 30

Damflask is a 115 acre (47 ha) compensation reservoir north-west of Sheffield. Being so close to a big city, the fishing pressure on Damflask is rather high but each year it produces some large fish, notably brown trout and pike. Roach are the predominant species but there are some big bream.

SPECIES Brown trout, rainbow trout, roach, perch, bream and pike.

TECHNIQUES AND BAITS Any recognised bait and lure can be used at Damflask, even for the trout. Most anglers float fish or leger with maggots, but worm legered at long range will often take the bigger bream and brown trout. A keepnet can be used to retain coarse fish only when they are in season. Trout must not be kept in a keepnet and only two trout may be retained. All other fish should be returned carefully to the water.

SEASON 25th March to 30th September (trout) and 1st June to 31st January (coarse fish).

ACCESS Damflask is reached by the B6077 road from Sheffield to Low Bradfield.

Permits are obtained at the reservoir. For further details contact The Division General Manager, Yorkshire Water Authority, Southern Division, Castle Market Building, Exchange Street, Sheffield.

Welsh Water Authority

The angling in Wales is primarily for game fish; the region is full of streams and small rivers containing brown trout. Very often a visitor can fish these waters simply by making enquiries to local farmers and landowners. The

Key	Page
1 Llyn Alaw	87
2 Llyn Aled and Aled Isaf Reservoirs	88
3 Brenig Reservoir	88
4 Alwen Reservoir	88
5 Celyn Reservoir	89
6 Cwmystradllyn Reservoir	89
7 Bala Lake or Llyn Tegid	89
8 Teifi Pools	90
9 Elan Valley Reservoirs	91
10 Llys-y-frân Reservoir	91
11 Llanllawddog Lake	91
12 Usk Reservoir	92
13 Talybont Reservoir	92
14 Llwyn-on Reservoir	93
15 Pontsticill Reservoir	93
16 Llandegfedd Reservoir	94
17 Upper and Lower Ynysyfro	94
18 Wentwood Reservoir	94
19 Llangorse Lake	95
20 River Wye – Hay-on-Wye	95
21 River Wye – Ross-on-Wye	95
22 River Lugg – Moreton Water	96
23 River Lugg – Mordiford	96
24 River Frome – near Mordiford	97

trout may not be large, but on light tackle they offer good sport. As a bonus, the scenery in these areas can be breathtaking, and it is often possible to fish all day and not see another angler. The Wye and the Usk are both salmon rivers, although both support a head of coarse fish in the lower reaches. The Wye, in the Hereford area in particular, is full of big chub, pike and perch, and visitors can take advantage of the sport after the salmon season closes. Some very large catches of chub are taken from the Wye.

There is plenty of good reservoir trout fishing in Wales for both brown trout and rainbow trout. The fishing on these reservoirs is often zoned, so that anglers can use different methods of fishing, rather than just fly fishing. Coarse fishing may also be had in some of the region's lakes. Lake Bala is a superb fishery set in magnificent scenery, and is full of big roach and pike. Llangorse Lake offers some fine fishing for bream and, furthermore, the fishing is free.

Llyn Alaw (Anglesey) Wales 1

The 770 acre (310 ha) Alaw Reservoir is located in open countryside on Anglesey. This reservoir is very rich in natural food, and has a head of good-sized native brown trout. It is also heavily stocked with brown and rainbow trout and the fish have an excellent growth rate. The size limit is 10 in (25 cm) and the bag limit is six fish.

SPECIES Brown trout and rainbow trout.

TECHNIQUES AND BAITS This is 'method zoned reservoir'. The fishing on the north and east banks is restricted to fly fishing only. Worm fishing and spinning are allowed on the south shore between the Main Dam and a marker post.

SEASON 1st April to 30th September. Fishing is from 7 am to 1 hour after sunset.

ACCESS Travelling north-west from Llangefni, turn off the B5109 road at Trefor and take the B5112 road to Llanerchymedd and then the unclassified road to Alaw.

Permits are obtained from the Fishing Office, Llyn Alaw, Llanerchymedd, Anglesey.

Llyn Aled and Aled Isaf Reservoirs
(near Cerrigydrudion, Clwyd) Wales 2

These are two reservoirs of 110 acres (45 ha) and 75 acres (30 ha), respectively, and are coarse fisheries full of rudd and perch. The average weight of fish of both species is about 6 oz (0.2 kg), but larger specimens are caught.

SPECIES Perch and rudd.

TECHNIQUES AND BAITS All methods are allowed.

SEASON 16th June to 14th March.

ACCESS These reservoirs are close to Brenig Reservoir and are reached by taking the unclassified road to Llansannan off the A543 road.

Permits are obtained from the interpretation centre, Brenig Reservoir, Cerrigydrudion, near Corwen.

Brenig Reservoir (near Cerrigydrudion, Clwyd) Wales 3

Brenig Reservoir covers 919 acres (372 ha) and is located near the Clocaenog Forest at an altitude of 1,400 ft (425 m). The fishing is for brown and rainbow trout, and the reservoir is stocked annually with up to 25,000 rainbow trout. The size limit is 10 in (25 cm) and the bag limit is six fish. Rowing boats and motor boats are available and can be booked in advance. The average size of the brown and rainbow trout is a little over 1 lb (0.5 kg).

SPECIES Rainbow trout and brown trout.

TECHNIQUES AND BAITS Fly fishing only. For the best results use lure fishing early in the season, then all types of fly fishing.

SEASON 1st April to 15th October (bank fishing), 1st May to 30th September (boat fishing). Fishing times from 8.30 am to 10.30 pm or half an hour after sunset (whichever is earlier) for bank fishing. Boat fishing starts at 9.30 am and finishes at the same time as bank fishing.

ACCESS Take the A5(T) road to Cerrigydrudion and then the B4501 road to Brenig.

Permits are obtained from the Interpretation Centre, Brenig Reservoir, Cerrigydrudion, near Corwen.

Alwen Reservoir (near Cerrigydrudion, Clwyd) Wales 4

This upland reservoir is in a particularly attractive setting. The water covers 368 acres (149 ha) and is at an altitude of 1249 ft (380 m) above sea-level. As well as the usual brown and rainbow trout the reservoir holds an enormous head of perch. No boats are available. The bag limit is six trout.

SPECIES Rainbow trout, brown trout and perch.

TECHNIQUES AND BAITS Fly fishing must be used for the trout. Spinning and worm fishing are allowed for the perch.

SEASON 1st March to 30th September (trout) and 16th June to 14th March (coarse fish).

ACCESS The reservoir is located near Brenig Reservoir, about 3 miles (4.8 km) north of Cerrigydrudion on the B4501 road.

Permits are obtained from the Reservoir Keeper, Alwen Reservoir, Cerrigydrudion, near Corwen.

Celyn Reservoir (near Bala, Gwynedd) Wales 5

This massive 800 acre (324 ha) reservoir lies in the superb setting of the Snowdonia National Park. The surrounding countryside is mountainous and magnificent. The fishing is mainly for wild brown trout, which is stocked, together with a few rainbow trout. No boats are available. The size limit is 8 in (20 cm) and the bag limit is six fish.

SPECIES Brown trout and rainbow trout.

TECHNIQUES AND BAITS Fly fishing, spinning and worm fishing are all allowed.

SEASON 1st April to 30th September. Fishing from 7 am to 1 hour after sunset.

ACCESS The reservoir is alongside the A4212 road from Bala to Trawsfynydd.

Permits are obtained from Fron-goch Post Office, Fron-goch, Bala; or from the Reservoir Keeper

Cwmystradllyn Reservoir (near Porthmadog, Gwynedd) Wales 6

This reservoir, in the magnificent setting of the Snowdonia National Park, covers 95 acres (38 ha) and is regularly stocked with rainbow trout. No boats are available. The size limit is 7 in (18 cm) and the bag limit is six fish.

SPECIES Rainbow trout.

TECHNIQUES AND BAITS Fly fishing, spinning and worm fishing may be used. Float fishing is not allowed so worms must be fished freelined or legered.

SEASON 3rd March to 30th September. Fishing from 1 hour before sunrise to 1 hour after sunset.

ACCESS This reservoir is reached by taking the minor road off the A487(T) road, north of Porthmadog.

Permits are obtained from the Cwmystradllyn Reservoir Treatment Works, Cwmystradllyn, near Garn Dolbenmaen, Gwynedd.

Bala Lake or Llyn Tegid (Gwynedd) Wales 7

Bala is the largest natural lake in Wales, being over 4 miles (6.4 km) long and $\frac{3}{4}$ mile (1.2 km) wide. This lake is managed jointly by the local council and the Snowdonia National Park Committee. As a fishery, the potential of Bala is tremendous, but the casual angler may experience difficulties coming to terms with it simply because it is so big. The lake contains most species of fish, many of which can grow to specimen proportions. The pike fishing is superb, with fish to nearly 30 lb (13.6 kg) being caught. The roach fishing is also excellent, with bags of fish totalling 50 lb (22.7 kg).

This lake forms the headwaters of the River Dee, and the grayling in the Dee have moved into Bala, making it one of the few lakes in the country to support a natural head of grayling. Bala also supports the very rare gwyniad, a whitefish which is seldom caught because it prefers the deepest areas of the lake, which go down to 150 ft (47 m) in places. Even salmon enter the lake, although not many are caught. The trout fishing is good, with fish to 3 lb (1.4 kg) not uncommon – in fact, the trout can grow to over 10 lb (4.5 kg). The bag limit for trout is six fish.

This is the ideal venue for an angling holiday in Wales. The scenery is magnificent, there are toilets at the parking ground and camping is available on both sides of the lake. During the summer, 15 to 20 boats are available to anglers and these can be rented from the Lake Warden at the parking ground.

SPECIES Pike, roach, perch, brown trout, salmon, grayling and eels.

TECHNIQUES AND BAITS There are no restrictions, and any legal method of fishing can be enjoyed.

SEASON 16th June to 14th March (coarse fish) and 15th June to 14th August (trout). No night fishing is allowed.

ACCESS The A494(T) road runs along the west bank of Bala Lake. Permits are obtained from Mr W E Pugh, 74 High Street, Bala.

Teifi Pools (near Pontrhydfendigaid, Dyfed) Wales 8

Teifi Pools are a series of six moorland lakes situated 1400 ft (425 m) above sea-level. The lakes are at the headwaters of the River Teifi, and will be appreciated especially by anglers who love wide open spaces. The lakes vary in size from Llyn Teifi at 61 acres (25 ha) to Pond-y-Gwaith at 8 acres (3.2 ha). The fishing is for brown trout and a few brook trout. The size limit is 9 in (23 cm) and the bag limit is six fish. No boats are available. Good waterproof clothing is advisable early in the season.

SPECIES Brown trout and brook trout.

TECHNIQUES AND BAITS Fly fishing only, except on Llyn Teifi where fly fishing, spinning and worm fishing are permitted.

SEASON 10th March to 20th September. Fishing from 8 am to 1 hour after sunset.

ACCESS The approach road to the lakes leaves the B4343 road at Ffair Rhôs, north of Pontrhydfendigaid. Permits are not available on site and must be obtained in advance from fishing licence distributors in Aberystwyth, Tregaron and Pontrhydfendigaid.

For further information contact the Fishery and Recreation Officer.

Elan Valley Reservoirs (near Rhayader, Powys) Wales 9

These are a group of five reservoirs in an upland setting, 1200 ft (360 m) above sea-level. The largest reservoir of the group is Claerwen at 650 acres (263 ha) and the smallest is Penygarreg at 124 acres (50 ha). The fishing is for wild brown trout, although some restocking does take place. One of the reservoirs, Craig Goch, is quite heavily stocked with brook trout. Claerwen is well known as a picturesque wild brown trout fishery. Both rowing boats and motor boats can be hired. The size limit is 10 in (25 cm) and the bag limit is six fish.

SPECIES Brown trout and, on Craig Goch only, brook trout.

TECHNIQUES AND BAITS Fly fishing only is allowed on the reservoirs but spinning and worm fishing may be used on the streams.

SEASON 1st March to 30th September (Claerwen only) and 28th March to 30th September on the other reservoirs. Worm fishing is allowed until 31st August and spinning until 30th September. Fishing is from half an hour before sunrise to half an hour after sunset.

ACCESS From Rhayader take the B4518 road to Elan Village.

Permits are obtained from the Elan Estate Office, Elan Village, Rhayader, Powys.

Llys-y-frân Reservoir (near Haverfordwest, Dyfed) Wales 10

This reservoir covers 187 acres (76 ha) and is an ideal venue for a family fishing trip. The brown and rainbow trout fishing is good and non-angling members of the family are catered for with a cafe, picnic tables, walks and nature trails. Boats can be hired and there are launching facilities for those who own their own boats. The size limit for trout is 9 in (23 cm) and the bag limit is six fish.

SPECIES Brown trout and rainbow trout.

TECHNIQUES AND BAITS Fly fishing, spinning and worm fishing are allowed over the entire reservoir.

SEASON 1st April to 30th September. Fishing from half an hour before sunrise to half an hour after sunset.

ACCESS The reservoir lies alongside the minor road connecting Haverfordwest with the B4313 at Maenclochog, and is a few miles north of the village of Clarbeston Road.

Permits are obtained from The Reservoir Superintendent, Llys-y-frân Reservoir, near Haverfordwest, Dyfed.

Llanllawddog Lake (near Carmarthen, Dyfed) Wales 11

This is a 2½ acre (1 ha) lake, managed as a trout fishery. It is U-shaped with clear, open banks allowing unhindered casting from every part of the lake. Llanllawddog Lake is stocked with both brown and rainbow trout, and the average size of the fish is $1\frac{1}{2}$–2 lb (0.7–0.9 kg). The lake is also stocked with some big rainbow trout weighing over 5 lb (2.2 kg). The number of rods is limited to nine a day. The bag limit is four fish.

SPECIES Brown trout and rainbow trout.

TECHNIQUES AND BAITS Fly fishing only. Lures are probably best early in the season, but the fish are free rising and dry fly fishing works well in the summer.

SEASON Mid February to the end of November (the actual dates may vary). Fishing is from 9 am to 9 pm.

ACCESS Llanllawddog Lake is 6 miles (9.7 km) north of Carmarthen on the A485 road.

For further information or booking contact Mr H W Olive, Home Farm, Llanllawddog, Carmarthen, Dyfed.

Usk Reservoir (near Trecastle, Powys) Wales 12

An excellent trout reservoir, Usk covers 280 acres (113 ha) and is situated in an attractive woodland setting 1050 ft (320 m) above sea-level. The reservoir is stocked with both brown and rainbow trout. The size limit is 8 in (20 cm) and the bag limit is six fish. Two motor boats are available for anglers and can be booked in advance. There are also special facilities for disabled anglers.

SPECIES Brown trout and rainbow trout.

TECHNIQUES AND BAITS Fly fishing is possible on all parts of the reservoir, and spinning and worm fishing are allowed in specially zoned areas, which are clearly marked.

SEASON 4th April to 14th October.

ACCESS To reach Usk Reservoir, turn south off the A40(T) Brecon to Llandovery road at Trecastle.

Permits are obtained from the Reservoir Keeper, Usk Reservoir, Trecastle, near Brecon, Powys.

Talybont Reservoir (near Brecon, Powys) Wales 13

This reservoir is located in a beautiful wooded valley in the Brecon Beacons National Park. The reservoir covers 318 acres (129 ha) and is richer in natural food than most of the nearby reservoirs. This reservoir has a good head of natural brown trout, but is also well stocked with rainbow trout. There is a nature reserve on the reservoir and anglers are asked to respect this and not cause any disturbance to wildlife. Rowing boats can be hired for the day. The size limit is 8 in (20 cm) and the bag limit is six fish.

SPECIES Brown trout and rainbow trout.

TECHNIQUES AND BAITS Fly fishing is allowed on the entire reservoir and spinning is permitted from a section of the west shore.

SEASON 4th April to 14th October. Fishing from 8 am to dusk.

ACCESS The reservoir is reached by taking the unclassified road south of Talybont near Brecon.

Permits are obtained from the Reservoir Superintendent, Talybont Reservoir, Talybont-on-Usk, near Brecon, Powys.

Llwyn-on Reservoir (near Merthyr Tydfil, Mid Glamorgan)
Wales 14

Covering 150 acres (60 ha), Llwyn-on is a good brown and rainbow trout fishery surrounded by a mature conifer forest. Bank fishing only is allowed. A fishing pontoon has been specially constructed for disabled anglers. The size limit is 9 in (23 cm) and the bag limit is six fish.

SPECIES Brown trout and rainbow trout.

TECHNIQUES AND BAITS Fly fishing only.

SEASON 21st March to 30th September. Fishing from 8 am to 1 hour after sunset.

ACCESS The reservoir is alongside the A470(T) road from Merthyr Tydfil to Brecon and is about 4 miles (6.4 km) north of Merthyr Tydfil.

Permits from the Fishing Office, Llwyn-on Filter House, Llwyn-on Reservoir, Merthyr Tydfil, Mid Glamorgan.

Pontsticill Reservoir (near Merthyr Tydfil, Mid Glamorgan)
Wales 15

Covering 253 acres (102 ha), Pontsticill Reservoir is in an attractive wooded valley north of Merthyr Tydfil. The reservoir is managed as a mixed fishery and, as well as being regularly stocked with brown and rainbow trout, the lake has a natural head of pike, perch and roach. Serious coarse fishing is not allowed until the end of the trout season but, obviously, coarse fish are going to be caught on baits intended for trout before this date. No boats are available. The size limit for trout is 9 in (23 cm), and the bag limit is six fish.

SPECIES Brown trout, rainbow trout, perch, pike and roach.

TECHNIQUES AND BAITS Fly fishing, spinning and worm, maggot and cereal baits are allowed. Groundbaiting and loose feeding are not allowed.

SEASON 21st March to 30th September (trout) and 1st October to the last day of February (coarse fish). Fishing is from 8 am to 1 hour after sunset.

ACCESS The reservoir is at the bottom of the Taf Fechan Valley, north of Merthyr Tydfil.

Permits are obtained from The Stores, Pontsticill Depot, Pontsticill Reservoir, near Merthyr Tydfil.

Llandegfedd Reservoir (near Pontypool, Gwent) Wales 16

Llandegfedd Reservoir covers 429 acres (174 ha) and is the premier trout reservoir in Wales. Being situated fairly near the Severn Bridge, it is also easily accessible. The reservoir is heavily and regularly stocked, and the trout grow on naturally to reach a large size. Motor boats and rowing boats are available and can be booked in advance. The size limit is 11 in (28 cm) and the bag limit is six fish.

SPECIES Brown trout and rainbow trout.

TECHNIQUES AND BAITS Fly fishing only. Most types of fly fishing will catch fish, but lures work best early in the season.

SEASON 4th April to 14th October. Fishing times are from 6 am to 2 hours after sunset for bank fishing, and 8 am to 1 hour after sunset (boats).

ACCESS Turn off the A4042(T) Pontypool to Newport road to Llandegfedd.
    Permits are obtained from Sluvad Treatment Works, Llandegfedd Reservoir, Panteg, Pontypool, Gwent.

Upper and Lower Ynysyfro (near Newport, Gwent) Wales 17

These two small reservoirs of 10 acres (4 ha) and 16 acres (6 ha) are adjacent to one another. The lower reservoir is stocked with brown trout and the upper reservoir is stocked with rainbow trout. The fishing permit entitles the angler to fish both waters. Rowing boats are available and can be booked in advance. The size limit is 8 in (20 cm) and the bag limit is six fish.

SPECIES Rainbow and brown trout.

TECHNIQUES AND BAITS Fly fishing only.

SEASON 4th April to 14th October. Fishing is from 8 am to dusk.

ACCESS The reservoirs are at Rogerstone on the A467 Newport to Risca road. Permits are obtained from The Reservoir Superintendent, Ynysyfro Reservoir, Newport, Gwent.

Wentwood Reservoir (near Newport, Gwent) Wales 18

Wentwood Reservoir, covering 41 acres (17 ha), is in a beautiful setting below Wentwood Forest with a panoramic view across the Bristol Channel. The fishery is well stocked with both brown and rainbow trout. The bag limit is six fish and the size limit is 8 in (20 cm).

SPECIES Brown trout and rainbow trout.

TECHNIQUES AND BAITS Fly fishing only.

SEASON 4th April to 14th October. Fishing from 8 am to dusk.

ACCESS Wentwood is located near the A48 Newport to Chepstow road. Turn off to Llanvaches. Permits from The Reservoir Superintendent, Wentwood Reservoir, Llanvaches, Penhow, Newport, Gwent.

Llangorse Lake (Llangorse village, near Brecon, Powys) Wales 19

This is a 400 acre (162 ha) lake, which is full of bream. It is certainly the best bream fishing in Wales and, although really big bream are seldom caught, catches in excess of 50 lb (22.7 kg) are often taken, usually from the boats. The bank fishing is good but to really make the most of the water's terrific potential, a boat should be hired. In addition to the bream, the water holds some large pike, although they are not heavily fished.

SPECIES Bream, roach, perch, pike and eels.

TECHNIQUES AND BAITS The best bream fishing is from a boat. Anchor the boat at either end and, after plumbing the depth correctly, fish a waggler float (driftbeater if windy) and use maggot, worm or bread bait over a carpet of groundbait. From the bank, swing tip legering with a swimfeeder is the best technique.

SEASON 16th June to 14th March. There is no restriction on fishing times.

ACCESS Access is from the A40(T) road and then the B4560 to Llangorse village.

Boats can be hired at the lakeside. The fishing is free.

River Wye – Hay-on-Wye (near Hereford, Hereford and Worcester) Wales 20

The middle Wye is a magnificent river and the water on this stretch varies from fast glides to deep pools. Over 4 miles (6.4 km) of the river can be fished for coarse fish after the salmon season has closed. The chub and dace fishing is excellent. The chub average $2\frac{1}{2}$ lb (1.1 kg) with fish up to 5 lb (2.3 kg). In the deeper pools the river holds some enormous pike. It is worth trying for these as 20 lb (9.1 kg) fish are not uncommon.

SPECIES Chub, dace, pike, perch and a few barbel.

TECHNIQUES AND BAITS The best chub are taken on bread flake either trotting down with an Avon-type float or by legering. Luncheon meat is another good chub bait. The dace are best fished for with a stick float and casters. The pike can be caught by spinning or with deadbait.

SEASON 10th October to 20th January. (This is during the salmon close season.)

ACCESS The stretch is at Bredwardine between Hay-on-Wye and Hereford. Bredwardine is reached via the B4352 road from Hay-on-Wye.

Permits can be booked by telephone from The Red Lion Hotel, Bredwardine, near Hereford.

River Wye – Ross-on-Wye (near Hereford, Hereford and Worcester) Wales 21

This fishery covers 1 mile (1.6 km) of the River Wye on the south bank, 2 miles (3.2 km) north of Ross-on-Wye. The water is managed as a mixed fishery with both game and coarse fish. This is a fairly deep stretch of river with a good flow. There are five named salmon pools along the length. Salmon fishing has precedence over coarse fishing, and during the salmon season coarse fishing spots are restricted.

SPECIES Salmon, brown trout, chub, roach, dace, perch and pike.

TECHNIQUES AND BAITS Maggots are not allowed for coarse fishing until the salmon season has closed on 14th October. From that date, until 14th March, maggots can be used. A good bait for the chub is bread flake on float tackle, or bread crust on leger tackle.

SEASON 26th January to 30th September (salmon), 1st March to 30th September (brown trout) and 16th June to 14th March (coarse fish).

ACCESS The river is approached off the A40 at Ross-on-Wye.

Permits are obtained in advance from Mr C W Bateman, Wye Lea, Bridston, Ross-on-Wye.

River Lugg – Moreton Water (near Hereford, Hereford and Worcester) Wales 22

This fishery covers the south bank of the River Lugg for 1 mile (1.6 km) downstream from Moreton on Lugg. The river is wide, fast flowing and very deep in places. There are a few slower pools and these fish best in the winter. The banks are fairly open with flood bankings in places. The main species are chub and grayling with a few trout. The chub fishing is very good.

SPECIES Chub, dace, grayling and trout.

TECHNIQUES AND BAITS Float fishing using a stick float with maggots and casters as bait. The chub can be caught using float tactics but the larger fish are taken on leger using big baits such as cheese, bread crust or luncheon meat. During the winter, 'laying on' in the slacker pools is a good method.

SEASON 16th June to 14th March.

ACCESS Moreton on Lugg is just north of Hereford and is reached by taking the A49(T) road and then taking the minor road to the village.

River Lugg – Mordiford (near Hereford, Hereford and Worcester) Wales 23

The River Lugg is a major tributary of the River Wye and rises in the hills above Presteigne, where it flows first east and then south to join the Wye below Mordiford. This fishery on the Lugg covers 1¼ miles (2 km) of the south bank at Mordiford. The fishing for coarse fish is excellent with chub to a large size. The grayling fishing is also good with the occasional trout and salmon being caught. The stretch is very picturesque with plenty of

Part of the vast acreage of Grafham Water (see page 137).

The dream of most pike anglers, a 30 lb (13.5 kg) pike.

bankside vegetation in places. The flow of the river varies with fast glides and deeper, slacker areas.

SPECIES Chub, dace, grayling, perch, eels and pike.

TECHNIQUES AND BAITS Legered bread, luncheon meat and cheese are effective for the chub. The grayling and dace are taken float fishing with a stick float using maggots or casters as hookbait.

SEASON 16th June to 14th March.

ACCESS Mordiford is reached via the B4224 road east of Hereford.

Permits are obtained from Mr J Wright, Larport Court, Dormington, Hereford.

River Frome – near Mordiford (Hereford, Hereford and Worcester) Wales 24

The Frome, like the Lugg, is a tributary of the Wye system. The Frome rises above Bromyard and flows south to join the Lugg just north of Mordiford. This fishery on the Frome is $\frac{1}{2}$ mile (800 m) of double bank and a further $\frac{1}{2}$ mile (800 m) of single bank. A short section of the river has been canalised and the fishing on this section is not very good. The rest of the stretch, which in places twists and bends creating deep pools, is excellent, especially for chub. This is a good winter fishery, as grayling are also present.

SPECIES Chub, dace, grayling and trout.

TECHNIQUES AND BAITS Leger for the chub using a quiver tip rod. Big baits such as luncheon meat, cheese, bread flake or bread crust are best. Float fishing with a stick float and using casters or maggots will take the smaller chub, dace and grayling.

SEASON 16th June to 14th March.

ACCESS The river is reached by taking the B4224 road east from Hereford to Mordiford and then the minor road north via the village of Dormington.

Permits are obtained from Mr J Wright, Larport Court, Dormington, Hereford.

Severn Trent Water Authority

This is one of the largest water authorities in the country. From the River Humber the boundary runs south-westwards, taking in Newark-on-Trent, Grantham, Nottingham, Leicester, Warwick, Cheltenham and Gloucester down to the Severn Estuary. The western boundary takes in an area of Wales where the River Severn has its source, and includes all the tributaries of the Severn.

Key		Page
1	Ladybower Reservoir	99
2	Tittesworth Reservoir	100
3	Higham Farm Lakes	100
4	River Derwent – Belper	101
5	River Derwent – Duffield	101
6	River Trent – Swarkestone	103

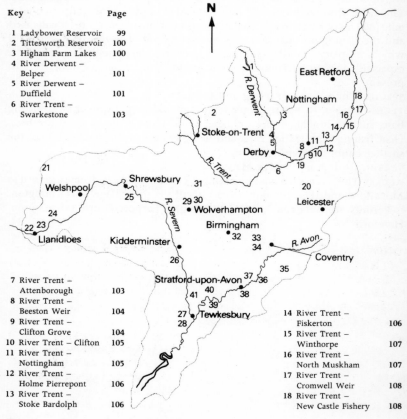

7	River Trent – Attenborough	103
8	River Trent – Beeston Weir	104
9	River Trent – Clifton Grove	104
10	River Trent – Clifton	105
11	River Trent – Nottingham	105
12	River Trent – Holme Pierrepont	106
13	River Trent – Stoke Bardolph	106
14	River Trent – Fiskerton	106
15	River Trent – Winthorpe	107
16	River Trent – North Muskham	107
17	River Trent – Cromwell Weir	108
18	River Trent – New Castle Fishery	108

19	Attenborough South Lakes	108		Ribbesford	114	35	Napton Reservoirs	118
20	Nanpantan Reservoir	109	27	River Severn – Ripple	114	36	Compton Verney Lake	119
21	Lake Vyrnwy	109	28	River Severn – Hawbridge	115	37	River Avon – Eckington	119
22	River Severn – Llanidloes	111	29	Church Pool	115	38	River Avon – Stratford-upon-Avon	120
23	River Severn – Dinam Estate Fishery	112	30	Great Pool	116	39	River Avon – Offenham	120
24	River Severn – Penstrowed	112	31	Gailey Trout Fishery	116	40	River Avon – Evesham	121
25	River Severn – Atcham	113	32	Edgbaston Reservoir	117	41	River Avon – Hampton Ferry	121
26	River Severn –		33	Packington Trout Lakes	117			
			34	Packington Coarse Lakes	118			

The rivers Severn, Trent and Avon are the major water courses in the area. These rivers offer something to all anglers: the game fishing on the upper Severn and its tributaries is excellent; in the middle reaches of the Severn, there are some big barbel, chub, pike and roach; and in the lower reaches there are some splendid bream to be caught. The middle reaches of the River Trent, around Thrapston and Beeston, is fishing extremely well for barbel. Most of these fish are still small but growing fast, so sport in the next few years looks set to improve still further.

The Trent and Severn are heavily match-fished at weekends and, before travelling to a fishery, visiting anglers would be wise to check on the availability of bank space for individual fishing. This advice also applies to some lakes, such as Coombe Abbey near Coventry.

There are many day ticket waters in the Severn and Trent area from which the visitor can choose a place to fish. Anglers living in the region can widen this choice still further by purchasing a yearbook issued by one of the big angling associations such as Birmingham. For the price of the book – a few pounds – they have the right to fish literally hundreds of different fisheries affiliated to the association.

Ladybower Reservoir (Peak District National Park, Derbyshire) ST 1

This is a large reservoir set in the Peak District National Park. The banks are well wooded and steeply sloping. The reservoir is very deep and, in places, the bottom drops away to over 100 ft (30 m). The bank fishing can be good, especially early in the season, but boat fishing produces the bigger fish in the deep water during the summer months. In recent years, several rainbow trout over 8 lb (3.6 kg) have been taken at Ladybower Reservoir. The reservoir has its own hatchery and is well stocked right through the season. Boats can be hired for the day or the evening.

SPECIES Rainbow trout, brown trout and brook trout.

TECHNIQUES AND BAITS Fly fishing only is allowed. Without any doubt, lure fishing works best at Ladybower. Black lures, such as an Undertaker or Viva catch plenty of fish. Lures with a tail, such as a Waggy lure, are also worth trying. During hot weather a lure fished deep on a sinking line

around the fish cages will catch some of the really big rainbow trout.
SEASON 1st April to 15th October. The fishing limit is four fish until 31st
May and six fish from 1st June to the end of the season.
ACCESS Ladybower is reached by taking the A57 Sheffield to Glossop road.

Permits must be obtained from Mr A Purnell at the Fishery Office at the
reservoir.

Tittesworth Reservoir (Leek, Staffordshire) ST 2

Tittesworth covers an area of 184 acres (74 ha) and is an extremely attractive
trout water with many bays and inlets. The scenery is superb and, in some
areas, the banking is very steep and wooded and these spots can only be
reached from a boat. The attraction of Tittesworth is its superb brown
trout. In addition to stock brown trout, there is a head of wild fish. The
condition of these brown trout is exceptional, and they sport bright red
spots on their flanks. Good areas to fish are Churnets Bay, Fosters Flats and
Badger Bay. There is a mayfly hatch at Tittesworth in late spring and early
summer.
SPECIES Brown trout to double figures, rainbow trout and brook trout.
TECHNIQUES AND BAITS Fly fishing only. Good lures on the reservoir are
Jack Frost, Black Chenille, Undertaker and Whiskey Fly.
SEASON 13th April to 15th October. Fishing from 1 hour before sunrise to 1
hour after sunset.
ACCESS From Leek take the A53 road north for 3 miles (4.8 km) and then
turn left on to the minor road for the reservoir before the village of Upper
Hulme is reached.

Permits are obtained at the reservoir. For information contact the Fishing
Lodge

Higham Farm Lakes (near Alfreton, Derbyshire) ST 3

These are four good coarse fishing lakes, covering a total of 12 acres (5 ha).
The lakes are very attractive and have an average depth of 10 ft (3 m). The
margins of the lakes are lush with rushes and reeds but the lakes are clear of
weeds. Carp are the main species of interest, with fish up to 30 lb (13.6 kg).
SPECIES Carp, tench, chub, roach, and bream to 6½ lb (2.9 kg).
TECHNIQUES AND BAITS Big fish tactics are needed for the carp, with
sweetcorn, high-protein baits and 'boilies' producing the best results. For
other species, float fishing, using a waggler float and maggots, casters and
bread as bait is effective.
SEASON 16th June to 14th March.
ACCESS Higham is reached via the A61(T) road north from Alfreton.

Permits are obtained from the Higham Farm Hotel, Old Higham, near
Alfreton.

River Derwent – Belper (Derbyshire) ST 4

This fishery covers 5 miles (8 km) of the River Derwent on both banks, and is controlled by the Belper Angling Club. The water flow is regulated by two weirs, and the river is fairly slow flowing and deep. This stretch runs from Ambergate Railway Bridge, through Belper to the downstream limit at Milford Road Bridge. The fishing is predominantly for chub, roach and grayling. In recent years, there has been an upsurge in the grayling population and some large catches can be made during the months of winter.

SPECIES Chub, roach, grayling, bream, perch and trout.

TECHNIQUES AND BAITS The best method to catch a good mixed bag of fish is with a stick float and maggot bait just tripping the bottom. The bigger chub are taken on legered bread or cheese. Casters are also a good chub and roach bait. During the winter 'laying on' with maggots in the slacker pools will take the grayling and chub.

SEASON 16th June to 14th March.

ACCESS Day permits are obtained from Mr A Henderson, Quality Tackle, 37 Bridge Street, Belper.

River Derwent – Duffield (Derbyshire) ST 5

Controlled by Derbyshire Angling Federation, this stretch of the river covers 2½ miles (4 km) between Milford and Allestree. The top end of the section is fast flowing below a derelict weir. Below the church section the river is slower and deeper and this is where the bream are most likely to be caught. In the faster upstream section, grayling are the main species, with a few sizeable chub and dace also.

SPECIES Grayling, roach, dace, chub, bream and trout.

TECHNIQUES AND BAITS Float fishing with a fine stick float is the best method, using maggots or casters as bait. Loose feeding should be kept 'little and often'. Light legering is also good for the chub and bream. Coloured maggots are banned in this water.

SEASON 16th June to 14th March.

ACCESS Day tickets are obtained from Mr A Henderson, Quality Tackle, 37 Bridge Street, Belper, Derbyshire

Introduction to the River Trent

The River Trent rises near Stoke-on-Trent and flows first east and then north, before entering the River Humber. A massive improvement in the quality of the water in the Trent has taken place in recent years, and the river is now extremely popular with anglers. Unlike most rivers, it was the upper reaches of the Trent which were the worst polluted and some of the major tributaries, such as the River Tame (which joins the Trent just south of Burton-upon-Trent) were little more than open sewers. The upper reaches of the Trent are still the least productive but at least fish can now live in the water. Even the Tame supports fish, although it could be made cleaner.

An interesting feature, since the Trent became cleaner, is the increase in the numbers of barbel and carp. In the early part of the last century the Trent supported a tremendous head of barbel but, as the river became grossly polluted during the Industrial Revolution, this species became virtually extinct in the river. A few fish managed to survive in the more oxygenated water of the weir pools, however, and, as the river became cleaner, they began to re-establish themselves along the river and are now the dominant species on a few stretches around Nottingham.

The success of the carp in the river is due largely to the large number of power stations sited along the River Trent. The river water is used in vast quantities for cooling purposes, and when it is returned to the river it is several degrees warmer. The carp like warm water and have thrived and bred in the river. As well as being present in reasonably large numbers, the carp have grown big and several specimens weighing over 30 lb (13.6 kg) have been caught in the river.

The river also holds a large head of roach but, in recent years, their numbers have declined, although the average size has increased. A number of 2 lb (0.9 kg) roach are caught in the river every year. The chub fishing in the river is excellent and the vast shoals of this species grow to a very respectable size with many 2–3 lb (0.9–1.4 kg) fish. Bream are mainly found in the lower reaches of the river but, again, they have increased in numbers and have spread upriver since it became cleaner.

Very few anglers fish for pike in the Trent but, with the massive numbers of food fish available, it is little wonder that this species has thrived. Some areas of the river are full of pike, and plenty of double figure fish can be caught. The river also swarms with smaller species, such as gudgeon and bleak, which can play an important part in matches if the river is running high after heavy rain. Double figure catches of bleak have regularly been taken from the river in matches.

The middle reaches of the Trent – between Burton-on-Trent and Nottingham – are very heavily match-fished, especially at weekends, and this is a matchman's water rather than a big fish water. There are undoubtedly some big fish in the Trent, especially chub and carp, but most of the stretches are too heavily fished to be of interest to the specimen hunter requiring peace and quiet.

The Trent is a wide river and the flow is fairly steady, making it a good water for the exponents of float fishing. When roach were the predominant species most anglers used float tackle and a free-running centre-pin reel. Even now a centre-pin gives the best control when float fishing the Trent. However, with the explosion in the numbers of chub and barbel, many matches are won legering with a swimfeeder. The feeders used by Trent regulars are big and hold a lot of feed, and they are well leaded so that they do not roll about in the current. Big, open-ended feeders need to be fished on fairly strong line and 4–5 lb (1.8–2.3 kg) breaking strain line is about right, with a hook length of 3 lb (1.4 kg) breaking strain line. The barbel are powerful fish and to fish light is risking a lot of breakages. The barbel in the Trent have a liking for hemp and tares, and casters are also a good bait. The usual barbel baits of luncheon meat and lobworms will catch both barbel and chub but not at the same rate, although they will probably attract the bigger fish.

The Trent is a river with plenty of opportunities for the visiting angler to obtain day tickets, especially from Burton-upon-Trent downstream.

River Trent — Swarkestone (near Burton-upon-Trent, Nottinghamshire) ST 6

This is an excellent stretch of the Trent, controlled by Derby Angling Association. The fishing begins above Willington Bridge and extends downstream on both banks, with a few short breaks, to below Swarkestone Bridge. The river is fast with gravelly runs and deeper pools. There are beds of weed during the summer. The depth of the river varies from 4 to 7 ft (1.2 to 2.1 m). Chub are, without doubt, the predominant species but the number of barbel is on the increase. During the summer the best fishing is in the shallows, but during the winter the chub pack into the deeper glides.

SPECIES Chub, roach, dace, barbel, bream and pike.

TECHNIQUES AND BAITS Long trotting with a stick float and maggot or caster as bait is the best technique to use. Some anglers have had good bags of fish using float-fished luncheon meat. Hemp seed is another bait worth trying in summer. Swimfeeder rigs will catch plenty of chub and an increasing number of barbel.

SEASON 16th June to 14th March.

ACCESS Swarkestone is downstream from Burton-upon-Trent.

Permits are obtained from the Rising Sun Inn at Willington or the Crewe and Harpur Inn, Swarkestone, or from local tackle dealers. The Secretary of Derby Angling Association is Mr B Sharratt, 64 Haig Street, Alvaston, Derby.

River Trent — Attenborough (near Long Eaton, Nottinghamshire) ST 7

Leisure Sport control 8285 ft (2525 m) of the fishing on the left bank of the river at Attenborough adjacent to the club's gravel-pit fisheries. The river is permanently pegged and pegs 50 to 60 are in a highly rated area. The river varies in character with deep glides and shallow runs. The chub fishing is excellent, and a lot of barbel are now present, too. This section of the river also holds shoals of good sized bream.

SPECIES Chub, barbel, roach, bream and pike.

TECHNIQUES AND BAITS Use feeder rigs for the chub and barbel with maggots or casters for bait. Hemp is an excellent barbel attractor. For the roach try float-fished caster using a stick float.

SEASON 16th June to 14th March.

ACCESS There is an anglers' car park at the end of Meadow Lane, Long Eaton.

Permits are obtained from Mr G Plummer, 45 Beresford Road, Sawley, Long Eaton, Nottingham

River Trent – Beeston Weir (near Beeston, Nottingham) ST 8

This stretch of the river, which includes Beeston Weir, is possibly the best, if present trends continue. The barbel population has increased considerably in the last two seasons, and anglers are regularly taking 50 lb (22.7 kg) each of fish during the summer. On the left-hand bank the water, which is controlled by Nottingham Angling Association, starts at Beeston Weir and extends to below the island. On the right-hand bank, the stretch begins above Beeston Weir and extends downstream to the boundary with Nottingham and District Federation Angling Society private water. The water is streamy and fairly shallow, and is full of chub and barbel.

SPECIES Chub, barbel, carp, bream, roach, perch and pike.

TECHNIQUES AND BAITS Mostly feeder tactics with big, open-ended feeders for the chub and barbel. Float fishing with a stick float is best for the chub and roach. Best baits are maggots, casters, tares and hemp.

SEASON 16th June to 14th March.

ACCESS Permits are available from bailiffs on the bank. The Secretary of Nottingham Angling Association is Mr E J Collin.

River Trent – Clifton Grove (Nottingham) ST 9

This water is controlled by Nottingham and District Federation Angling Society and covers the right bank of the Trent from just below Beeston Weir for $\frac{3}{4}$ mile (1.2 km). The society reserve half of this stretch for members only (signposted); the other half is open to visiting anglers. The river is very shallow and fast flowing, but is full of chub and barbel, including a few fish to double figures. There are also some good roach to be caught.

SPECIES Chub, barbel, roach, carp, bream, perch and pike.

TECHNIQUES AND BAITS Swimfeeders fished in conjunction with maggots, casters and hemp are usually used for the chub and barbel. Anglers have recently been taking some large barbel on liver.

SEASON 16th June to 14th March.

ACCESS Permits are available from bailiffs on the bank. The Secretary of Nottingham and District Federation Angling Society is Mr W Belshaw.

River Trent — Clifton (Nottingham) ST 10

This stretch of river at Clifton, on the right-hand bank, is controlled by Nottingham Waltonians. The river is shallow, about 3 ft (0.9 m), and swift flowing. Even so, a lot of the barbel can be caught right under the rod tip. The water gives excellent fishing for chub, barbel and roach and several roach over 2 lb (0.9 kg) are taken each season.

SPECIES Chub, bream, dace, roach, barbel, perch and pike.

TECHNIQUES AND BAITS Swimfeeders should be used, fished in conjunction with maggots, casters and hemp. On this stretch, hemp and tares are good baits for roach and barbel. A lot of barbel are taken fishing with a stick float right under the rod tip.

SEASON 16th June to 14th March.

ACCESS Access is through the riverside housing estate.

Permits are obtained from bailiffs on the bank. The Secretary of Nottingham Waltonians is Mr M Phillips, 123 Widecombe Lane, Nottingham.

River Trent — Nottingham ST 11

On the stretch of river known as the Victoria Embankment, the fishing in the city of Nottingham is free to holders of a Severn Trent Water Authority licence. The fishing is for $1\frac{1}{2}$ miles (2.4 km) and runs between Trent Bridge and Wilford Bridge. The river is wide and strong-flowing and roach are the predominant species. The fishing is from the embankment steps and the water is very popular, especially during the school holidays. However, during the winter the water is less heavily fished and some good catches of roach, chub and skimmer bream can be taken. The depth of the river varies between 5 and 15 ft (1.5 and 4.6 m).

SPECIES Roach, chub, bleak, gudgeon, bream, carp, tench and pike.

TECHNIQUES AND BAITS Stick float fishing, two rod lengths out with the bait just tripping bottom, is best. The best baits are tares, hemp, casters and maggots. Leger in the middle of the river for the bigger chub, bream and carp. Luncheon meat and cheese are good baits.

SEASON 16th June to 14th March.

ACCESS Parking is available in the city car parks.

The fishing is free.

River Trent – Holme Pierrepont (near Nottingham) ST 12

Holme Pierrepont is just 3½ miles (5.6 km) from Nottingham city centre and is the National Watersports Centre. The river is wide and chub and roach are the main quarry. The fishery also includes the Winfield Lagoon, alongside the Trent. The fishing is good, as are the facilities at the Watersports Centre, with accommodation and camping available.

SPECIES Roach, chub, bream, carp, gudgeon, bleak and pike.

TECHNIQUES AND BAITS Trotting with a stick float two rod lengths out from the bank is best for the roach and small chub. Legering with a feeder is the best tactic for the chub and bream.

SEASON 16th June to 14th March.

ACCESS Holme Pierrepont is reached by the A52 road from Radcliffe on Trent.

Permits are obtained at the Watersports Centre. Excellent car parking facilities are available. For details contact Mr R Broadley, Holme Pierrepont National Watersports Centre, Adbolton Lane, Nottingham.

River Trent – Stoke Bardolph (Nottingham) ST 13

This stretch of the river includes the famous Golden Mile Road. The water is controlled by Nottingham and District Federation Angling Society and the available fishing is on the left bank of the river, from just below Radcliffe Viaduct to Gunthorpe Bridge. The river at this point is lined by rocks, and the fishing is good close to the bank. Chub are the predominant species but there are some good bream and carp.

SPECIES Carp, chub, bream, roach and dace.

TECHNIQUES AND BAITS Feeder fishing with a big, open-ended feeder is best for the chub and bream. Float fish well out across the river in summer, but fish close to the bank in the winter. Casters, hemp and tares are the best baits.

SEASON 16th June to 14th March.

ACCESS Permits can be obtained from bailiffs on the bank. The Secretary of Nottingham and District Federation Angling Society is Mr W Belshaw.

River Trent – Fiskerton (near Newark on Trent, Nottinghamshire) ST 14

This is a good stretch of the Trent for chub and roach, with catches of 50 lb (22.7 kg) being taken by pleasure anglers. The fishery is on the left bank from Hazelford Lock downstream.

SPECIES Chub, roach, dace and bream.

TECHNIQUES AND BAITS Legering with an open-ended swimfeeder is best

for the chub and bream. Maggots, casters, hemp and tares are all good baits.
Float fish for dace, roach and chub with casters or hemp. Tares are a good
bait for the roach during the summer.

SEASON 16th June to 14th March.

ACCESS Access to the river is via the car park of the Bromley Arms pub at
Fiskerton. Fiskerton may be reached by turning south-east off the A612
Nottingham to Newark on Trent road at Southwell.

Permits are obtained from the Bromley Arms pub.

River Trent – Winthorpe (near Newark on Trent, Nottinghamshire) ST 15

This stretch consists of 4 miles (6.4 km) of the right-hand bank of the river
from Crankley Point to Holme Marsh, and is controlled by Worksop
Angling Society. The river is fairly shallow and the predominant species is
chub. The chub run to 4 lb (1.8 kg) and there are also some good bream and
carp on this stretch. This section of the river still fishes well in flood
conditions.

SPECIES Chub, bream, roach, carp, dace, gudgeon and pike.

TECHNIQUES AND BAITS Legering with a big, open-ended feeder is best on
this stretch of river. Casters, hemp and tares are all good baits. Sweetcorn
will catch the carp and will also take some good chub and roach. Float
fishing will catch mainly chub and roach.

SEASON 16th June to 14th March.

ACCESS The river is reached via Winthorpe village.

Worksop Angling Society issue temporary membership tickets from
bailiffs on the bank.

River Trent – North Muskham (near Newark on Trent, Nottinghamshire) ST 16

The fishing on this stretch of the Trent is controlled by Walter Bower, and
is a superb chub fishery with some good carp and bream also present.
Catches of over 100 lb (45.4 kg) of carp have been taken, comprising fish in
the 2–4 lb (0.9–1.8 kg) range. There are also three lakes which can be fished,
and these have an excellent stock of chub, tench and carp.

SPECIES Roach, chub, bream, dace, pike, bleak and gudgeon.

TECHNIQUES AND BAITS Legering, using luncheon meat or cheese,
produces the best results with the chub and swimfeeders in conjunction
with maggots and casters are also good for the chub and bream. Float fishing
with a stick float will produce the usual mixed bag of roach, chub and
skimmer bream.

SEASON 16th June to 14th March.

ACCESS The North Muskham fishery is just off the A1(T) north of Newark
on Trent, on the west bank of the river.

Permits are obtained from Mr W Bower at his house which is at the entrance to the fishery.

River Trent — Cromwell Weir (Collingham, Nottinghamshire) ST 17

This fishery covers the Trent, from Cromwell Weir, downstream to Besthorpe Wharfe, on the right-hand bank of the river. The fishery is controlled by Collingham Angling Association and visitors should note that the water is heavily match-fished at weekends, although a section is reserved for pleasure fishing. Cromwell Weir is the tidal limit of the Trent. The fishing is predominantly for roach, chub and bream.

SPECIES Chub, roach, bream, dace, pike and gudgeon.

TECHNIQUES AND BAITS Leger with a swimfeeder in conjunction with maggots, casters, tares and hemp for the chub and bream. Stick float fishing with casters, tares and hemp is best for the roach and chub.

SEASON 16th June to 14th March.

ACCESS Access is on minor roads off the A1133 Newark to Gainsborough road, at Collingham and Besthorpe.

Permits are obtained from bailiffs on the bank. The Secretary of Collingham Angling Association is Mrs J Wilson.

River Trent — New Castle Fishery (North Clifton, Nottinghamshire) ST 18

This is a 6 mile (9.7 km) section of the lower Trent, controlled by Sheffield Amalgamated Anglers Society. The stretch is on the right bank of the river from the first fence, near the railway viaduct at North Clifton, upstream via South Clifton and Girton to the confluence with Fleet Dyke. A further 1640 ft (500 m) of fishing is available from Besthorpe Wharfe to Collingham. The fishing is predominantly for chub, roach and bream.

SPECIES Chub, roach, bream, carp and dace.

TECHNIQUES AND BAITS Legering with an open-ended feeder is best for chub and bream. Casters, maggots and hemp are the best baits. Float fish for chub and roach using the same baits.

SEASON 16th June to 14th March.

ACCESS Access to the river is possible at South Clifton, North Clifton and Girton.

Day tickets are obtained from Mr A Baynes, 39 Sparken Hill, Worksop, Nottingham.

Attenborough South Lakes (Long Eaton, Nottinghamshire) ST 19

These are two gravel-pits of 28 acres (11 ha) and 114 acres (46 ha), controlled by Leisure Sport. They support a mixed head of coarse fish, notably bream and roach. The bream average 2–3 lb (0.9–1.4 kg) and total catches of 20 lb (9.1 kg) are not uncommon. Club matches can be booked (100 pegs), and are held on the north end of the largest lake.

SPECIES Roach to 3 lb (1.4 kg), pike to 18 lb (8.2 kg) and bream to 6½ lb (2.9 kg).

TECHNIQUES AND BAITS The big bream catches for which the water is well known are taken by swing tip legering with a feeder and maggots. The roach are caught using a waggler float and fine tackle.

SEASON 16th June to 14th March. No night fishing is allowed.

ACCESS Proceed to Station Road, Long Eaton. New Tythe Street will be found almost opposite Horseshoe Sports (a tackle shop). Follow New Tythe Street for about 1 mile (1.6 km), keeping to the main road until the entrance to the municipal car park, with its height barrier, is reached. Cars should be parked in this car park at the far end of the parking area. There is another car park at the north end of the big lake, reached by Barton Lane, crossing the railway and the bailey bridges. Car parking is to the left and right of the road and in the designated area at the far end beyond the bailey bridges.

Permits are available from Mr F Russell, 'Wotsits' Tackle Shop, 8 Archer Road, Stapleford, Nottingham.

Nanpantan Reservoir (Loughborough, Leicestershire) ST 20

This is an 8 acre (3.2 ha) reservoir managed as a coarse fishery. The water was drained several years ago and stocked with a fast-growing strain of carp which have now grown on to double figures, with some over 20 lb (9.1 kg). The water is fairly deep near the dam and there is some marginal weed and rushes. The water is limited to 30 rods per day.

SPECIES Carp to 23 lb (10.4 kg), roach, perch, bream and tench.

TECHNIQUES AND BAITS Specimen tactics are necessary for the bigger carp. It is preferred that carp are returned immediately to the water. Luncheon meat is a good bait, together with sweetcorn and high-protein baits. Maggots and casters are best for the smaller species, and should be presented on waggler float. For the bream use light leger tackle with a swing tip. Groundbaiting is banned.

SEASON 16th June to 14th March.

ACCESS The reservoir is located on the outskirts of Loughborough on the B5350 road to Nanpantan.

Permits are obtained from Mr Wortley, W H Wortley and Son, 45 Baxter Gate, Loughborough.

Lake Vyrnwy (near Welshpool, Powys) ST 21

Lake Vyrnwy lies at the foot of the Berwyn Mountain range. The lake is over 4 miles (6.4 km) long and covers 1120 acres (455 ha). It is in a particularly beautiful setting with heavily wooded banks sloping up the valley sides. The fishing is for the wild brown trout and stocked rainbow trout. Boats must be used, and there are 13 boats available each taking three anglers. The trout are not large but the average size is good with most fish weighing at least 1 lb (0.5 kg), and 2 lb (0.9 kg) fish are plentiful. Rhiwargor Bay, at the top end of the lake, is one of the shallowest areas and is a productive 'hot spot'. Most fish are caught drifting close to the bank. The limit is eight fish per day.

SPECIES Brown trout and rainbow trout.

TECHNIQUES AND BAITS Fly fishing only. Use lures on sinking lines early in the season and loch-style drift fishing later on in the season.

SEASON 1st March to 15th October. Fishing from 8.30 am to sunset.

ACCESS Take the A490 from Welshpool and then the B4393 after passing through Llanfyllin.

Permits to fish are obtained through the Hotel Vyrnwy.

Introduction to the River Severn

The River Severn provides many opportunities for the visiting angler, with scores of good day ticket waters. The river also supports a tremendous head of fish of just about every species; even zander are starting to establish themselves in the lower reaches of the river.

The Severn is 180 miles (290 km) long and rises on Plynlimon (Pumlumon Fawr) in Powys, only a short distance from the source of the River Wye. In the upper reaches the river is fast flowing and narrow, with just a few deeper glides. Between Llanidloes and Newtown, the river flows close to the main A470(T) and A489(T) roads and is in a very attractive setting. The river alternates between gravel glides and fast broken runs. The banks have a lot of vegetation which gives the angler plenty of cover. The main species are trout and grayling, the latter being the dominant species. Chub and dace are also present, especially in the deeper glides.

At Welshpool, coarse fish become much more common and barbel, for which the river is famous, begin to feature in catches. Then, between Welshpool and Shrewsbury, the Severn is joined by the River Vyrnwy, one of its major tributaries. During the summer, water is released from Lake Vyrnwy to flow down the Severn. This has mixed results because, although the extra water increases the flow when the river is low, the water from the lake is very cold, and the sudden introduction of cold water can cause the fish to go off feed temporarily. Barbel are among the first species to stop feeding in cold water.

At Atcham, near Shrewsbury, the barbel fishing can be really outstanding in summer, with some spectacular catches taken by pleasure anglers. Even in matches several catches of over 100 lb (45.4 kg) have been recorded. Most barbel tend to be in the 2–4 lb (0.9–1.8 kg) size range but bigger fish to 12 lb (5.4 kg) have been taken. Further downstream at Ironbridge the barbel fishing is also excellent and there are also some large chub to be caught. The barbel in this middle reach of the Severn have so much feed thrown at them by anglers that they have become addicted to small baits such as maggots, hemp or casters. They will take luncheon meat but, for consistency, small baits work best. The Severn in these middle reaches alternates between deep glides and fast shallows. On most of the banks, there is a lot of willow and other vegetation, but periodically the Severn Trent Water Authority drainage engineers clear the banks, supposedly in the interests of improved land drainage and flood prevention.

From Bridgnorth to Bewdley roach become more prolific and, although they are not present in the numbers they once were, they can offer good sport, especially in the winter months. Chub, too, are prolific in these reaches and they replace the barbel during the winter as the anglers' main target. Very little serious pike fishing is undertaken on the middle Severn, yet they are numerous and grow to a large size.

From Stourport downstream to Tewkesbury the river is much deeper and slower flowing. There are less barbel in these reaches, and bream up to 6 lb (2.7 kg) roam this part of the river. It is in these reaches that zander have started to put in an appearance.

The River Severn is a very popular match fishing venue and in the middle and lower reaches it is always worth checking that the stretch you intend to fish has not been pegged, especially if you hope to fish at a weekend. The Severn Trent Water Authority operates a service to anglers which informs them of the river levels. This is extremely useful in winter and can save wasted journeys.

River Severn – Llanidloes (Powys) ST 22

This upper reach of the Severn is very attractive with the river running into pools and then shallow glides. The bed is gravel and shingle and the fishing is predominantly for trout and grayling with a few coarse fish present.

The fishery covers 1970 ft (600 m) of the right-hand bank downstream from the boundary fence of the sewage works.

SPECIES Brown trout, grayling to 1 lb (0.5 kg), dace, and chub to 3 lb (1.4 kg).

TECHNIQUES AND BAITS Try float fishing with a stick float in the glides for the best results. Maggots and casters are good baits, although small redworms will often tempt the larger grayling, especially in cold weather when maggots tend to 'stiffen up'. Cheese, bread crust and luncheon meat will tempt the bigger chub on leger tackle.

SEASON 16th June to 14th March.

ACCESS The water is at Llanidloes, near the sewage works. The fishing is free to Severn Trent Water Authority (S T W A) licence holders. For further details contact the STWA (Upper Severn Division).

River Severn – Dinam Estate Fishery (Llandinam, Powys) ST 23

This well-stocked fishery is in the upper Severn Valley between Llanidloes and Caersws, and provides excellent trout fishing with the opportunity for some coarse fishing. There is also the chance of catching a few salmon from July onwards. The river runs through a picturesque open valley with numerous gravel riffles and pools. Some $4\frac{1}{2}$ miles (7.2 km) of double-bank day ticket fishing is available.

Excluding the very short length between the two bridges and Llandinam, the 2 miles (3.2 km) from the Afon Trannon confluence upstream to the upper limit board can be fished for trout and grayling but is restricted exclusively to fly fishing. The catch limit is four trout and four grayling. The remainder of the fishery is reserved exclusively for coarse fishing. This includes both banks from the Trannon confluence to the upper boundary of Caersws recreation ground, the right bank only from Caersws road bridge to the lower limit (clearly marked), and both banks of the Afon Trannon to the first road bridge upstream of Carnedd Farm.

SPECIES Brown trout, grayling, chub, dace and salmon (occasional).

TECHNIQUES AND BAITS On the fly-only game section small wet and dry flies work best using light river fly tackle. A size 5 floating line is about right and, using this, wet flies can be worked deeper by degreasing the nylon leader with fuller's earth. On the coarse fishing section, the method likely to catch the most fish is a stick float with maggot and caster bait. In the colder weather, try redworms for the grayling as they are more lively in low temperatures. To catch the larger chub try legered luncheon meat or cheese.

SEASON 18th March to 30th September (trout), 2nd February to 30th September (salmon) and 16th June to 14th March (coarse fish including grayling).

ACCESS Day permits are obtained from Mr Wilden, The Lion Hotel, Llandinam.

River Severn – Penstrowed (near Newtown, Powys) ST 24

This stretch of the Severn is probably the best water in the area for grayling. The length of the fishery is $1\frac{1}{4}$ miles (2 km) and runs from the top of the first meadow, above the railway bridge, to the boundary fence behind the garage on the right bank. This is an attractive length of river with the water alternating between deeper glides and broken ripples. There are lots of bushes along the bank, although, in places, the banking is rather high. The trout fishing is quite good with a few large trout to be caught.

SPECIES Brown trout, grayling to $1\frac{1}{2}$ lb (0.7 kg), chub and dace.

TECHNIQUES AND BAITS This is a good fly fishing water for both trout and grayling. Small dry flies will take the grayling with patterns such as Greenwell's Glory and Grey Duster. During the autumn and winter, bait fishing will catch the grayling, trotting down with stick float and maggots or redworms. During the winter a few matches are held and the winning weight is usually made up of grayling with double figure catches not uncommon.

SEASON 18th March to 30th September (brown trout) and 16th June to 14th March (coarse fish).

ACCESS The water is reached by the A492 road, $2\frac{1}{2}$ miles (4 km) west of Newtown. The river is reached past Penstrowed Hall, which is a black and white farmhouse, on the opposite side of the road to a quarry. Parking is allowed at the quarry entrance.

Permits are obtained from the Mid Wales Angling Centre, 22 Park Street, Newtown, or Mr L Bebb, 15 Shortbridge Street, Newtown.

River Severn – Atcham (near Shrewsbury, Shropshire) ST 25

This stretch of the Severn is capable of producing some huge catches of barbel. The river is perfect for this species, alternating between shallow gravelly glides and holes up to 16 ft (4.9 m) deep. Atcham is one of the areas along the Severn where big barbel are caught quite frequently and consequently receives the attention of big fish anglers. The fishing on this length is controlled by the Severn Trent Water Authority (STWA). Both banks can be fished for a short distance above Atcham Bridge, and the right bank downstream of the bridge for $3\frac{1}{2}$ miles (5.6 km). This length of river is regularly match-fished but several sections are reserved for individual pleasure anglers. The river at Atcham also has a good head of other coarse fish besides the barbel.

SPECIES Barbel, chub, roach, dace, pike and perch.

TECHNIQUES AND BAITS Legering with large feeders is best for the barbel. Do not be tempted to fish too light for the barbel, even when using small hooks; 4–5 lb (1.8–2.3 kg) breaking strain line is about right, in conjunction with a size 14 or 16 hook for maggots. With big baits, such as cheese or luncheon meat, use a size 8 to 10 hook. Hemp seed is a good attractor for barbel but do not overfeed. Some of the slow glides are perfect for float fishing with a stick or waggler float. Some of the best barbel swims are very snagging so expect to lose a few feeders.

SEASON 16th June to 14th March.

ACCESS Atcham is 6 miles (9.7 km) south-east of Shrewsbury on the A5 road. Access is by the lane next to Atcham Bridge that runs to Cross Houses on the A458. A car park is on the left-hand side of the lane.

Permits are obtained from the filling station at Cross Houses near the junction of this access lane and the A458 road. For further details contact the STWA (Upper Severn Division).

River Severn – Ribbesford (Stourport-on-Severn, Hereford and Worcester) ST 26

Barbel are less numerous on this length of the Severn but there are some excellent dace and roach. The fishing is controlled by Lyttleton Angling Association, and the fishery is on the right-hand bank. The fishery begins at the caravan site below Stourport Bridge and extends upstream for $1\frac{1}{2}$ miles (2.4 km). The depth of the river at Stourport varies between 5 and 10 ft (1.5 and 3 m). The best area to fish is between the concrete slipway and the spinney.

SPECIES Barbel, chub, bream, roach, dace and pike.

TECHNIQUES AND BAITS This is a good float fishing stretch, and the pace of the river is fairly even. Trot down with a stick float, holding back slightly and letting the bait just trip bottom. Good baits are hemp seed, tares, casters and maggots. Legering with a quiver tip in mid-river will bring the larger chub and barbel, using luncheon meat as bait.

SEASON 16th June to 14th March.

ACCESS There is a car park next to Stourport Bridge.

Permits are obtained from J White, Tackle Shop, Raven Street, Stourport; or Mal Storey, 106 Sutton Road, Kidderminster, Hereford and Worcester. The Secretary of Lyttleton Angling Association is Mr E Wilkes.

River Severn – Ripple (near Tewkesbury, Gloucestershire) ST 27

The Severn Trent Water Authority (STWA) control the fishing for 1 mile (1.6 km) of the River Severn near the village of Ripple, north of where the M50 motorway crosses the river. The fishery extends for 1 mile (1.6 km) on the east bank only. The river is wide and deep, with bream and chub being the predominant species. Barbel are also caught but they are not as widespread as further upstream. The pike fishing is good and is worthy of more serious attention than it receives.

SPECIES Chub, roach, bream, perch, pike, barbel and carp.

TECHNIQUES AND BAITS Legering with bread flake is best, especially for the bream, chub and large roach. Float fishing with a stick or waggler float one-and-a-half rod lengths from the bank will catch the roach, dace and chub. Maggots, casters and tares are good roach baits.

SEASON 16th June to 14th March.

ACCESS The river is approached via the village of Ripple, 4 miles (6.4 km) north of Tewkesbury. A car park is provided near the fishery.

The fishing is free to holders of an STWA licence. Further details are available from the STWA (Lower Severn Division).

River Severn – Hawbridge (near Tewkesbury, Gloucestershire) ST 28

This fishery is controlled by Gloucester United Angling Association and centres around Hawbridge. The right-hand bank of the river for 1 mile (1.6 km) upstream and 1 mile (1.6 km) downstream of the bridge can be fished on a day ticket. The left-hand bank can be fished downstream of the bridge for one meadow only. The river in this area is very wide and deep and the fishing for pike and bream is extremely good.

SPECIES Roach, chub, pike, bream, dace and gudgeon.

TECHNIQUES AND BAITS Stick float and waggler fishing using maggots or casters as bait about one-and-a-half rod lengths from the bank should be used. If the river is carrying extra water 'laying on', with a stick float close to the bank, works well. For the bream, legering with bread-flake using an open-ended feeder crammed with groundbait is effective.

SEASON 16th June to 14th March.

ACCESS Hawbridge is just outside Tewkesbury. Parking is available at the bridge and boundary fence.

Permits are obtained from F Harvey; Allsports; Tredworth Tackle; Rod and Gun Room, Gloucester; or The Tackle Shop, 56 Church Street, Tewkesbury. The General Secretary of the Gloucester United Angling Association is Mr J Gibby, 70 Robert Raikes Avenue, Tuffley, Gloucestershire.

Church Pool (Patshull Park, Wolverhampton, West Midlands) ST 29

This is an exceptionally good big fish water, set in Patshull Park and covering 10 acres (4 ha). The fishery has only recently opened to the public and already it has produced several carp over 25 lb (11.3 kg). The best fish so far is a mirror carp of 26 lb (11.7 kg). The interesting feature of this lake is that most of the carp are fully scaled common carp and not the usual mirrors. Other species are present and these also grow to huge proportions. The setting of the lake is idyllic with lilies and rushes in the water, and trees surrounding the site. The lake is also fairly deep, up to 18 ft (5.5 m) in places. Local hotel accommodation is available.

SPECIES Carp to 26 lb (11.7 kg), bream to 10 lb (4.5 kg), roach to 2 lb 14 oz (1.3 kg) and tench.

TECHNIQUES AND BAITS Specimen fish tactics are best on this lake. During the summer a good bait for the carp is dog food 'mixer'. During the autumn and early winter the regular anglers do best using 'boilies'. The baits are fished on hair rigs usually in conjunction with bolt rigs. No keepnets are allowed.

SEASON 16th June to 14th March.

ACCESS Patshull is reached by taking the A41(T) and A464(T) roads west from Wolverhampton and turning left a couple of miles past Tettenhall on to the minor road to the village of Pattingham. From here turn right to Patshull (signposted).

Permits are obtained from the Lakeside Lodge Hotel, Patshull Estate.

Great Pool (Patshull, Wolverhampton, West Midlands) ST 30

This 68 acre (28 ha) lake is managed as a trout fishery. The lake varies greatly in depth from shallows of 3 ft (0.9 m) to areas which are 30 ft (9 m) deep. The lake is set in attractive, partly wooded surroundings, with lily beds and weed beds in places. The fishing is from both banks and boats. Thirty special fishing punts can be hired at the fishery. The water is regularly stocked right through the season. The catch limit for a full day is six fish and for a half day permit, three fish. The facilities at Patshull are excellent with easy access, good parking, toilets and hotel accommodation. The Troutmasters Final fishing competition is usually held at Patshull.

SPECIES Rainbow trout.

TECHNIQUES AND BAITS Fly fishing only. Lure fishing is best early and late in the season. Buzzer, nymph and dry fly fishing is best in the summer.

ACCESS Patshull is reached by taking the A41(T) and A464(T) roads west from Wolverhampton and turning left a couple of miles past Tettenhall on to the minor road to the village of Pattingham. From here turn right to Patshull (signposted).

Permits are obtained from the Lakeside Lodge Hotel, Patshull Estate.

Gailey Trout Fishery (near Cannock, Staffordshire) ST 31

A good sized trout lake covering 35 acres (14 ha), Gailey has an average depth of 15 ft (4.6 m). There are 15 boats available for anglers and plenty of open bank space where casting is unhindered. Day and evening permits are available and have a bag limit of six fish and three fish, respectively. The average size of the fish is good, and some very large rainbow trout are caught every season. Party bookings from small clubs are welcome and the management will give free tuition and advice to beginners.

SPECIES Rainbow trout to 13 lb 14 oz (6.3 kg) and brown trout to 6 lb 12 oz (3.1 kg).

TECHNIQUES AND BAITS Fly fishing only. Sinking lines work better than floaters at Gailey. Green Nymphs on a slow sink line, and Viva lures on a fast sinker are recommended.

SEASON 1st March to 31st October. Fishing from 8.30 am to dusk.

ACCESS Gailey is very close to Junctions 11 and 12 on the M6 motorway.

Permits can be obtained from Gailey Trout Fishery, Gailey Lea Lane, Penkridge, Staffordshire.

Edgbaston Reservoir (Birmingham, West Midlands) ST 32

Although in the heart of Birmingham, the 65 acre (26 ha) Edgbaston Reservoir is a very good coarse fishery. Edgbaston is a canal feeder reservoir and can be fished all round except on the dam face. The water is not very deep, with an average depth of 5 ft (1.5 m). Each year the Department of Recreation and Community Services run the City of Birmingham Angling Festival on several of the city's park lakes and the final is usually held at Edgbaston. Roach and small bream are the main species and some good catches are taken, especially during the summer and autumn.

SPECIES Roach, bream, tench and eels.

TECHNIQUES AND BAITS Legering with an open-ended feeder with a swing tip rod or float fishing using a waggler float is best. At all times, use fine tackle and small hooks.

SEASON 16th June to 14th March.

ACCESS From the Birmingham city centre, the reservoir is to the right of the A456 road, travelling west towards the M5 motorway.

Permits can be obtained from local tackle shops or direct from the Department of Recreation and Community Services, City of Birmingham, Auchinleck House, Five Ways, Birmingham.

Packington Trout Lakes (Meriden, near Birmingham, West Midlands) ST 33

There are three trout lakes at Packington open to day ticket anglers. The lakes are disused gravel-pits and fishing is from both the bank and from boats. The banks of the lakes are easily accessible all round. The lakes are continually stocked right through the season with both brown and rainbow trout. The bag limit is 15 trout.

SPECIES Brown trout and rainbow trout.

TECHNIQUES AND BAITS Fly fishing only. During the early part of the season lures fished deep on sinking lines work best. During the summer, a lot of fish are taken on buzzer, nymph and dry fly.

SEASON 18th March to 15th November. (The lakes may stay open to mid December some years.) Fishing from 6 am to 1 hour after sunset.

ACCESS To reach Packington, take the A45 road east from Birmingham and at Meriden take the B4102 road to the fishery entrance.

Permits are obtained from the Fishery Lodge, Maxstoke Lane, Meriden.

Packington Coarse Lakes (Meriden, near Birmingham, West Midlands) ST 34

There are four coarse fishing lakes at Packington. They are 12 acre (5 ha) Molands Mere, 6 acre (2.4 ha) Geary's Level, 2 acre (0.8 ha) Anniversaries, and 1½ acre (0.6 ha) Siblings. Molands Mere is a mixed coarse fishery with some good carp and tench. This lake is also stocked with trout and between 18th March and 1st June is a fly only, trout fishery. This means that there is a fair residue of trout remaining when the coarse fishing season re-opens on 16th June. Geary's Level is a carp fishery and the remaining two lakes are mixed coarse fisheries. The lakes are all matured gravel-pits with easily accessible banks.

SPECIES Carp, tench, bream, roach, rudd, perch, crucian carp and rainbow trout (Molands Mere only).

TECHNIQUES AND BAITS Legering should be used for the bigger fish. Good catches are taken on float tackle using a waggler float with maggots, casters, bread flake and sweetcorn as bait.

SEASON *Molands Mere*: 16th June to 28th February (coarse fish) and 18th March to 1st June (fly only trout). *Other lakes*: 16th June to 14th March.

ACCESS To reach Packington take the A45(T) road east from Birmingham and at Meriden take the B4102 road to the fishery entrance.

Permits are obtained from a self-service machine on site. Information is available from the Fishery Lodge, Maxstoke Lane, Meriden, near Birmingham.

Napton Reservoirs (Southam, Warwickshire) ST 35

These are two lakes near the Grand Union Canal below Calcott Locks. The largest lake covers 20 acres (8 ha) and has some lush weed beds in the shallows and deeper clear areas. This lake holds some specimen tench and a good head of roach. The smaller lake covers 3 acres (1.2 ha) and has some big carp to over 20 lb (9.1 kg). The carp in both these lakes are difficult to catch.

SPECIES Carp, tench, roach, bream and perch.

TECHNIQUES AND BAITS Specimen tactics are best for the carp, and should be used with high-protein paste baits. For the other species float fishing, using a waggler float set to just over depth, is best. Best baits are maggots, casters, bread and sweetcorn.

SEASON 16th June to 14th March.

ACCESS Southam is reached by travelling on the A425 road east from Warwick. Continue on this road beyond Southam for 2 miles (3.2 km) to the village of Napton for access to the lakes.

Permits are available from bailiffs on the bank. The water is controlled by

Coventry and District Angling Association whose Secretary is Mr P O'Connor, 48 Loxley Close, Wood End, Coventry.

Compton Verney Lake (Kineton, Warwickshire) ST 36

This is a long narrow lake, covering 20 acres (8 ha). The lake is nearly $\frac{1}{2}$ mile (0.8 km) long and 330 ft (100 m) wide with depths varying from 3 to 24 ft (0.9 to 7.3 m). Set in picturesque surroundings, the east bank is wooded and fishing is from clearings. On the west side of the lake, fishing jetties have been constructed. The pike fishing is very good with plenty of double figure catches and during 1983 a 38 lb (17.2 kg) specimen was taken.

SPECIES Pike, roach, perch, bream and carp.

TECHNIQUES AND BAITS Deadbaiting or spinning is best for the pike. The other species respond to float fishing using a waggler float and maggots, casters, bread or sweetcorn as bait. In the deeper water try swing tipping using the same baits.

SEASON 16th June to 14th March. Fishing is from dawn to dusk (6 pm in summer). No night fishing is allowed.

ACCESS Take the B4056 road from Stratford-upon-Avon and travel east through Wellesbourne Hastings, on to the B4086 and across the Foss Way. Once across the Foss Way turn right after 200 yards into the driveway to the farm. Parking is in the fisherman's car park.

Tickets are available at the waterside. For further details contact Mrs E Towns, Park Farm, Compton Verney.

Introduction to the River Avon

The River Avon is the largest and, from an angling point of view, the most important tributary of the River Severn. It rises near Naseby and from there flows steadily in a south-westerly direction to join the River Severn near Tewkesbury, and provides some excellent sport along most of its length. The best of the fishing is below Stratford-upon-Avon, especially around Evesham and Eckington. It is also a beautiful river, with lush bankside vegetation in most places. The fishing throughout the river is mainly for chub, roach and dace but, in the lower reaches, some big barbel are caught. Bream are also found in the lower reaches, although they tend to shoal and are not always easy to locate. Boats can cause problems for anglers, especially during the summer around Stratford-upon-Avon.

River Avon – Eckington (Hereford and Worcester) ST 37

This is a first-class stretch of river and is controlled by Cheltenham Angling Association. The Avon can be fished at Eckington, Strensham Locks and Weir, Nafford and Birlington. The river here is wide, slow flowing and very deep in places. The banks are pegged for match fishing. Some good bream

are to be found between pegs 27 and 29 and again between pegs 50 and 70. The stretch between the locks and weir is excellent for pike fishing. From the pipe bridge swim to the rowing club, bream, roach and chub are the main species. The water is probably the best for big fish on the Avon.
SPECIES Bream, pike, roach, chub and the occasional large barbel.
TECHNIQUES AND BAITS Legering with an open-ended feeder packed with groundbait and maggots is effective. For hookbait, maggots, casters or bread are best. Waggler fishing with maggots or casters will catch the chub and roach.
SEASON 16th June to 14th March.
ACCESS Eckington is reached by the A440 road from Evesham and then the B4080 road from Pershore.

Permits are obtained from The Bell Inn, Eckington (after 8.30 am); or Mrs Stayt, Boon Street, Eckington (near Bell Inn, 7.15 am onwards). They are also available from local tackle shops. The Cheltenham Angling Association Secretary is Mr F T Selley, 2 Hollis Gardens, Hatherley, Cheltenham, Gloucestershire.

River Avon – Stratford-upon-Avon (Warwickshire)
ST 38

The fishery here is at the Old Lido and the recreation ground. This water fishes better in winter as it is less busy. The fishing is predominantly for roach. During the summer, a few barbel are caught on this stretch.
SPECIES Chub, roach, dace, perch, barbel (few) and pike.
TECHNIQUES AND BAITS Waggler and stick float fishing is best, using maggots, casters or hemp as baits. Leger with a small feederlink for the chub, using casters or bread as bait.
SEASON 16th June to 14th March.
ACCESS Day permits are obtained from bailiffs on the bank or from the Senior Bailiff, Mr J Boag, 8 Coppice Close, Stratford-upon-Avon.

River Avon –Offenham (Hereford and Worcester) ST 39

The fishing on this stretch is controlled by the Fish and Anchor public house. The fishery is on the left bank of the river upstream of the pub (except the weir). This is a good water for chub and dace, with roach more plentiful above the weir. The shallow sections fish better in summer, and the deeper water fishes better in winter.
SPECIES Dace, roach and chub.
TECHNIQUES AND BAITS Stick float fishing should be tried in the faster water, and float fishing with waggler in the deeper swims. Legering with a small feeder using maggots or casters as bait will also bring results.
SEASON 16th June to 14th March.

ACCESS Turn right over the bridge at Bidford-on-Avon on to the B4085 road and then right again on to the B4510. Cars may be parked in the pub car park. Permits are obtained from the Fish and Anchor Inn (during licensing hours) or from the bailiff's caravan.

River Avon– Evesham (Hereford and Worcester) ST 40

This is an excellent stretch of river which is very popular at weekends. Chub are the predominant species and some large catches of them are taken. This part of the river fishes best in the autumn and winter. The fishing is on the right-hand bank, and some of the best swims are just above the A435 road bridge, the culvert pegs downstream from the road bridge and opposite the sidestream confluence.

SPECIES Chub, roach, dace and pike.

TECHNIQUES AND BAITS Float fishing with either a stick float close to the river bank, or a waggler float in the middle of the river, using maggots, casters or hemp as bait. Legering in the middle or under the far bank with casters or bread will also take chub.

SEASON 16th June to 14th March.

ACCESS Permits are obtained from bailiffs on the bank. For further information contact Mr T H Pitcher who is Secretary of the Evesham Angling Association.

River Avon – Hampton Ferry (Evesham, Hereford and Worcester) ST 41

This stretch of the Avon is often referred to as Huxley's, and is a popular match-fishing venue. Chub are the predominant species with some good roach and dace fishing. The fishing is on both banks of the river upstream of the railway bridge. The upstream end of the fishery is the shallowest while the bottom end of the stretch has depths of up to 16 ft (4.9 m).

SPECIES Roach, chub, dace, perch, bream and pike.

TECHNIQUES AND BAITS Float fish with a stick float in the upper part of the stretch, and try waggler fishing in the lower stretch. Maggots or casters are the best bait. Leger with bread or casters for the bigger chub.

SEASON 16th June to 14th March.

ACCESS Access is via the A44 Evesham to Pershore road.

Permits are obtained from E W Huxley and Son (cafe) at Hampton Ferry.

Anglian Water Authority

The Anglian Water Authority covers a large area from Lincolnshire in the north to Essex in the south. The area is a mass of waterways and rivers, and is especially blessed with new gravel-pit fisheries – especially in the Northampton area.

The major river in the area is the Great Ouse which, although having suffered in recent years, is still fishing well. Sadly, the once-superb fishing on the Norfolk Broads has declined greatly. Although parts of the Broads and associated rivers are still good fisheries, some are now very poor. Hickling Broad and Heigham Sound are typical examples. These waterways, part of the Hickling Broad National Nature Reserve, were once the finest pike fisheries in the country. In 1969 the toxic alga *Prymnesium parvum* appeared in the waters and virtually wiped out the entire fish population. Since then *Prymnesium* has reared its ugly head in May and June in most years, with the result that very few fish are caught in these waters now. Unfortunately many anglers visiting the area still associate the names of the waters with big fish, and are soon disappointed.

As well as some excellent coarse fisheries, the Anglian region is blessed with very good trout fisheries. There are the massive reservoirs, such as Rutland, Grafham and Pitsford, and the new smaller waters such as Ringstead Grange and Vicarage Spinney.

Key	Page
1 Barton Broads	123
2 The Poplars	124
3 Hill View Lakes	124
4 Rutland Water	125
5 River Welland	126
6 Folly River	126
7 River Great Ouse – Ten Mile Bank	126
8 River Great Ouse – Littleport	127
9 River Wissey – Hilgay	127
10 Edgefield Hall Lake	128
11 Swanton Morley Lakes	128
12 Booton Clay Pit	129
13 Hevingham Lakes	129
14 Taverham Gravel Pits	130
15 River Ant – Ludham	130
16 River Thurne – Martham	131
17 River Bure – South Walsham	131
18 Fritton Decoy	132
19 Eyebrook Reservoir	132
20 River Nene – Oundle	133
21 St Ives Complex	133
22 River Great Ouse	135
23 Fen Drayton Complex	135
24 Thrapston Complex	136
25 Ringstead Grange Trout Fishery	137
26 Grafham Water	137
27 Pitsford Reservoir	138
28 Overstone Solarium	138
29 Billing Aquadrome	139
30 Castle Ashby Lakes	139
31 Little Paxton Fishery	140
32 Vicarage Spinney Lake	140
33 Linford Lakes Complex	141
34 River Great Ouse – Buckingham	143
35 Loughton Lakes	143
36 River Great Ouse – Haversham	143
37 Waveney Valley Lakes	144
38 Weybread Pits	144
39 Swan Lake – Woolpit	145
40 Lakeside Caravan Park	145
41 River Stour – Flatford Mill	146
42 Abberton Reservoir	146
43 Chigborough	147
44 South Ockendon Carp Fishery	147

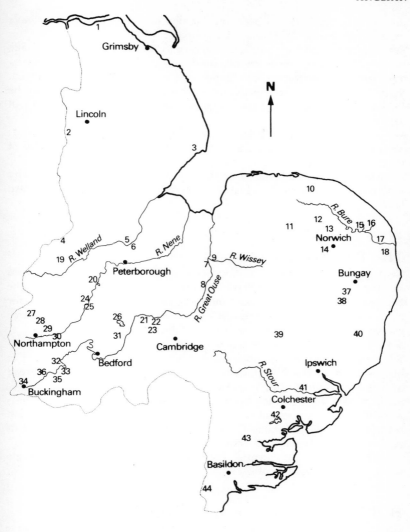

Barton Broads (Barton-upon-Humber, Humberside) A 1

This site should not be confused with the Norfolk broad of the same name. The fishery consists of two lakes of 1 acre (0.4 ha) and 10 acres (4 ha), respectively. The smaller lake is managed as a carp fishery, and the number of anglers fishing at any one time is restricted. This lake is also more expensive to fish. The larger lake is a good mixed coarse fishery. The lakes are old clay-workings with an average depth of 5 ft (1.5 m). They have muddy bottoms and the water is coloured.

SPECIES The carp lake is stocked with carp to 20 lb (9.1 kg). The other lake has a good head of roach, bream, rudd and tench.

TECHNIQUES AND BAITS No hemp seed or groundbaiting is allowed. Standard carp baits are effective in the carp lake. The other lake can be fished with a waggler float and maggot or caster hookbait. Sweetcorn will also catch plenty of fish.

SEASON 16th June to 14th March. Night fishing is permitted.

ACCESS The lakes are situated at Barton-upon-Humber on the south side of the Humber Bridge.

Tickets are obtained from the site shop. There is a caravan site nearby with facilities for tourists. Advance booking is advisable for the small carp lake.

The Poplars (near Lincoln) A 2

Two clay-pits of 1 acre (0.4 ha) each. One of the lakes contains much weed but the other is clear. The average depth of the lakes is 5 ft (1.5 m). The banks are accessible all the way round the lakes. The fishing is mainly for carp, with plenty of double figure fish and some over 20 lb (9.1 kg). Three caravans are available for hire near the lakes.

SPECIES Carp, roach, perch, tench and bream.

TECHNIQUES AND BAITS Specialist tactics are needed for the carp. The other species can be taken on waggler floats using maggots, casters or bread as bait. No groundbaiting is allowed.

SEASON 16th June to 14th March. Night fishing is allowed.

ACCESS The fishery is reached by taking the A46(T) Foss Way from Lincoln towards Newark for 8 miles (12.9 km). Turn right towards the village of Eagle (signposted) and then continue to North Scarle village.

Advance booking is essential. Contact Mr L W Day, The Poplars, Eagle Road, North Scarle, Lincoln.

Hill View Lakes (near Skegness, Lincolnshire) A 3

Hill View comprises two lakes, one for trout fishing and the other for coarse fishing. The trout lake covers 2 acres (0.8 ha) and has an average depth of 6 ft (1.8 m). The lake has been carefully landscaped to look attractive yet allow unhindered casting. The fishing is for rainbow and brown trout which are stocked twice weekly throughout the season. The limit is four fish, and the average catch rate is two fish per rod. The smaller coarse fishing lake has an average depth of 7 ft (2.1 m) and covers $\frac{3}{4}$ acre (0.3 ha). The coarse fishing lake holds a good head of fish, notably carp, which grow to 20 lb (9.1 kg). In the interests of fish preservation only barbless hooks are allowed on the coarse lake, and these can be bought at the warden's caravan.

SPECIES *Trout lake*: rainbow trout (record: 12 lb 8 oz/5.7 kg), and brown trout (record: 6 lb 8 oz/2.9 kg). *Coarse lake*: carp to 20 lb (9.1 kg) and also tench, roach, rudd and bream.

TECHNIQUES AND BAITS *Trout lake*: fly fishing only. Small wet flies and nymphs are most effective. Dry fly fishing is good from June to August. In late May there is a good hatch of pond olives in the lake. *Coarse lake*: float fishing works best with the float set slightly overdepth. Good baits for the tench and carp are sweetcorn, maggots and small balls of high-protein mix.

SEASON *Trout lake*: 1st April to 29th October. Fishing from 10 am to dusk. *Coarse lake*: 1st April to 29th October. Fishing on this water is from 10 am to dusk.

ACCESS Hill View is on the A52 road at Chapel St Leonards, north of Skegness.

Permits are available on site and advance booking is not essential. Information from Mr K Raynor, Hill View Lakes, Skegness Road, Hogsthorpe, near Skegness.

Rutland Water – Empingham (near Oakham, Leicestershire) A 4

Rutland Water is probably the most well-known reservoir trout fishery in England. Since it first opened for fishing in 1977, Rutland's 3000 acres (1215 ha) has attracted anglers from all over the country. Fishing is from both the bank and from boats. Many anglers find the sheer size of the water very daunting. The bank fishing is best early and late in the season. During the summer, especially in hot weather, the best fishing is from the boats. The water is a very irregular shape with the north and the south arms of the reservoir being separated by the Hambleton peninsula. A popular area of the reservoir which produces a lot of fish is the Whitwell Creek where a lot of big brown trout are likely to be caught. The bag limit at Rutland is eight fish.

SPECIES Brown trout and rainbow trout.

TECHNIQUES AND BAITS Fly fishing only. From the shore long casting with lures seems to produce the best results and most anglers use shooting heads to achieve greater distance. Large brown trout are caught from the boats by fishing big brightly coloured lures very deep. A lead core line is sometimes used to get the lure down deep. In a good wave, traditional loch-style fishing from a boat will produce some good catches.

SEASON 1st April to 29th October.

ACCESS Rutland is at Empingham on the A606(T) road west from the A1(T) at Stamford.

Permits are available on site.

River Welland (near Market Deeping, Cambridgeshire) A 5

The Welland at Market Deeping is controlled by the Deeping St James Angling Club, and the stretch covers 6¾ miles (10.9 km) on both banks from the town to Deeping High Bank. The river flows at a medium pace over a gravel bottom through farmland. The banks are good and firm, and the river is accessible in most places for disabled anglers. The main species are chub and roach. The chub fishing is exceptionally good, with plenty of fish weighing 3 lb (1.4 kg) or more. Tench and bream are also present and, although not particularly numerous, they do grow big.

SPECIES Chub to 6 lb (2.7 kg), bream to 8½ lb (3.9 kg), tench to 6½ lb (2.9 kg), and also roach, perch and pike.

TECHNIQUES AND BAITS Float fishing with a stick float alongside the weeds is the best technique for chub and roach. Casters and maggots are the most popular baits. The chub will also take bread, cheese and luncheon meat. Quiver tip legering can be used in slacker areas for the bream and tench, and also for the bigger chub. The controlling club does not encourage coloured maggots although, as yet, they are not banned.

SEASON 16th June to 14th March. Fishing from dawn to dusk. No night fishing.

ACCESS Parking in Market Deeping. The river runs through the town.

Permits are obtained from Pets Pantry, Market Deeping; Market Deeping Waterlife; and Walkers Newsagents, Deeping St James. For further information contact Mr J Cran, Secretary of the Deeping St James Angling Club.

Folly River (Peakirk, near Market Deeping, Lincolnshire) A 6

This is not a true river, but a land drain which was once part of a Roman canal system connecting the River Witham to the River Nene. The permit stretch covers 2 miles (3.2 km) of single bank. The Folly River is very slow flowing and very weedy. The main species are roach and tench.

SPECIES Roach, tench, bream and chub.

TECHNIQUES AND BAITS Float fishing with a waggler float in conjunction with maggot or caster hookbait is best. In the really weedy areas, stronger tackle and lobworm are needed for the tench.

SEASON 16th June to 14th March.

ACCESS The Folly River runs close to the Peakirk to Northborough road. Parking is allowed alongside the road.

Permits are obtained from Pets Pantry, Market Deeping; Market Deeping Waterlife; or Walkers Newsagents, Deeping St James, Lincolnshire.

River Great Ouse – Ten Mile Bank (Denver Sluice, Norfolk) A 7

This fishery covers the 4½ mile (7.2 km) length between Danby Drove and

Denver Sluice. The flow is controlled by Denver Sluice and in a dry summer the river becomes stagnant. The fishing is on both banks. Bream and roach are the most common species taken but some sizeable pike are caught during the winter. The fishing on this length of the river was poor for a number of years but has now improved considerably and can be very good. There is a run of sea trout every year and a few fish in the 4–6 lb (1.8–2.7 kg) range are taken. These fish, however, are a bonus and it is not worthwhile seriously fishing for them. Below Denver Sluice the river is tidal.

SPECIES Roach, bream and pike.

TECHNIQUES AND BAITS Waggler fishing with maggots or casters should be used. Redworm is worth trying for the bream. Deadbaiting sink-and-draw style is best for the pike.

SEASON 16th June to 14th March.

ACCESS Access is off the A10 Downham Market road.

Permits are obtained from local tackle shops. The fishing is controlled by King's Lynn Angling Association, Secretary, Mr G T Bear, 1 Cock Drive, Downham Market.

River Great Ouse – Littleport (Cambridgeshire) A 8

The fishing is controlled by the Littleport Angling Club and covers both banks of the river for 1 mile (1.6 km) from Sandhill Bridge to Littleport Bridge. The river is 90 ft (27.4 m) wide and slow flowing, and the average depth is 13 ft (4 m). At this point the river is non-tidal.

SPECIES Mainly roach and bream, with some eels.

TECHNIQUES AND BAITS Waggler fishing slightly overdepth with fine tackle is the best technique. Maggots and casters are the most widely used baits but redworms will tempt the bream. Legering tends to attract eels.

SEASON 16th June to 14th March. Night fishing is allowed.

ACCESS Littleport is 5 miles (8 km) north of Ely on the A10 Ely to King's Lynn road.

Permits are obtained from the Black Horse Inn, Sandhill Bridge, Littleport, or the fishing tackle shop in Littleport. Information can be obtained from Mr J W Shelsher, Honorary Secretary, Littleport Angling Club.

River Wissey – Hilgay (Norfolk) A 9

This is a very attractive tributary of the Great Ouse and a 7 mile (11.3 km) stretch controlled by King's Lynn Angling Association can be fished on a day permit. The river can be fished from Dereham Belt down to the confluence with the River Great Ouse, below Ten Mile Bank railway bridge. The fishing is mainly for roach, chub and bream. As with the Great Ouse, a few big sea trout make their way up the River Wissey each year and may be caught.

SPECIES Chub, roach and bream.

TECHNIQUES AND BAITS Stick float fishing with maggots, casters or bread is the best technique in the streamier water. Legering with caster or bread yields the best results in the deeper pools.

SEASON 16th June to 14th March.

ACCESS Hilgay is 3 miles (4.8 km) south of Downham Market on the A10 road.

Permits are obtained at local tackle shops or direct from the Bailiff, Mr W Delph, Old Bridge, Hilgay. The fishing is controlled by King's Lynn Angling Association, Secretary, Mr G T Bear, 1 Cock Drive, Downham Market.

Edgefield Hall Lake (near Holt, Norfolk) A 10

This is a 4½ acre (1.8 ha) man-made lake with the River Glaven running through the fishery. The river valley is attractive and the surroundings have been well landscaped. There is an island in the lake, and anglers can cross a rustic bridge to reach it and fish from a casting platform. The water is rich in natural food, and the trout have a good growth rate. Weed growth can be prolific in summer but the management try to control it. Good areas on which to concentrate are near the dam and in the deeper water around the weir end. The fishing is restricted to 15 anglers a day and the bag limit is four fish.

SPECIES Brown trout and rainbow trout to 8 lb (3.6 kg).

TECHNIQUES AND BAITS Fly fishing only. Lure fishing with Baby Dolls, Appetizers or Black Cheniles will catch fish, but this is a water that lends itself particularly to nymph and buzzer fishing with floating lines.

SEASON April to September. Fishing from dawn to dusk.

ACCESS Edgefield Hall is just south of Holt on the B1149 Norwich to Holt road.

Permits are available on site.

Swanton Morley Lakes (East Dereham, Norfolk) A 11

This site, of nearly 65 acres (26 ha), comprises three flooded gravel-pits and ¾ mile (1.2 km) of the adjacent River Wensum. The gravel-pits offer some excellent fishing, notably for roach. The Wensum is a river which has always produced some good fish, especially roach and chub. This particular length has produced chub to 6 lb (2.7 kg). Barbel are also present, and in recent years the Wensum has become one of the few rivers in the country capable of producing double figure barbel.

SPECIES *Lakes*: bream to 8 lb (3.6 kg), roach to 2 lb (0.9 kg), pike to 25 lb (11.3 kg), tench to 6 lb (2.7 kg), and also carp, perch, rudd and eels. *River Wensum*: roach, chub, dace, barbel, perch, eels and pike.

TECHNIQUES AND BAITS Bread flake, worms and maggots are all good baits. As a rule, the larger fish are taken on leger, but float fishing close to the margins is also worthwhile. On the river, bread crust is best for the chub. Some good chub are also taken on sweetcorn.

SEASON 16th June to 14th March. Fishing from sunrise to sunset.

ACCESS From Norwich take the A47 road to East Dereham and then the B1147 road to Bawdeswell. Swanton Morley is about half-way between East Dereham and Bawdeswell.

Permits can be obtained after 8 am from Mrs V Marsham, Waterfall Farm, Swanton Morley. Anglers wishing to fish before this time can obtain tickets in advance from Chambers Tackle Shop, Market Place, Dereham; Rod and Gun, Norwich Street, Dereham; or Mrs Marsham at Waterfall Farm. Please enclose a SAE.

Booton Clay Pit (near Aylsham, Norfolk) A 12

This is an old clay working covering 1½ acres (0.6 ha), and having a depth of 9 ft (2.7 m). The bottom of the lake is clay. The fishing is accessible in most places, and there is a safe path round the lake. The fishing is exceptionally good for such a small lake, producing some huge carp, bream and tench.

SPECIES Carp to 30 lb (13.6 kg), bream to 9 lb (4.1 kg) and tench to 6 lb 12 oz (3.1 kg).

TECHNIQUES AND BAITS Big fish tactics and strong tackle are recommended. Baits for carp are high-protein paste, and particle baits such as sweetcorn and tic beans. Worms and bread can be used to take the tench and bream.

SEASON 16th June to 14th March.

ACCESS To reach Booton take the B1145 road from Aylsham to Cawston. The village of Booton is 1 mile (1.6 km) south of Cawston on a minor road.

Permits must be obtained in advance from Cawston village post office. The fishing is controlled by Aylsham and District Angling Society, and further information can be obtained from the Secretary, Mr Sutton.

Hevingham Lakes (near Norwich, Norfolk) A 13

These are three small lakes totalling 4 acres (1.6 ha), set amid surrounding heathland. The lakes are sheltered by alder trees and gorse bushes. The depth of the lakes varies from 3 to 9 ft (0.9 to 2.7 m). In one of the lakes there is an irregularly shaped island. The lakes are extremely well stocked with coarse fish, and produce some very big carp. There are toilet facilities on site and areas for camping.

SPECIES Mirror carp to 32 lb (14.5 kg), common carp, tench, roach, rudd, bream and crucian carp.

TECHNIQUES AND BAITS Float fishing with a waggler float, set so that the bait is just touching the lake bed, will produce the best results. The tackle

should be shotted so that only the very tip is visible when fishing for the shy-biting crucian carp. Maggots, casters or bread are good baits here. Big fish tactics are needed for the carp and tench. Groundbaiting is not allowed.
SEASON 16th June to 14th March. Fishing is from dawn to dusk. No night fishing is allowed for day ticket holders.
ACCESS Hevingham is 8 miles (12.9 km) north of Norwich on the A140 Norwich to Aylsham road.

Permits are obtained at the entrance to the fishery. For further information contact Mr C Matthewson, Hevingham Lakes, Hevingham, near Norwich.

Taverham Gravel Pits (Old Costessey, near Norwich, Norfolk) A 14

Taverham Gravel Pits are a complex of seven lakes totalling $11\frac{1}{2}$ acres (4.7 ha). The lakes are tucked away in a very secluded area of woodland and offer some good fishing for coarse fish. There is some interesting wildlife in this area and otters are still to be found on the nearby River Wensum. The lakes are small and intimate; the largest one is $3\frac{1}{2}$ acres (1.4 ha).
SPECIES Bream to 6 lb 8 oz (2.9 kg), tench to 5 lb 12 oz (2.6 kg), roach to 2 lb 5 oz (1 kg), common carp to 19 lb (8.6 kg), crucian carp to 1 lb (0.5 kg), and pike (small).
TECHNIQUES AND BAITS General float fishing will catch most species. During the winter months the pike can offer good sport, although they do not run to a great size.
SEASON 16th June to 14th March. Day ticket holders are only allowed to fish between dawn and dusk but season permit holders may night fish.
ACCESS Take the A47(T) road from Norwich past Costessey and turn right at Roundwell Public House (Longwater Lane). Turn left at Old Costessey at the T-junction, and keep left at Ringland Lane. Proceed 1 mile (1.6 km), then turn right into an unmade road. The bridge over the river is immediately in front of you. After crossing the river bridge, follow the road between the lakes, taking two left bends, and the parking area is immediately visible.

Day tickets are obtained from Huntsman Motor Caravanette Centre and Filling Station, West End, Old Costessey, Norwich.

River Ant – Ludham (Norfolk) A 15

The River Ant is one of the smallest and narrowest of the Norfolk Broads rivers. It is below Barton Broad that the river is of most interest to anglers. During the summer the fishing is poor, due to the constant boat traffic, but during the winter some good fish are caught, notably roach, bream and pike. The Anglian Water Authority controls the fishery on the left-hand bank of the river from Ludham Bridge upstream for 2 miles (3.2 km).

SPECIES Roach, bream, pike and perch.

TECHNIQUES AND BAITS Waggler fishing using maggots, casters or bread is best for the roach. Light legering with a small open-ended feeder, using maggot or bread as bait, is effective for the bream. The pike fall to livebaiting or deadbaiting, the former producing the best results on this river.

SEASON 16th June to 14th March.

ACCESS The river is reached via the B1354 road and Ludham Bridge.

The fishing is free to Anglian Water Authority licence holders. For further details contact the Anglian Water Authority, Norwich Division.

River Thurne – Martham (Norfolk) A 16

The River Thurne is the shortest Norfolk river. It rises near the village of West Somerton and flows in a south-westerly direction through Martham Broad to join the River Bure near South Walsham. During the summer, the fishing on the river is best described as moderate but, during the winter, many fish move out of the shallower broads into the deeper river channel and the fishing can be excellent. The match record for the Thurne was taken in February 1977 and stands at 83 lb (37.6 kg). The stretch of river between Martham and Repps Staithe on the left-hand bank is controlled by the Anglian Water Authority and covers $3\frac{1}{2}$ miles (5.6 km) of bank. A few short areas, where private gardens back on to the river, cannot be fished. The river at this point is tidal.

SPECIES Roach, bream, pike, perch, eels and rudd.

TECHNIQUES AND BAITS Float fishing should be used for the roach and skimmer bream with a stick float or waggler. Maggots, casters and bread are the best baits. Most of the bream catches are taken by legering with an open-ended feeder and maggots as bait.

SEASON 16th June to 14th March.

ACCESS The river is reached at Potter Heigham Bridge or the minor road from Martham village.

The fishing is free to Anglian Water Authority licence holders. Further details can be obtained from the Anglian Water Authority, Norwich Division.

River Bure – South Walsham (Norfolk) A 17

The River Bure is one of the larger Norfolk rivers. It rises in north Norfolk near Melton Constable and flows south, through Wroxham and Horning, before being joined by the River Ant near South Walsham. The Bure then flows first south and then east to join the Yare estuary at Great Yarmouth.

The river at South Walsham is tidal and the fishing is controlled by the Anglian Water Authority. The fishery covers $4\frac{1}{2}$ miles (7.2 km) of the Bure, 1 mile (1.6 km) of Fleet Dyke (which links the Bure with South Walsham Broad) and all of Upton Dyke. The fishery on the main river stretches from South Walsham to Upton Dyke. The best fishing is in autumn and winter.
SPECIES Roach, bream and pike.
TECHNIQUES AND BAITS Legering with an open-ended feeder is best for the roach and bream. Maggots, casters and bread are good baits. Use float fishing with a waggler and stick float in order to take large numbers of roach.
SEASON 16th June to 14th March.
ACCESS Access is from South Walsham and Upton.

The fishing is free to holders of an Anglian Water Authority rod licence. For further details contact the Anglian Water Authority, Norwich Division.

Fritton Decoy (near Great Yarmouth, Norfolk) A 18

This is a very attractive lake set in a country park. The lake covers 175 acres (70 ha) and is $2\frac{1}{2}$ miles (4 km) long. Some of the bank is overgrown but areas have been cleared for angling and boats are available. Windsurfing takes place on the lake but in an area which is segregated from the angling. The water varies in depth but drops to 20 ft (6.1 m) in places. Bream are the main attraction, with some very large catches taken. Some sizeable pike are also caught.
SPECIES Bream, pike and eels.
TECHNIQUES AND BAITS Float fishing with a waggler float using maggots, redworm or bread as hookbait is effective. Legering with an open-ended feeder in the deeper water using the same hookbait should also be tried.
SEASON 16th June to the end of September. Fishing from 7 am to 7 pm.
ACCESS Fritton Decoy is 5 miles (8 km) from Great Yarmouth on the A143 Beccles road.

Permits are available on site from the kiosk. For further details contact the Warden, Mr K Mussett.

Eyebrook Reservoir (Uppingham, Leicestershire) A 19

Eyebrook is managed as a trout fishery and covers 400 acres (162 ha). Both boat and bank fishing are allowed and there is no catch limit imposed. The Stockerston Bridge end of the reservoir is shallow and, since it becomes very weedy during the summer, it fishes best early in the season. The dam wall fishes well, as does the area around Robbo's Cabin. If fishing from a boat, it is worth concentrating on the area between the Island and Robbo's Cabin.
SPECIES Brown trout and rainbow trout.

TECHNIQUES AND BAITS Fly fishing only. Lure fishing will catch trout right through the season but it is worth concentrating on nymph and buzzer fishing during the summer.

SEASON 1st April to 30th September.

ACCESS Eyebrook is reached from the A6003 road between Uppingham and Corby, Northamptonshire.

The water is controlled by Corby and District Water Company, Geddington Road, Corby.

River Nene — Oundle (Northamptonshire) A 20

This stretch of the Nene is controlled by the Oundle Angling Association and covers 5 miles (8 km) of river fishing around the town. The river at this point forms a massive bend near the village of Polebrook before flowing north again. The bend of the river at Polebrook is a noted 'hot spot' for a large bream shoal. The river was dredged recently to give an average depth of 12 ft (3.7 m) and a lot of the weed was removed. This, however, is expected to grow again within a year or two and the bream fishing is still good. The roach fishing is also good and catches of 12–13 lb (5.4–5.9 kg) at a sitting are to be expected.

SPECIES Predominantly roach and bream, with chub, pike, dace, perch, carp and eels.

TECHNIQUES AND BAITS Waggler fishing with maggot or caster bait is best for the roach. For the bream and bigger roach quiver tip legering with maggot or worm bait is best.

SEASON 16th June to 14th March. Night fishing is allowed.

ACCESS Oundle is reached from the A1 by taking the A605 road.

Permits are obtained from Greens Newsagents, Market Place, Oundle, or the Riverside Hotel, Oundle. For information regarding the fishing contact Mr D Laxton, the Secretary of the Oundle Angling Association.

St Ives Complex (St Ives, near Huntingdon, Cambridgeshire) A 21

This is a massive gravel-pit complex near St Ives, including ten stillwaters and a stretch of the Great Ouse, all of which can be fished on a single permit. The fishing has been developed by the Amey Anglers Association and the potential is tremendous. The permit for this complex also covers the nearby Fen Drayton Complex.

Meadow Lake

This is the largest lake in the complex at 100 acres (40 ha) and is also used for sailing, but there is a no-go area for boats within 100 ft (30 m) of the banks.

The average depth is 12 ft (3.7 m), dropping away to 24 ft (7.3 m) in places. The lake is well stocked wtih big pike, bream, roach, tench and carp. Meadow Lake has recently been restocked with 8500 roach, bream and perch fingerlings.

The Fjords

This lake covers 80 acres (32 ha) and is a good summer and autumn fishery containing big tench and pike. Some massive catches of bream are also taken.

Island Lagoon

Island Lagoon is a smaller water and, as its name suggests, has a whole series of vegetated islands on it. There are deepwater channels between the islands, providing secluded swims. This water holds sizeable tench, carp, bream, roach and pike, and is an excellent winter fishery.

Long Reach

This is another big water of 60 acres (24 ha) and provides excellent winter fishing for pike. The average depth of the water is 15 ft (4.6 m). As well as the usual roach, tench, bream and carp, this water has a good head of chub and rudd.

St Ives Water

This lake covers 20 acres (8 ha) and has an average depth of 13 ft (4 m). The lake holds plenty of carp (averaging 8 lb/3.6 kg), bream, tench and small pike. There is an excellent stock of roach in the $\frac{1}{2}$–$\frac{3}{4}$ lb (0.2–0.3 kg) range. This water fishes better in summer than in winter.

Ivo

Slightly smaller than St Ives Water, this lake holds some big pike weighing up to 20 lb (9.1 kg). The average depth of the lake is 10 ft (3 m) and the winter pike fishing is good. During the summer and autumn the fishing is good for small roach, tench, and bream up to 5 lb (2.3 kg).

Andersons

This lake is similar in size to Ivo, but is shallow and weedy. The average depth is 3 ft (0.9 m) dropping to 10 ft (3 m) in places. Two special features of this water are that it produces specimen rudd to over 2 lb (0.9 kg) and that it contains zander. Other species include tench, small roach and bream, and pike to 20 lb (9.1 kg).

Lowrys

This is an excellent early season water with very good tench and rudd fishing. The lake is shallow, being only 6 ft (1.8 m) at its deepest. There are plenty of small roach and also some big pike and zander.

The Pond

As the name suggests, this is a small lake near the banks of the Great Ouse. The average depth is 8 ft (2.4 m) and most of the fish are small. There are large numbers of small roach, rudd, bream and pike. The lake has a few chub to 3 lb (1.4 kg) plus.

The Nursery

This lake is next to The Pond but, although it is almost the same depth and shape, it holds some bigger fish. The bream, tench, roach and rudd all grow reasonably big.

River Great Ouse A 22

The permit covers 2000 yards (1830 m) of the bank of the River Great Ouse, extending from the St Ives Complex to the nearby Fen Drayton Complex. The fishing in the river is for roach, bream, dace and chub, and a few zander are present. Boats are a nuisance in summer, but during the autumn and winter the fishing is excellent, especially for the chub and dace. Extending off the river is a drain, which provides good fishing in winter when the water is high and flood conditions concentrate a lot of fish from the river into the drain.

SPECIES Roach, bream, dace, chub and zander.

TECHNIQUES AND BAITS There is no one method that can be described to fish this complex. Float fishing will produce large numbers of small fish, while legering with feeders or large baits will produce less fish but will give better specimens of each species.

SEASON 16th June to 14th March.

ACCESS The St Ives Complex is on the St Ives by-pass. Two car parks are available, one near Meadow Lake and the other next to St Ives Water. All the lakes on this fishery are within walking distance of these two car parks.

Permits are available at Toys 'n' Tackle, St Ives. Enquiries regarding the fishing should be made to Mr B Hunt.

Fen Drayton Complex (near Huntingdon, Cambridgeshire) A 23

This large gravel-pit complex is managed by Amey Anglers Association. There are four gravel-pits and a section of the River Great Ouse, which runs alongside the gravel-pits. A single permit enables anglers to fish this complex and the nearby St Ives Complex. The river fishing extends through both gravel-pit complexes and is detailed under the St Ives Complex.

Drayton Fen

This is the largest water on the site, and covers 100 acres (40 ha). There are some very large fish in this lake and it is visited by specialist pike anglers, as the water holds pike to at least 25 lb (11.3 kg). Large carp, tench, bream and roach are also present. The water generally fishes best in summer, and during the winter most of the fishing is for pike. Some big pike and carp have recently been stocked.

Holywell Lake

Holywell Lake is a much smaller lake than Drayton Fen and is a better all-round fishery, although the fish are not as big. Pike up to 20 lb (9.1 kg) in weight are caught and the lake is a good winter fishery. The lake holds many fairly small roach, bream, rudd and perch which, despite their size, can still provide good sport.

Holywell Pond

This is a small water alongside Holywell Lake, heavily stocked with tench, roach, perch and rudd.

Plains Water

This new lake in the complex is about half the size of Holywell Lake. It lies alongside the Great Ouse and is still in the process of being developed as a fishery. It already holds plenty of small roach and bream, and also a few chub. Stocking is continuing and it will take a few years to mature as a fishery.

SPECIES See individual lakes.

TECHNIQUES AND BAITS All general coarse fishing tactics can be employed. Float fishing with maggots and casters can be used for the roach, perch and rudd, and legering for the larger species. Specimen hunting tactics are probably best for Drayton Fen.

SEASON 16th June to 14th March.

ACCESS Fen Drayton is reached by the A604 Huntingdon to Cambridge road. A minor road from Fen Drayton leads to the fishery.

Permits are obtained from Toys 'n' Tackle, St Ives, Cambridgeshire. Enquiries should be made to Mr B Hunt.

Thrapston Complex (Thrapston, Northamptonshire) A 24

This is a huge fishing complex covering not only the 150 acre (60 ha) Thrapston Lagoon but also including 4 miles (6.4 km) of fishing on the nearby River Nene. Thrapston Lagoon is an extensive water providing good year-round sport and some excellent catches of bream, roach and tench. The northern side of the lake has numerous tree-covered islets and can be booked by clubs for fishing matches. The depth of the lake varies from 3 to 15 ft (0.9 to 4.6 m). The fishing on the River Nene is in segmented stretches at Ditchford, Irthlingborough, Ringstead and Thrapston. A permit covers all the fishing, and detailed maps are provided.

SPECIES *Thrapston Lagoon*: pike to 20 lb (9.1 kg), bream to 7 lb (3.2 kg), roach to 2½ lb (1.1 kg), perch to 3 lb (1.4 kg), eels to 4 lb (1.8 kg) and tench. *River Nene*: pike, chub, bream, roach, tench, perch and eels.

TECHNIQUES AND BAITS Waggler fishing with maggots or casters should be used on the river. In the lagoon, legering with a swing tip and maggot is the best technique for the bream. Float fishing will catch plenty of smaller fish.

SEASON 16th June to 14th March.

ACCESS The fishery is located near the town of Thrapston off the A604.

Permits are obtained from W Jaques, High Street, Thrapston, or The Head Bailiff at The Workshop Compound at Thrapston Lagoon. Information can be obtained from Mr C Morehen.

Ringstead Grange Trout Fishery (near Kettering, Northamptonshire) A 25

This is a 36 acre (15 ha) trout fishery with an excellent reputation for good fishing. The fishery is stocked twice weekly right through the season. Recently, experimental stocking with salmon has also been tried and quite a number of these have been caught. The average depth of the lake is 6 ft (1.8 m) and it contains plenty of natural food with good hatches of buzzer, pond olive and sedge each season. There is a useful fishing lodge, complete with a gas stove for anglers to use, and seven boats are available for hire.

SPECIES Rainbow trout (record: 14 lb 4 oz/6.5 kg), brown trout, brook trout and salmon.

TECHNIQUES AND BAITS Fly fishing only. Lure fishing is best early and late in the season. From the boats, loch-style wet fly fishing works well. During the summer, nymph fishing and dry fly fishing are best.

SEASON 1st April to 29th October. Fishing is from 7 am to 1 hour after sunset.

ACCESS The fishery is at Ringstead Grange Farm, just south of Thrapston on the A605 road. The fishery is alongside the River Nene.

Advance booking is advisable for weekends. Contact Mr H Foster, Ringstead Grange Trout Fishery, Ringstead, near Kettering.

Grafham Water (Huntingdon, Cambridgeshire) A 26

Until the opening of Rutland Water, Grafham was considered to be the premier trout reservoir in the country. It is still extremely popular and the bank fishing, in particular, is good at Grafham. During the 1982 and 1983 seasons, the catches at Grafham declined slightly and many anglers blamed the lack of *Daphnia* and the rich feed that this had afforded the trout in previous years. However, during 1984 the catch rate and the average size of fish returned to normal and plenty of 2–4 lb (0.9–1.8 kg) rainbow trout were taken. Fishing on Grafham's 1500 acres (605 ha) is from both the bank and from boats. The catch limit at Grafham is eight fish.

SPECIES Rainbow trout and brown trout.

TECHNIQUES AND BAITS Fly fishing only. Long casting with lures works best from the bank, especially early and late in the season. During the summer, buzzer and nymph fishing also works well. From the boats, deeply fished lures will take the bigger brown trout.

SEASON 1st April to 29th October.

ACCESS To reach Grafham Water, take the A604(T) road west from the A1(T) at Huntingdon and at the village of Ellington, take the minor road south.

Permits are obtained on site.

Pitsford Reservoir (near Northampton) A 27

Pitsford Reservoir covers 740 acres (300 ha). It is stocked with both brown and rainbow trout and there is a limited amount of spawning success by the brown trout. In an attempt to produce some excellent brown trout fishing, the water authority are stocking the reservoir each November with thousands of small trout. During the 1984 season the brown trout record for the water was broken with a fish of 8 lb 9 oz (3.9 kg). Weed can be a problem on this reservoir and, in some areas, can seriously interfere with bank fishing. The catch limit at Pitsford is eight fish.

SPECIES Brown trout and rainbow trout.

TECHNIQUES AND BAITS Fly fishing only. Lures will catch plenty of fish at Pitsford but this is a water where the trout do a lot of surface feeding and floating lines work well in summer. There is a good hatch of pond olives, and when they are hatching dry fly works very well.

SEASON 1st April to 29th October.

ACCESS Pitsford is about 6 miles (9.6 km) north of Northampton on the A508(T) road. Turn off at the village of Brixworth.

Permits are available on site.

Overstone Solarium (Northampton) A 28

These are two large lakes surrounded by woodland. The lakes are deep, up to 30 ft (9.1 m), and offer some good coarse fishing. Night fishing is allowed, and some of the better specimens are taken at night or dawn.

SPECIES Carp, tench, bream and roach.

TECHNIQUES AND BAITS Legering with bread or maggots in conjunction with an open-ended feeder should be used. Waggler fishing with maggots or casters is best for the smaller species of fish.

SEASON 16th June to 14th March.

ACCESS Overstone Solarium is at Ecton Lane, Sywell, 4 miles (6.4 km) north-east of Northampton, near Sywell Private Airport.

Permits are obtained on site.

Billing Aquadrome (Northampton) A 29

This is a leisure complex of 13 lakes, covering 30 acres (12 ha). One of the lakes is, however, a marina. The fishery also includes a $\frac{1}{2}$ mile (0.8 km) stretch of the nearby River Nene. Billing Aquadrome contains some large carp, but they are far from easy to catch. However, in 1966 a carp weighing 42 lb (19.1 kg) was caught at Billing. Roach and perch are the predominant species with some chub in the River Nene.

SPECIES Roach, perch, pike and carp with chub and bream in the River Nene.

TECHNIQUES AND BAITS Waggler fishing or long-range legering with maggots or casters as hookbait is best. Try deadbaiting for the pike.

SEASON 16th June to 14th October. Fishing from 6 am to 9 pm. No night fishing.

ACCESS Billing Aquadrome is reached by taking the new A45(T) road from Northampton for 5 miles (8 km). The lakes are also 6 miles (9.7 km) from Junction 15 on the M1 motorway.

Permits are obtained on site.

Castle Ashby Lakes (near Grendon, Northamptonshire) A 30

There are three lakes, which can all be fished with a day permit, at Castle Ashby close to the Castle Ashby to Grendon road. All the waters are fairly shallow with an average depth of $3\frac{1}{2}$ ft (1 m). The surroundings are beautiful with lush undergrowth and trees. The lakes have lily beds and reeds.

The largest lake, at $6\frac{1}{2}$ acres (2.6 ha), is the Grendon Quarter Pond, which at the start of each season produces big tench catches. The water also holds double figure bream. Access to this lake is such that it is suitable for a disabled angler to fish. Scotland Pond covers an area of $5\frac{1}{2}$ acres (2.2 ha) and also holds some good tench. This lake also offers good pike fishing right through the winter with plenty of double figure fish. The third, and smallest, water is Brickyard Pond, which is 2 acres (0.8 ha). This water contains mixed coarse fish.

SPECIES Tench, bream, roach, perch and pike.

TECHNIQUES AND BAITS Float fishing using a waggler float set to depth or just over depth is best. The ideal baits are sweetcorn, bread flake, worm, maggots and casters. Groundbaiting is banned during long, hot summer spells.

SEASON 16th June to 14th March.

ACCESS From Northampton take the A428(T) road south for 6 miles (9.7 km) and then turn left on the minor road to Castle Ashby and Grendon. This road runs alongside Grendon Quarter lake.

Permits are available from the bailiffs on the bank.

Little Paxton Fishery (St Neots, Cambridgeshire) A 31

This fishery consists of three lakes totalling 30 acres (12 ha) and a ½ mile (0.8 km) stretch of the River Great Ouse. The lakes have plenty of cover and marginal vegetation, and vary in depth from 4 to 8 ft (1.2 to 2.4 m). The lakes are well stocked with coarse fish, and the car park lake has been specially stocked with large carp to 20 lb (9.1 kg). This part of the river is best known for its chub and roach fishing. The land surrounding the lakes is part of a farm, and anglers must keep to the footpath and not interfere with or feed the animals.

SPECIES Bream, roach, tench, rudd, perch, pike and carp. Chub and roach are present in the river.

TECHNIQUES AND BAITS Most recognised coarse fishing tactics will work in the lake and a specialist approach will lure the bigger specimens, including the carp. In the river, stick float fishing with maggots or casters should be used for the roach and chub. Legered bread will catch the larger chub.

SEASON 16th June to 14th March. Fishing from 7.30 am to sunset. Advance day ticket holders may fish from sunrise to sunset. Only season permit holders with a special arrangement with the manager can night fish for carp.

ACCESS The fishery is at the end of Little Paxton Lane, Little Paxton. One lake is adjacent to the car park, the other two are on the other side of the road. The river is at the end of the long narrow lake, which is on your left after crossing the stile.

Weekday anglers must obtain their tickets from the site office adjacent to the car park before proceeding to the waters. At weekends only, anglers may commence fishing after 8 am without tickets. The bailiff will come round. Manager: Mr I May, 8 Davis Close, Little Paxton.

Vicarage Spinney Lake (near Newport Pagnell, Buckinghamshire) A 32

Vicarage Spinney Lake is a 6 acre (2.4 ha) former gravel-pit set in the pleasant surroundings of the Great Ouse Valley, situated between Dovecote Sailing Lake (adjacent to the A R C Wildfowl Centre) and Vicarage Spinney – from which it takes its name. Stocked with quality rainbow and brown trout to a density well in excess of 100 fish per acre (0.4 ha), it is sure to provide an enjoyable day's sport for the discerning trout angler. There are two boats which can be hired for the day, and 25 anglers are allowed to fish each day. The bag limit is four fish and the average weight of the fish is $2\frac{3}{4}$ lb (1.2 kg). Half-day tickets are available.

SPECIES Rainbow trout to 11 lb (5 kg) and brown trout to 5 lb (2.3 kg).

TECHNIQUES AND BAITS Fly fishing only. Depending on the prevailing weather conditions, all methods of fly fishing will take trout on this water.

SEASON 1st April to 29th October. Fishing times are from 9 am to sunset.

ACCESS Vicarage Spinney is very close to the Newport Pagnell service area on the M1 motorway. Bookings and enquiries to Mr M Sando, 6 Kipling Drive, Newport Pagnell, Buckinghamshire

Linford Lakes Complex (near Newport Pagnell, Buckinghamshire) A 33

This is a massive gravel-pit complex managed by Amey Anglers Association. The gravel-pits total over 500 acres (200 ha) of water and the total site covers 780 acres (315 ha). In addition, permit holders may fish 3 miles (4.8 km) of the River Great Ouse.

Dovecote

This is the largest gravel-pit in the complex, and it is rated the best summer fishery. The roach fishing is excellent, and some good tench and bream are also present. During the winter, the main sport is with roach and the pike, which grow up to 20 lb (9.1 kg). Sailing also takes place on this lake.

Red House and Rocola Lakes

These two adjacent lakes are on the opposite side of the Great Ouse to Dovecote. Rocola is the larger of the two, but both have a good head of roach and medium-sized bream. The other species present are tench and pike. The pike reach weights of at least 20 lb (9.1 kg).

Black Horse

This is the best water in the complex for specimen fish, notably tench, with fish to 7 lb (3.2 kg) recorded. Big bream and roach can also be caught. Some of the big roach may, however, be suspect, as roach/bream hybrids are also present. The pike fishing is excellent, with fish weighing up to 30 lb (13.6 kg) recorded. Anglers should note that this lake is also used for sailboarding.

Alder and Poplar

These two pits are of similar size and are located next to one another. As well as roach, bream and tench, they also contain dace and chub.

River Pool

This small pit offers the best winter fishing and is completely surrounded by the River Great Ouse, which divides into two at this point. The roach and pike fishing is very good.

Arboretum

This is one of the smallest pits in the complex and is full of small roach, bream and pike. Tench are present but do not grow much over 2 lb (0.9 kg).

Haversham and Bradwell Lakes

Both these lakes have only recently been completed and will take a few years to mature with a really healthy stock of fish. Haversham has been stocked with roach and bream fry. The management have indicated that Haversham may also be used for other leisure activities at a later date.

Farmhouse, Serpentine and Linford Lakes

These lakes are out of bounds to day ticket holders, and are reserved for season ticket game fishing only.

Stantonbury Lake

Strictly no entry to this lake, which is run by the Game Conservancy.

River Great Ouse

The River Great Ouse, which twists through the centre of the complex, can be fished for 3 miles (4.8 km) of both double and single bank. The fishing is mainly for roach, dace and chub, but a few barbel are also present.

SPECIES *Gravel-pits*: roach, bream, tench, pike, perch, dace and chub. *River Ouse*: roach, dace, chub and barbel.

TECHNIQUES AND BAITS Legering is best for the bigger fish, using baits such as worm, corn and paste. Roach can be caught on flake or caster baits. Maggots, either float fished or legered, will take most species. On the river use float fishing with a stick float for chub and dace. Chub and barbel are also taken on swimfeeder maggot baits.

SEASON 16th June to 14th March.

ACCESS The Linford Lakes Complex is at Little Linford near Newport Pagnell. The nearest turn-off on the M1 is Junction 14.

Permits can be obtained from Agrora Tackle Shop, Wolverton, near Milton Keynes. One permit covers the whole complex. The site warden is Mr R Thomlinson.

River Great Ouse – Buckingham A 34

This fishery covers $4\frac{1}{2}$ miles (7.2 km) of the river through Buckingham. The water is fairly shallow but there are a few deeper glides. The river fishes better in the winter than it does in the summer. The fishing is mainly for chub and roach.

SPECIES Chub, roach, bream and pike.

TECHNIQUES AND BAITS Use a stick float with caster for the chub and roach. Long trotting is the best method in the shallower sections. Legering with bread flake or cheese is effective for the bigger chub.

SEASON 16th June to 14th March.

ACCESS A detailed map of the exact boundaries is available from the tackle shop in Buckingham.

Permits from Fish and Field (Tackle Shop), 62 Nelson Street, Buckingham.

Loughton Lakes (near Milton Keynes, Buckinghamshire) A 35

This is a miniature parkland with four lakes which have a small brook flowing between them. Only three of the lakes are open to fishing, the fourth lake being kept as a bird sanctuary. The three fishing lakes are 1 acre (0.4 ha), $1\frac{1}{2}$ acres (0.6 ha) and 2 acres (0.8 ha), respectively. The lakes are fairly new but they are maturing each season. They are excellent fisheries for youngsters, being fairly shallow and extremely well stocked. The waters are teaming with small crucian carp which can be obliging even to clumsily presented tackle!

SPECIES Tench, carp and crucian carp.

TECHNIQUES AND BAITS Light float tackle, using maggots as hookbait, will catch plenty of fish. A thin waggler float shotted so that the bait fishes on 'the drop' works best.

SEASON 16th June to 14th March.

ACCESS Loughton Lakes are at the village of Loughton. The village is reached by the minor road from Wolverton, or the A5 from Bletchley.

Permits are obtained from Dots Tackle, Victoria Road, Bletchley, Buckinghamshire. For further information contact Mr M Sando, 6 Kipling Drive, Newport Pagnell, Buckinghamshire.

River Great Ouse – Haversham (near Milton Keynes, Buckinghamshire) A 36

The fishing is on 5 miles (8 km) of the River Great Ouse between Stony Stratford and Haversham. The river at this point is fairly fast and shallow over a gravel bed. The fishing is mainly for chub, with a few bream shoals roving along the stretch.

SPECIES Chub, bream, roach and dace.

TECHNIQUES AND BAITS Because the river is narrow, the best tactics are to fish 'fine and far off' – trotting, using a stick float and maggot or caster hookbait. Legering under willows or in the deeper pools with bread crust will take the larger chub. Cheese is also a good chub bait.

SEASON 16th June to 14th March. Night fishing is allowed.

ACCESS Parking is available near the river.

Permits are obtained from Agrora Tackle, Agrora Centre, Wolverton, near Milton Keynes. Information about the fishing can be obtained from Mr M Sando, 6 Kipling Drive, Newport Pagnell, Buckinghamshire.

Waveney Valley Lakes (Wortwell, near Harleston, Norfolk) A 37

This fishery consists of eight lakes totalling 18 acres (7 ha) situated on the Norfolk/Suffolk border. The lakes are in an attractive setting partly surrounded by trees. The depths vary and are up to 12 ft (3.7 m). The fishery specialises in carp fishing but there are big fish of most species in the waters. There is a caravan site nearby for anglers who want to arrange fishing holidays.

SPECIES Big carp and tench, also roach, rudd and bream.

TECHNIQUES AND BAITS Fishing with particle baits (for instance, corn, tic beans, etc.) is not allowed. High-protein paste baits are best for the carp, and should be used in conjunction with big fish tactics.

SEASON 16th June to 14th March.

ACCESS The fishery is at Wortwell village, east of Harleston on the A143 Bungay road.

Permits are obtained at the shop at the entrance to the fishery. Information is available from Mr M Symonds, Waveney Valley Lakes, Caravan Park, Wortwell, Harleston.

Weybread Pits (near Harleston, Norfolk) A 38

These are four gravel-pits totalling 50 acres (20 ha), with good mixed coarse fishing. A fifth pit will soon become part of the fishing complex. The depths vary greatly, with the smaller pits having depths of 3–6 ft (0.9–1.8 m) while the largest pit has holes as deep as 40 ft (12.2 m). As with many gravel-pits there are also ledges and sand-bars, and the bottom should be explored with a plummet to get a 'picture' of the underwater topography. Access is good round the banks, and some pegs are reserved for the use of disabled anglers.

SPECIES Carp to over 20 lb (9.1 kg) are caught every year. Roach, bream, rudd, tench and pike are also present.

TECHNIQUES AND BAITS As with most gravel-pits, legering on the sides of the gravel-bars using big fish tactics will catch the larger specimens. Float fishing with a waggler float and small hooks, using maggots, casters and bread bait, will catch plenty of smaller fish. Set the tackle to fish on 'the drop' to catch the rudd.

SEASON 16th June to 14th March. Fishing from 8 am to sunset. No night fishing.

ACCESS Weybread itself is just inside the Suffolk border on the B1116 Harleston to Framlingham road on the south side of the River Waveney. Harleston is actually in Norfolk on the north side of the River Waveney.

Permits are obtained from G Denny and Sons Ltd, Market Place, Harleston; 'Catch 22', Diss, Norfolk; or The Cherry Tree Inn, Harleston. For further information contact Mr J Adamson, Honorary Secretary, Harleston, Wortwell and District Angling Club.

Swan Lake – Woolpit (near Bury St Edmunds, Suffolk) A 39

Swan Lake is a disused clay-pit covering 1¾ acres (0.7 ha) and is situated in a pleasant wooded area. The lake is deep, up to 19 ft (5.8 m) in places. The banks are not totally accessible and there are 12 fishing places. This limits the numbers of rods, so advance booking is advisable. Bream and roach are the main species, with a few big pike. The record pike for the water is 29 lb 8 oz (13.4 kg), which is impressive for a small lake.

SPECIES Pike, roach, bream and eels.

TECHNIQUES AND BAITS Waggler fishing with maggots, bread and casters is best for the roach and bream. The deadbaiting 'sink-and-draw' method should be used for the pike.

SEASON 16th June to 14th March. Fishing from dawn to dusk. No night fishing.

ACCESS Woolpit village is 9 miles (14.5 km) from Bury St Edmunds on the A45 Stowmarket road.

Tickets are available on site.

Lakeside Caravan Park (Saxmundham, Norfolk) A 40

This ¾ acre (0.3 ha) lake contains double figure carp and good-sized tench. The lake is fairly shallow at one end and about 8 ft (2.4 m) deep near the dam. During the summer, there is usually too much disturbance from the nearby caravans for serious daytime fishing but night fishing is allowed. However, during the autumn it is quieter and some good roach catches are taken.

SPECIES Carp, tench, roach and bream.

TECHNIQUES AND BAITS Float fishing with a waggler float is best for the roach using bread or caster as bait. Floating bread crust works for the carp.

SEASON 16th June to 14th March.

ACCESS The lake is located just outside Saxmundham on the B1119 Framlingham road.

Tickets are obtained from the Caravan Park. Enquiries to Saxmundham Angling Centre.

River Stour – Flatford Mill (near Ipswich, Suffolk) A 41

This stretch of the Suffolk Stour covers $1\frac{1}{2}$ miles (2.4 km) of single-bank fishing. The river at this point is slow flowing and fairly shallow. There are a few deeper holes and these are always worth seeking out and fishing. The countryside around Flatford Mill is very picturesque, with meadowland and mixed farmland bordering the river. The banks of the river are good and firm for fishing. Flatford Mill is, of course, associated with the landscape artist John Constable, and was, at one time, owned by Constable's father. The mill is now owned by the National Trust. The area is very popular in summer, and can get crowded with visitors along the narrow approach road. The fishing is predominantly for roach and chub.

SPECIES Chub, roach, dace and good pike.

TECHNIQUES AND BAITS Float fishing with a stick float and maggot can be used for most fish. The larger chub and roach are taken on legered bread.

SEASON 16th June to 14th March. Fishing from dawn to dusk. No night fishing.

ACCESS Cars must be parked in the car park at the mill. To reach the fishing available on the south side of the river cross the river over the wooden bridge.

Tickets are only available from the bailiff on the bank. The fishing is controlled by Elm Park, Hornchurch and District Angling Association. For further information contact the Secretary, Mr Driscoll.

Abberton Reservoir (Colchester, Essex) A 42

This is a very large, shallow reservoir and, because it is a very important wildlife sanctuary, the fishery is restricted to either side of the two causeways which cross the reservoir. The total area of the reservoir is 1,200 acres (480 ha) and the deepest water is near the dam. Only 30 anglers a day are allowed to fish the water so advance booking is advisable. The pike fishing is superb, with fish to 30 lb (13.6 kg), and there are bream to double figures. Carp and tench are present but because of the restricted fishing areas they are not often caught.

SPECIES Bream, pike, rudd, roach, tench and carp.

TECHNIQUES AND BAITS Deadbaiting with sea fish should be used for the pike. Most bream are caught on legered bread, worms or maggots. Float fishing on 'the drop' is effective for the roach and rudd.

SEASON 16th June to 14th March. Fishing from 6 am to dusk.

ACCESS The water is located at the village of Layer-de-la-Haye on the B1026 road, south of Colchester.

Permits can be obtained on site. For further information contact the Essex Water Company, Layer-de-la-Haye, near Colchester.

Chigborough (Maldon, Essex) A 43

These are two lakes of 1¼ acres (0.5 ha) and 7¼ acres (2.9 ha), controlled by Leisure Sport. The lakes have produced some very big eels in recent years and the larger lake actually produces a few flounders. The coarse fish do not grow to specimen size, although some good perch are caught.

SPECIES Perch to 2½ lb (1.1 kg), roach to 1½ lb (0.7 kg), tench to 2½ lb (1.1 kg), bream to 3½ lb (1.6 kg), rudd to 1 lb (0.5 kg) and eels.

TECHNIQUES AND BAITS Most methods of fishing will catch fish here but worm baits are especially effective for the perch, eels and bream.

SEASON 16th June to 14th March inclusive. Night fishing is allowed.

ACCESS From Chelmsford take the A414 road to Maldon and then the Colchester road to Scraley Road. The entrance to the fishery is from Scraley Road. Both the lakes are easily accessible on foot from the car park.

Day tickets must be bought in advance from Last's Sports, 79 High Street, Maldon

---

South Ockendon Carp Fishery (South Ockendon, Essex) A 44

This fishery consists of three matured gravel-pits covering 10 acres (4 ha). There is an average depth of 12 ft (3.7 m) in all the pits. The maximum weight attained by all the species in the lakes is extremely high when compared with other small lakes, with the carp weighing up to 30 lb (13.6 kg) and the tench up to 8½ lb (3.9 kg). During the winter, the predominant species are roach and pike.

SPECIES Carp to 30 lb (13.6 kg), tench to 8½ lb (3.9 kg), roach to 2¾ lb (1.2 kg), perch to 3½ lb (1.6 kg), and pike to 24 lb (10.9 kg).

TECHNIQUES AND BAITS There are no bait restrictions, and most methods will catch fish. Because of the undoubted presence of specimen fish, strong tackle is recommended. Line-shy carp can be caught on hair rigs.

SEASON 16th June to 14th March.

ACCESS The fishery is on the outskirts of the village of South Ockendon in Essex.

Permits are obtained on the bank.

Thames Water Authority

The Thames Water Authority centres, not unnaturally, around the River Thames and its many tributaries. The Thames in the centre of London is a much improved river. Above the cleansed tidal reaches the fishing is generally good, but the river is plagued by boats during the summer and serious fishing often must be restricted to early mornings, evenings or during the night, where this is allowed. If peace and tranquility is one of the requirements of your fishing, then the Thames on a sunny Sunday in July is not the place to find it!

Regardless of the boat traffic, the Thames still produces some good fish, especially around the Oxford area. Massive bream catches are a thing of the past, although it is still possible to drop lucky on a shoal and take over 100 lb (45.3 kg) at a sitting. The barbel on the Thames are rather elusive and difficult to catch in great numbers, although there is no doubt that the river is capable of producing a few double figure fish. Some of the best catches of coarse fish are now taken in the lower reaches and the dace fishing can be great fun with 20 lb (9.1 kg) bags not at all uncommon.

The best specimen water in the area is the River Kennet, but day ticket facilities on the river are not very extensive.

The Oxford area is very rich in gravel-pit fisheries, and these offer excellent fishing for specimen bream, carp and pike.

Key	Page
1 Blenheim Palace Lake	149
2 Stoneacres	150
3 Tring Reservoirs	150
4 Grand Union Canal – Tring	150
5 Savay Lake	151
6 Grand Union Canal – Kings Langley	151
7 Wraysbury Gravel Pits	152
8 Deans Farm Fishery	152
9 Holwell Hyde Lake	153
10 Kings Weir Fishery	154
11 Hooks Marsh	154
12 Bowyers Lake	155
13 Claverhambury Carp Lake	155
14 Coppermill Stream – Walthamstow	155
15 River Roding – Buckhurst Hill	156
16 Bedfords Park Lake	156
17 Fairlop Lake	157
18 Raphael Park Lane	157
19 Harrow Lodge Lake	158
20 Mayesbrook Park Lakes	158
21 River Thames – Lechlade	160
22 River Thames – weir pools between Lechlade and Benson	160
23 River Thames – Tadpole Bridge	160
24 River Thames – Newbridge	161
25 River Thames – Oxford	161
26 River Thames – Dorchester	162
27 River Thames – weir pools between Benson and Henley	162
28 River Thames – Reading	162
29 River Thames – weir pools between Henley and Windsor	163
30 River Thames – Marlow	163
31 River Thames – Maidenhead	164
32 River Thames – Maidenhead	164
33 River Thames – Windsor	164

34 River Thames –
   weir pools between
   Windsor and Molesey 165
35 River Thames –
   Molesey 165
36 River Thames –
   Teddington 166

37 River Thames –
   Richmond 166
38 River Thames –
   Chiswick 166
39 Roughgrounds Farm
   Lake 167
40 Queenford Lagoon 167
41 Dorchester Gravel
   Pit Complex 168

42 Theale Complex 169
43 River Kennet –
   Manton Fishery 169
44 Trilakes 170
45 Holly Bush Lane
   Fishery 170
46 Basingstoke Canal
   – Odiham to Byfleet 171
47 Old Bury Hill Lake 171

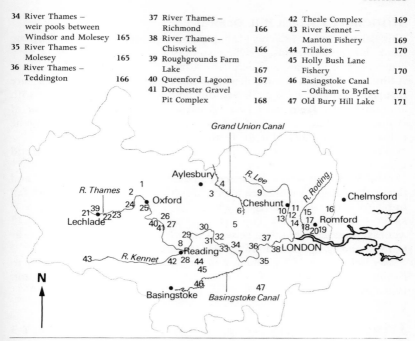

Blenheim Palace Lake (Woodstock, near Oxford, Oxfordshire) T 1

This large lake is famous for its tench and pike fishing. It is set in the grounds of Blenheim Palace, and has attractive lily beds and reed-fringed margins. The limited amount of bank fishing is restricted to use by local residents, and visitors to the water must fish from one of the 13 boats available. The tench fishing in summer is very good, with plenty of fish to 4 lb (1.8 kg) being taken. Really big hauls of tench are unlikely as there is a groundbait ban on the water. During the winter, lots of double figure pike are taken from the lake, and fish to over 20 lb (9.1 kg) are present.

SPECIES Tench, pike, roach and perch.

TECHNIQUES AND BAITS From the boats, fishing with a waggler float set over depth alongside the weed beds is best. Good baits are lobworm, sweetcorn and bread flake. The pike are taken on deadbaits fished sink-and-draw fashion, or by spinning.

SEASON 16th June to 14th March. Fishing from 6 am (or dawn) to dusk.

ACCESS Woodstock is reached on the A34(T) road, 7 miles (11.3 km) north-west of Oxford.

Information and permits are obtained from Blenheim Palace Estate Office, Woodstock.

Stoneacres (Linch Hill, Oxford) T 2

This fishery covers 58 acres (23 ha) and is regularly stocked with young trout, but also contains excellent stocks of coarse fish. It offers very economic trout fishing and excellent coarse fishing throughout the year. Additional facilities for families, including a picnic and play area, are planned. Keepnets are not allowed during the period 15th March to 15th June inclusive. Trout must be returned to the water immediately or, if required or damaged, be killed and paid for at reception prior to leaving the fishery. Boats are available for fishing.

SPECIES Rainbow trout, carp, barbel, chub, tench, roach, bream, perch and pike.

TECHNIQUES AND BAITS No special method is needed at Stoneacres, and float-fished maggots will catch plenty of fish. In general, the larger fish fall to bigger baits fished on leger tackle.

SEASON No close season. This fishery is open all year.

ACCESS Stoneacres is located between Standlake and Stanton Harcourt near Oxford, and is signposted off the B4449 road.

Day tickets should be obtained at the fishery reception office prior to fishing. Advance bookings and enquiries to Linch Hill Fishery, Stanton Harcourt, Oxfordshire.

Tring Reservoirs (Tring, near Aylesbury, Hertfordshire) T 3

These three large reservoirs, Wilstone, Startops and Marsworth, are owned by British Waterways and are used to feed the Grand Union Canal. Startops Reservoir is completely concreted around the banks, and the other two have partly concreted areas and partly natural banks. The fishing potential of all three reservoirs is excellent. The British record catfish came from Wilstone and weighed 43 lb 8 oz (19.7 kg). The waters also contain specimen pike, bream and tench.

SPECIES Catfish, bream, roach, pike, tench and perch.

TECHNIQUES AND BAITS Specimen tactics are required for the larger fish. Long-range legering with lobworms is a good tactic for tench and big bream.

SEASON 16th June to 14th March.

ACCESS The reservoirs are just outside Tring on the A41 road from Aylesbury.

Permits are obtained on the banks.

Grand Union Canal – Tring (Hertfordshire) T 4

The stretch of the Grand Union Canal between Red House Lock and the Main Marsworth Basin is controlled by Tring Anglers. During the summer and autumn this stretch of the canal is full of carp, and some excellent catches are taken. There is a very high percentage of fully scaled common carp as well as the usual mirror carp. Most of the carp are in the 2–5 lb (0.9–2.3 kg) range but there are bigger fish present.

SPECIES Carp, roach, perch and bream.

TECHNIQUES AND BAITS Float fishing using a slim-bodied waggler float and maggots or casters as bait is effective. Early in the season sweetcorn and bread flake are also good baits. Some of the bigger carp are taken on light leger tackle.

SEASON 16th June to 14th March.

ACCESS The canal is reached via the A489 road at Marsworth.

Permits are obtained from bailiffs on the bank. The water is controlled by Tring Anglers whose Secretary is Mr B Boucher.

Savay Lake (near Denham, Buckinghamshire) T 5

Renowned to carp anglers, Savay Lake covers 60 acres (24 ha) and is a good all-round fishery. It is as a carp fishery that Savay has become famous, with many carp of 20 lb (9.1 kg) and over caught every year. Some individual carp are caught several times and have become well known to specimen hunters. The lake also holds specimen tench and bream. Approximately half of the lake is now open to the public, providing well over 100 good bank swims. Parts of the lake are very deep close to the side, and unaccompanied juniors are not permitted on the fishery unless in possession of a season permit.

SPECIES Carp to 30 lb (13.6 kg), tench, bream, pike, roach and perch.

TECHNIQUES AND BAITS Legering for the carp using hair rigs and bolt rigs seems to produce the best results. Because the carp grow so large at Savay, they attract a lot of specialist anglers and have just about every flavour of carp bait presented to them. In any case, legering on a gravel-pit is the best way of catching the larger fish. Roach and tench can be caught on float tackle using a waggler float and maggots, casters or bread as bait.

SEASON 16th June to 14th March.

ACCESS The lake is situated south of Moorhall Road, Harefield, near Denham, and is flanked by the River Colne to the west and the Grand Union Canal to the east. Permits must be obtained before fishing and are available from Peverills Newsagents, 3 Moorhall Road, Harefield, – $\frac{1}{2}$ mile (0.8 km) from the fishery entrance; or Balfours Newsagents, 12 Station Parade, Denham (near the railway station). The Fishery Manager is Mr P Broxup, 309 Shirland Road, London W9.

Grand Union Canal – Kings Langley (near Watford, Hertfordshire) T 6

This stretch of the Grand Union Canal is from Hunton Bridge Lock to Grove

Mill. It is a good canal fishery and includes the Lady Capels stretch, where big chub, bream and carp are caught. Normally, anglers associate canals with tiny stunted fish but this stretch produces some really prime specimens of most species. Fishing is from the towpath along the canal and the average depth of the canal is between 4 and 5 ft (1.2 and 1.5 m).

SPECIES Carp, roach to $1\frac{1}{2}$ lb (0.7 kg), chub to 5 lb (2.3 kg), bream to 7 lb (3.2 kg), gudgeon, perch and pike.

TECHNIQUES AND BAITS Tackle should be very fine, and probably the best tactic is to use a very slim-bodied waggler float, shotted so that just the tip is showing above the surface. Light legering, using a very small feeder, will also work.

SEASON 16th June to 14th March.

ACCESS The canal is reached via Grove Mill Lane off the A411 Hemel Hempstead to Watford road.

Permits are obtained from bailiffs on the bank. The fishery is managed by Kings Langley Angling Society whose Secretary is Mr Anderson.

Wraysbury Gravel Pits (near Staines, Middlesex) T 7

These are two big gravel-pits; one is 61 acres (25 ha) and the other is $76\frac{1}{2}$ acres (31 ha). Both lakes, especially the smaller of the two, regularly produce specimen-size fish. Night fishing is allowed on these waters. Kingsmead Fish Farms share these waters with Leisure Sport (who control the fishing), and anglers are not permitted to fish within casting distance of any trout pens which may be moored on the lake. On the smaller lake near Welley Road, the west bank is private.

SPECIES Carp to 31 lb 5 oz (14.2 kg), pike to 28 lb 6 oz (12.9 kg), tench to 9 lb 10 oz (4.4 kg), bream to 10 lb 2 oz (4.6 kg), roach to 3 lb 6 oz (1.6 kg), perch to 3 lb 2 oz (1.5 kg) and eels to 5 lb (2.3 kg).

TECHNIQUES AND BAITS These are big fish waters and, although good catches can be taken on standard float tackle, the best results are had by long-range legering at night, dawn or dusk. The carp respond to high-protein baits, although quite a number are still falling to sweetcorn.

SEASON 16th June to 14th March.

ACCESS The two lakes are separated by Station Road, leading from Wraysbury Station. Cars should be parked in the car parks at Douglas Lane, Wraysbury Club, or the entrance to the lake near the village school.

Day tickets are obtained from Wraysbury Newsagents, near Douglas Lane in Wraysbury High Street; Davies Angling, 47 Church Street, Staines; or LSA Thorpe Park, Staines Road, Chertsey, Surrey.

Deans Farm Fishery (near Reading, Berkshire) T 8

Deans Farm is a mature gravel-pit fishery covering 60 acres (24 ha). This is a specimen hunter's water, and is not the easiest of lakes to fish, but it holds some large tench and bream. The tench fishing is excellent, and the fishery can claim a string of 8 lb (3.6 kg) fish as well as a monster of 10 lb 2 oz (4.6 kg). The bream also grow very large, with several double figure specimens being caught in recent years. The permit also entitles the holder to fish $\frac{1}{2}$ mile (0.8 km) of the nearby River Thames. The Thames at this point holds barbel among other species. The fishery is surrounded by farmland, and anglers are requested to close all gates and not to interefere with or feed the animals.

SPECIES Tench, carp, roach, bream, pike and perch. In the river, roach, bream, chub and dace predominate, with a few perch and barbel.

TECHNIQUES AND BAITS Big fish tactics are best in the lake: legered lobworm is the most successful for the tench and bream. In the river float fishing will catch most species but, again, legering will lure the bigger specimens.

SEASON 16th June to 14th March.

ACCESS Turn off the M4 motorway at Junction 10 on to the A329(M). At the end of the A329(M), turn left on to the A4 into Reading, following signpost directions to Henley, and cross Reading Bridge. After 600 yards, turn right at the traffic lights and continue to the T-junction at the end of the road and then turn right again into Star Road. At the end of this road continue down the track to Deans Farm and then follow signpost directions to the car park.

Permits must be obtained from Deans Farm before commencing to fish. Resident Manager: Mr J Lucas.

Holwell Hyde Lake (Welwyn Garden City, Hertfordshire) T9

This is a mixed coarse fishery covering $2\frac{1}{2}$ acres (1 ha) controlled by Redland Angling. The lake is well stocked with some big carp and tench. The lake was private and has only recently been opened to the public for fishing.

SPECIES Carp, tench, roach and rudd.

TECHNIQUES AND BAITS Float fishing using a waggler float is best for most species. Good baits are maggots, casters, worms and sweetcorn.

SEASON 16th June to 14th March. Fishing from 8.30 am to sunset.

ACCESS Access is off the B195 road near Welwyn Garden City via Holwell Hyde Lane. The entrance to the lake and the car park is $\frac{1}{2}$ mile (0.8 km) down the lane on the left-hand side (immediately after the farm on the right).

Permits are obtained from the bailiff on the bank. For further information contact Mr G Rowles, Lakeview Farm, Old Bury Hill, Westcott, near Dorking, Surrey.

Kings Weir Fishery (Wormley, Hertfordshire) T 10

This well-known fishery comprises ½ mile (0.8 km) of the River Lee (both banks), ¾ mile (1.2 km) of the flood relief channel (both banks) and ¾ mile (1.2 km) of the bank of Langridge Lake. The focal point of the fishery is Kings Weir itself, which is well known for its catches of chub and barbel. Double figure barbel have been caught on this stretch of the Lee. The flood relief channel is well stocked with roach and bream. Langridge Lake fishes well for several species of coarse fish, notably tench and bream. Few fisheries in the UK can offer such a range of fishing, and the water produces fish in both summer and winter. The flood relief channel is available for club/match bookings. The weir pool itself may only be fished from punts, which are bookable. No keepnets are allowed in the river.

SPECIES Chub, barbel, roach, bream and carp in the river. Bream, roach, tench and pike in the lake.

TECHNIQUES AND BAITS Legered luncheon meat, maggots and cheese are best for the larger chub and barbel in the river, and stick float maggots and casters for the roach and smaller chub. In the lake, use a waggler float with maggots, casters or bread as bait.

SEASON 16th June to 14th March. Fishing from sunrise to sunset.

ACCESS Take the A10 road to Broxbourne and turn right into Station Road. Cross the railway bridge and continue for ½ mile (0.8 km) and then turn right at the Keysers Estate signpost. After 100 yards turn left into Green Lane. At the end of the road continue down the track and park where indicated. The flood relief channel is on the left, the lake is straight ahead and the river is approximately 330 yards (300 m) to the right of the lake and is reached by walking along the lakeside path.

Tickets are available on site.

Hooks Marsh (Waltham Abbey, Essex) T 11

This 40 acre (16 ha) gravel-pit is controlled by Leisure Sport. The average depth of the gravel-pit is about 10 ft (3 m); the shallowest end is the north bank. This is a good all-round coarse fishery, and has produced a number of pike in excess of 20 lb (9.1 kg). Night fishing is allowed on this lake, so specimen hunters can fish for the big bream and tench at favourable times.

SPECIES Bream to 6 lb (2.7 kg), tench to 7 lb (3.2 kg), roach to 1½ lb (0.7 kg), perch to 2 lb (0.9 kg) and pike to 26 lb (11.7 kg).

TECHNIQUES AND BAITS Float fishing with antenna floats set to fish slightly over depth will catch plenty of the smaller fish. Big bream catches and the larger tench are usually caught on leger, using a swimfeeder. The bigger pike are usually caught on dead baits.

SEASON 16th June to 14th March.

ACCESS The approach route to the fishery is the B194 north from Waltham Abbey towards Broxbourne. Turn left at the sharp bend in the main road on to the concrete road leading to Fishers Green Farm. The lake is to the left of the suspension footbridge immediately past the car park.

Day tickets are available from P & B Hall, 44 Highbridge Street, Waltham Abbey, Essex

Bowyers Lake (Waltham Cross, Hertfordshire) T 12

This is a well-matured gravel-pit fishery, covering 32 acres (13 ha). The average depth is 5 ft (1.5 m) but the banks drop away in places to 15 ft (4.6 m). The lake is oval in shape with an island in the middle. The banks are flat and accessible.

SPECIES Tench, carp, bream, roach and eels.

TECHNIQUES AND BAITS Big fish tactics work best for the bigger tench, carp and bream. High-protein baits are effective for the carp, and lobworm and sweetcorn for the tench and bream. Waggler fishing with maggots and casters will lure the smaller fish.

SEASON 16th June to 14th March.

ACCESS The water is reached via Trinity Lane off the A1010 road at Waltham Cross.

Permits are obtained from the bailiff on the bank or from the gatekeeper. The fishery is operated by the Duke of Wellington Angling Society. Chairman: Mr A Curson.

Claverhambury Carp Lake (Waltham Abbey, Essex) T 13

This specially made carp fishery covers $1\frac{1}{2}$ acres (0.6 ha). The long, narrow lake was formed by damming a small stream. It is shallow at the top end and 10 ft (3 m) deep near the dam. One side of the lake is wooded and the other is open grassland. The lake is fringed with reeds and rushes, giving plenty of cover. Rods are limited to ten a day.

SPECIES Carp to double figures.

TECHNIQUES AND BAITS All specialist carp techniques using baits such as corn, high-protein pastes and particles such as tic beans work well.

SEASON 16th June to 14th March.

ACCESS The lake is situated at the end of Galley Hill Road (Claverhambury Road), Waltham Abbey.

Permits must be obtained in advance from P & B Hall, 44 Highbridge Street, Waltham Abbey.

Coppermill Stream – Walthamstow (Tottenham, Greater London) T 14

The Coppermill Stream is a small river fishery running 1 mile (1.6 km)

through the Walthamstow reservoir complex. The Coppermill Stream flows into the Lee Navigation near the West Warwick Reservoir in the complex. The stream is a prolific fishery and is regularly stocked by the water authority. Species such as grayling and barbel are present and thriving, with barbel up to 9 lb (4.1 kg) having been caught. Roach, dace and chub are the predominant species and dace over 1 lb (0.5 kg) have been taken in recent years.

SPECIES Barbel to 9 lb (4.1 kg), roach to $2\frac{1}{2}$ lb (1.1 kg), bream to 4 lb (1.8 kg), perch to 2 lb (0.9 kg), carp to 16 lb (7.3 kg), pike to 19 lb (8.6 kg), chub to $5\frac{1}{2}$ lb (2.5 kg), dace to $1\frac{1}{4}$ lb (0.6 kg) and grayling.

TECHNIQUES AND BAITS Float fishing with a stick float and maggots or casters as bait is the most widely used method. Light legering with a quiver tip rod works well for the chub and barbel, with cheese, luncheon meat or bread as bait. Loose feeding is allowed but groundbaiting is banned.

SEASON 16th June to 14th March. Fishing from 6.30 am to half an hour after sunset.

ACCESS The fishery is part of the Walthamstow reservoir complex and access from the A10 Stamford Hill High Road is via Ferry Lane. The nearest stations are South Tottenham, Tottenham Hale and Blackhorse Road.

Day permits are available from ticket machines on site.

River Roding – Buckhurst Hill (Essex) T 15

The River Roding rises near Great Dunmow in Essex. In its upper reaches it is a fast-flowing, narrow river. The River Roding eventually enters the Thames at Barking. Near Buckhurst Hill, on the south side of Epping Forest, $1\frac{1}{2}$ miles (2.4 km) of the River Roding are operated by Epping Forest District Council. The fishing is from Loughton Bridge downstream to Roding Lane Bridge. The fishing is mainly for dace, chub and roach.

SPECIES Roach, chub, dace, perch and pike.

TECHNIQUES AND BAITS Float fishing, using a stick float, is best. The best baits are maggots, casters, bread and hemp. During the winter, 'laying on' in the slacker water close to the bank is worth trying for the roach.

SEASON 16th June to 14th March.

ACCESS The river is approached from Buckhurst Hill off the A121 road. Access to the river is along a footpath at the Recreation Ground boundary.

The fishing is free to holders of a Thames Water Authority Rod Licence. Information is available from the Parks Officer, Epping Forest District Council.

Bedfords Park Lake (Brentwood, Essex) T 16

This is a $1\frac{1}{2}$ acre (0.6 ha) lake set in open parkland. The lake is circular with sloping grassy banks, and the edge of the lake is fringed with lots of rushes and weeds. The lake is about 6 ft (1.8 m) deep in the middle. The fishing is

very good – probably the best in the area – with plenty of tench.
SPECIES Tench, carp and roach.
TECHNIQUES AND BAITS Float fishing with a waggler float set to the exact
depth of the swim. Baits to use are maggots, bread and sweetcorn.
SEASON 16th June to 14th March.
ACCESS The fishery is off the B175 road at Chase Cross near Brentwood.
   Permits are obtained from bailiffs on the bank. The fishery is operated by
North Romford Angling Society and the Secretary is Mrs Partridge.

Fairlop Lake (Hainault, near Romford, Essex) T 17

This is an attractive and easily accessible lake with swims cut out where the
banking is steep. In front of the car park some swims have been created so
that disabled anglers can reach the waterside. The water is fairly deep and
drops away very close to the edge so that, although the lake is fringed with
rushes, they do not extend very far and there is little weed under water.
The main species in the lake are tench, carp and rudd.
SPECIES Carp to 25 lb (11.3 kg), rudd, roach, perch and tench.
TECHNIQUES AND BAITS The best method of fishing is with a slim-bodied
waggler float, using maggots or casters as bait. Most fish are caught on the
sloping shelf close to the bank. Loose feeding on the 'little and often' basis is
effective.
SEASON 16th June to 14th March.
ACCESS The water is reached via Forest Road from the A123 road.
   The water is owned by London Borough of Redbridge Recreation
Department and the fishing is controlled by Redbridge Angling Association
who allow a limited number of day permits. Permits are obtained from
'Bromages 75', 666 Green Lane, Goodmayes, Essex; or Avenue Cycles at
Gants Hill, Ilford, Essex.

Raphael Park Lake (near Romford, Essex) T 18

This is a 2½ acre (1 ha) lake, set in parkland. The average depth of the lake is
4 ft (1.2 m) and the lake is very long and narrow. The water is a mixed coarse
fishery with some large tench and carp.
SPECIES Carp, tench, roach, rudd, perch and pike.
TECHNIQUES AND BAITS Float fishing with a waggler float, using maggots,
casters or hemp, is effective for most species. The same tactics, but with
slightly heavier tackle and using sweetcorn or high-protein paste as bait, is
best for the carp and tench.
SEASON 16th June to 14th March.
ACCESS Turn off the A12 road from London at Gidea Park. Turn into Pettits
Lane and then into Parland Avenue.
   Permits are available from bailiffs on the bank. The fishing is operated by

the Southern Essex Group Angling Bodies Consultative whose Secretary is Mr R Smith, 46 Shortcrofts Road, Dagenham, Essex.

Harrow Lodge Lake (Hornchurch, Essex) T 19

This $\frac{3}{4}$ mile (1.2 km) long lake is only 260 ft (80 m) wide. The total acreage of the water is 8 acres (3.2 ha). The lake, set in open parkland, has an average depth of 5 ft (1.5 m) and has readily accessible banks. The fishing is for mixed coarse fish but mainly roach and rudd.

SPECIES Roach, rudd, carp, perch and pike.

TECHNIQUES AND BAITS Mainly float fishing using a waggler float set so that the bait fishes on 'the drop'. Baits to use are maggots, casters, bread and sweetcorn.

SEASON 16th June to 14th March.

ACCESS The lake is in Harrow Lodge Park, Hornchurch, and is reached via the A125 Rainham road.

Permits are available from bailiffs on the bank. OAPs and disabled persons can fish free of charge. The fishery is operated by the Southern Essex Group Angling Bodies Consultative whose secretary is Mr R Smith, 46 Shortcrofts Road, Dagenham, Essex.

Mayesbrook Park Lakes (Barking, Essex) T 20

These two lakes are set in open parkland and have a combined area of 6 acres (2.4 ha). They are roughly circular in shape with an average depth of 5 ft (1.5 m). The beds are gravel and hard clay. The fishing is for mixed coarse fish. During the winter the roach fishing is excellent with some good-sized specimens.

SPECIES Roach, rudd, carp, tench, perch and pike.

TECHNIQUES AND BAITS Float fishing using a waggler float and with maggots, casters or bread as hookbait is effective. Sweetcorn is good for the carp and tench during the summer.

SEASON 16th June to 14th March.

ACCESS The lakes are in Mayesbrook Park, Barking, off Lodge Avenue (A1153). Access is on foot from the car park.

Permits are available on the banks. The fishery is operated by the Southern Essex Group Angling Bodies Consultative whose secretary is Mr R Smith, 46 Shortcrofts Road, Dagenham, Essex.

Introduction to the River Thames

The Thames is probably the most famous river in England, and is the second longest, after the River Severn. The Thames rises near Cirencester in the

Cotswolds and then flows eastwards across the country to the City of London and the busy estuary. In the upper reaches of the Thames, between Cirencester and Lechlade, the fishing is mainly for trout. From Lechlade downstream to Oxford, coarse fish predominate and there are some sizeable fish in this area. Tadpole Bridge is a noted 'hot spot' for chub and barbel. The River Windrush is a major tributary of the Thames and this joins the main river at Newbridge downstream of Tadpole Bridge.

At Oxford the river flows in a big bend, first north and then south again. The river also widens considerably around Oxford, and from here onwards bream are one of the most important species. Gone are the days when anglers could sit down on the banks and take over 100 lb (45.4 kg) bream catches without really trying, but some huge hauls of this species can still be made. Chub are prolific everywhere in this stretch, and some big barbel are also taken from the river, but this species is difficult to locate consistently.

The area from Reading to Maidenhead is also good for bream, with some large roach catches, too. Teddington Lock marks the top of the tidal river and below the lock most of the fishing is for dace and roach with just a few chub and skimmer bream. In recent years, the Thames in the city of London has undergone a massive clean up and coarse fish, such as dace and roach, can now be caught, often in good numbers, right in the heart of London. Here the surroundings may not be up to much, especially at low tide, but the dace are of good average size. Salmon fry have been introduced to the Thames in an effort to re-establish runs of these fish, and some success has been achieved. The lower weirs at Teddington and Molesey are producing salmon to anglers specifically fishing for them using toby spinners.

The Thames is not noted for specimen fish, but plenty of 2 lb (0.9 kg) roach and some big chub are caught. The average size of Thames barbel is high but they are seldom caught in large numbers. Six barbel in a day would be considered a good catch. Pike abound in the river but, as on many rivers, very few anglers fish seriously for them. Most methods of fishing will catch coarse fish on the Thames, but the two most used are legering with a swimfeeder, in conjunction with maggot or caster baits, and stick float fishing using the same baits.

The biggest problem when fishing the Thames is avoiding the heavy boat traffic in summer. It is not only the cruisers plying holiday-makers up and down the river, but also the countless canoes, skiffs and rowing boats that can disrupt sport. This is why the Thames weir permits are such good value in summer. When you fish a weir pool you are not only fishing in the most oxygenated water, but also avoiding the heavy boat traffic.

In the tidal reaches below Teddington Lock account must be taken of the state of the tide. Care must also be exercised by anglers who stand in the river to fish. The best times to fish the tidal reaches are when the river is starting to flow faster as the tide is going out. The fishing will be at its best around low tide and then tail off as the water starts to flow back. The tidal

Thames is a very busy waterway with big boats creating heavy swells. Always allow for the wash from a boat, otherwise you could end up with a boot full of water, or much worse.

River Thames – Lechlade (Gloucestershire) T 21

The fishing on this section of the upper river covers $2\frac{1}{2}$ miles (4 km) on the towpath side only. The fishing is upstream from St John's Lock to Murdoch's Ditch (Round House). A separate ticket can be obtained to fish the weir pool and St John's Lock. The main species upstream of the lock is chub, and some large pike can be caught in the weir pool itself, together with a few trout.

SPECIES Chub, dace, roach, pike and brown trout (in weir pool).

TECHNIQUES AND BAITS Stick float with caster bait is best for the chub and dace but legered bread flake works well for the bigger fish. Pike and trout can be caught in the weir pool by spinning.

SEASON 16th June to 14th March.

ACCESS Permits are obtained from the Trout Inn, Lechlade.

River Thames – weir pools between Lechlade and Benson (Oxfordshire–Berkshire) T 22

One permit allows anglers to fish in the following Thames weir pools: Grafton, Radcot, Rushey, Shifford, Eynsham, Sandford, Culham and Day's Lock. The weirs offer very good fishing for chub, bream and barbel. The barbel fishing in the lower weir pools can also be very good.

SPECIES Chub, barbel, roach, bream, dace and pike.

TECHNIQUES AND BAITS Leger with cheese, bread and luncheon meat for the chub and barbel. Leger with a small feeder and casters for chub and roach. Float fishing with a stick float in the streamy water, using maggots or casters, works well for roach and dace.

SEASON 16th June to 14th March.

ACCESS A permit covering all these weirs can be obtained from the Finance Department of the Thames Water Authority.

River Thames – Tadpole Bridge (Oxfordshire) T 23

This fishery is on the right-hand bank of the river from Rushey Lock to Tenfoot Bridge. This is an excellent stretch for chub and barbel. Bream are also present with a few sizeable roach. The best spots for barbel are where the current pushes through faster.

SPECIES Chub, barbel, roach, bream, dace and pike.

TECHNIQUES AND BAITS Leger for chub and barbel with a quiver tip rod. Luncheon meat, cheese and bread crust are all good baits. Lobworm is also worth trying and, when the river is running above normal, some good

Loch Tummel, near Pitlochry, contains both coarse and game fish (see page 36).

(Above) Dedicated carp anglers settled down for a long fishing session.

(Below) Two anglers with a magnificent 30 lb (13.5 kg) mirror carp.

roach are taken on this bait.

SEASON 16th June to 14th March.

ACCESS The river is reached from the car park at Tadpole Bridge.

Permits are obtained from the Trout Inn at Buckland (just off the A420), near Faringdon.

River Thames – Newbridge (Oxfordshire) T 24

The fishing here is excellent for chub, barbel and bream. The fishery centres on the confluence of the River Windrush with the Thames. Some large barbel have been taken from this area and the bream fishing can be good. The fishery is for two fields downstream on the left-hand bank at Newbridge and from the road bridge to the confluence on the left-hand bank of the River Windrush.

SPECIES Chub, roach, perch, barbel, bream and pike.

TECHNIQUES AND BAITS Legering is best for the bigger fish. Luncheon meat, bread flake and cheese are good baits for the chub and barbel. Casters are good for chub and roach. Float fishing with a stick float and maggot or caster bait works well for the smaller species.

SEASON 16th June to 14th March.

ACCESS Newbridge is on the A415 road between Witney and Abingdon. The river is reached via Newbridge car park.

Permits are obtained from Rose Revived Hotel, Newbridge.

River Thames – Oxford T 25

There is very little day ticket fishing around the town of Oxford but the Abingdon and Oxford Anglers' Alliance issue a seven-day permit, which covers several stretches of the Thames in this area. The fishing is at Eynsham, Radley, Sandford and Clifton-Hampden. This stretch of the Thames is very good, especially for bream. Some big barbel are also caught in this area. Chub are probably the dominant species and some good catches are taken. A few very big carp have also been taken from the Thames at Oxford.

SPECIES Bream, chub, barbel, roach, pike, perch and (occasional) carp.

TECHNIQUES AND BAITS Legering is by far the most successful method. Legering with bit baits, such as cheese and luncheon meat, is effective for the chub and barbel. For the bream, an open-ended feeder filled with a mixture of groundbait and maggots works well.

SEASON 16th June to 14th March.

ACCESS The fisheries can be reached via Eynsham Bridge, Radley village, Sandford Lock and Clifton-Hampden Bridge.

Seven-day permits can be obtained from local tackle shops in the Abingdon/Oxford area, together with a map showing the extent of the fishing. The secretary of the Abingdon and Oxford Anglers' Alliance is Mr M J Ponting.

River Thames – Dorchester (Oxfordshire) T 26

This fishery is controlled by Dorchester Angling Association and stretches from the Thames Stream Bridge (the confluence of the River Thame) to the old Meat Ferry site, a distance of 1 mile (1.6 km). The fishery is on the Dorchester bank only. The best fishing is for bream but there are some sizeable barbel and chub. A good 'hot spot' is at the top of the stretch just below the bridge and another bream 'hot spot' is in the middle of the stretch.

SPECIES Bream, chub, barbel, roach, dace, perch, pike and eels.

TECHNIQUES AND BAITS The best bream catches are taken on leger tackle, using a quiver tip rod. Small to medium-sized feeders should be packed with groundbait and casters. Bread flake is also a good bait for the bream, and in addition will take the chub. Luncheon meat is the best barbel bait on this stretch.

SEASON 16th June to 14th March.

ACCESS Dorchester is on the A423(T) road, 10 miles (16.1 km) south of Oxford.

Permits are obtained on the banks. Further information is available from the Secretary of Dorchester Angling Association, Mr R V Bull, 15 Chiltern Gardens, Watlington, Oxfordshire.

River Thames – weir pools between Benson and Henley (Oxfordshire – Berkshire) T 27

The three weirs at Goring, Shiplake and Marsh Lock are covered by a single permit. The fishing in the weir pools is good, and boats can usually be hired locally to enable the angler to explore all parts of the weir. Some big chub and barbel can be caught in the white water at the sill of the weir.

SPECIES Chub, barbel, roach, bream, dace, perch, pike and a few carp.

TECHNIQUES AND BAITS Legering is best for the larger fish. Baits such as luncheon meat, cheese and bread work well. A swim feeder laced with maggots, casters or hemp is good for chub and bream in the smooth glides. Stick float fishing is effective for the smaller species such as roach and dace.

SEASON 16th June to 14th March.

ACCESS Parking is available near the various weirs. A weir permit can be obtained from the Finance Department of the Thames Water Authority.

River Thames – Reading (Berkshire) T 28

This area of the Thames is very good for bream with the possibility of 100 lb

(45.4 kg) catches in summer. Some large chub are also taken on this stretch of the Thames. The length of the fishery is roughly 3610 ft (1100 m). The Thames Water Authority section is on the right-hand bank upstream of a section controlled by Reading Borough Council which can also be fished on a day ticket. The river is picturesque and tree-lined but boat traffic is heavy in summer.

SPECIES Bream, roach, perch, chub, barbel and pike.

TECHNIQUES AND BAITS All the big weights of bream are taken on feeders filled with casters and hemp. The bream range in size from 2 to 6 lb (0.9 to 2.7 kg), so there is no need to fish very heavy. A 3–4 lb (1.4–1.8 kg) breaking strain line is sufficient to deal with the bream and any interloping chub.

SEASON 16th June to 14th March.

ACCESS Access to the river is via Scours Lane off the A329 road at Tilehurst. Fishing is free.

River Thames – weir pools between Henley and Windsor (Berkshire) T 29

The three weirs along this stretch of the Thames are at Hambleden, Marlow and Bray, and all three can be fished with a single weir permit. Good mixed coarse fishing can be enjoyed in the weir pools and boats can occasionally be hired locally to fish the river. The main species are chub, bream and barbel but the pike fishing can also be good in these weir pools.

SPECIES Chub, roach, dace, perch, bream, barbel and pike.

TECHNIQUES AND BAITS Legering with luncheon meat, bread and cheese is best for the better chub and barbel at the heads of the pools. For bream and chub from the tails of the pools, try legering with a feeder. Maggots or casters fished under a stick float in the streamy water are good for roach, dace and chub.

SEASON 16th June to 14th March.

ACCESS Parking is available near the weirs.

A weir permit is available from the Finance Department of the Thames Water Authority.

River Thames – Marlow (Buckinghamshire) T 30

This stretch is controlled by Marlow Angling Club and covers the left bank upstream from Marlow Bridge to opposite Temple Island. The river is wide and the fishing is mainly for bream, roach and chub.

SPECIES Roach, dace, chub, bream, pike and perch.

TECHNIQUES AND BAITS Leger for the chub and bream using a small open-ended feeder. Bread, maggots and casters are the usual baits. Float fishing works best fot the smaller species.

SEASON 16th June to 14th March.

ACCESS Access to the river is via the towpath.

Permits are obtained from Kings Fishing Tackle, 1 Ray Street, Maidenhead. Telephone: Maidenhead 29283. The Secretary of Marlow Angling Club is Mr G W Hoing, 15 Greenlands, Flackwell Heath, High Wycombe, Buckinghamshire.

River Thames – Maidenhead (Berkshire) T 31

There are two stretches of free fishing in Maidenhead. They are on the right bank from Boulter's Lock to Maidenhead Bridge and on the left bank from Maidenhead Bridge to the end of the public gardens. Chub and bream are the main species.

SPECIES Chub, bream, roach, perch, pike and dace.

TECHNIQUES AND BAITS Leger with a small feeder and maggots or casters as hookbait for the bream and chub. Float fishing is best for the smaller species, again using maggots or casters as hookbait.

SEASON 16th June to 14th March.

ACCESS Access to the right bank is from Ray Head Road. Access to the left bank is gained via Ellington Road.

The fishing is free.

River Thames – Maidenhead (Berkshire) T 32

Controlled by Maidenhead and District Angling Association, the fishery is on the right bank downstream from My Lady Ferry to the beginning of the public gardens. The river is wide with a steady flow. Bream offer the best sport, together with chub and roach.

SPECIES Chub, barbel, bream, roach, dace and pike.

TECHNIQUES AND BAITS Float fish with maggots or casters for most species. Legering is best for the bream, with an open-ended feeder packed with groundbait and maggots.

SEASON 16th June to 14th March.

ACCESS The river is reached via the towpath from the car park.

Permits are available on the bank. The Maidenhead and District Angling Association Chairman is Mr G W Rance, Ivydene, Forlease Road, Maidenhead.

River Thames – Windsor (Berkshire) T 33

The fishery is controlled by Salt Hill Angling Society and is on the left bank of the river upstream from the A332 road bridge to Long Bridge. The fishing is predominantly for roach, bream and chub.

SPECIES Roach, bream, chub, dace, gudgeon and perch.

TECHNIQUES AND BAITS Float fish with maggots or casters for the smaller fish. Legered caster and maggot with a small feeder is best for the bream, chub and larger roach.

SEASON 16th June to 14th March.

ACCESS Access is from the car park off Meadow Lane.

Permits are obtained from Windsor Angling Centre, 157 St Leonards Road, Windsor. Telephone: Windsor 67210. The Secretary of Salt Hill Angling Society is Mr H W Mayo, 16 Old Way Lane, Cippenham, Slough, Berkshire.

River Thames – weir pools between Windsor and Molesey (Berkshire – Surrey) T 34

A single permit allows anglers to fish the following weirs on the Thames around Staines: Bell Weir Lock, Shepperton, Sunbury and Molesey Main. The weir pools are the most productive areas in the lower Thames. Some can be fished from the bank, while others are best fished from a boat. Boats are occasionally available for hire locally and these allow anglers to fish right up to the white water. The main species of the weir pools are bream, chub and barbel. Some of the Thames weirs still hold a few big trout bqt these are not as common as they used to be.

SPECIES Roach, perch, pike, bream, chub, barbel, dace, and a few trout.

TECHNIQUES AND BAITS Legering with cheese or bread flake is effective for the chub and barbel. Luncheon meat is also a good bait. The smooth glides at the tails of the pools are the best areas for bream and, again, legering with a feeder is the best method. Float fishing with maggots and casters will take roach, dace and chub in the streamy water.

SEASON 16th June to 14th March.

ACCESS Parking is available near the various weirs.

A weir permit can be obtained from the Finance Department of the Thames Water Authority.

River Thames – Molesey (Surrey – Middlesex) T 35

This stretch of fishing covers the river from Molesey Weir downstream to Teddington. The weir at Molesey offers good fishing for chub, roach, dace and a few barbel. In recent years, salmon have again begun to run up the Thames and it is in the weir pools, such as Molesey, that a few are caught on spinners. The place to fish for salmon at Molesey Weir is in the rough water below the newly contructed salmon trap. A team from the Water Authority Fisheries Department have found a lot of salmon at Molesey while electro-fishing.

SPECIES Roach, chub, dace, bream, pike, barbel and salmon (occasional).

TECHNIQUES AND BAITS Legering in the weir pool works best for chub and barbel, using bread, cheese or worm as bait. In the streamy water try float-fished maggots or casters for the roach and dace. Spin with a toby lure if you fancy trying to catch a Thames salmon.

SEASON 16th June to 14th March (coarse fish) and 1st April to 30th

September (salmon).

ACCESS Access is possible at Canbury Gardens, Kingston upon Thames, and from the towpath on the south bank down to Teddington Weir.

A Thames weir permit is required to fish Molesey Weir. Boats can be hired locally to fish the weir and give access to the back weir. There is no fishing on the south bank of this stretch between Hampton Court and Kingston Bridges.

River Thames – Teddington (Middlesex) T 36

Larger coarse fish are more common on this length than further downstream and one or two sizeable bream have been caught. Dace and roach are still the predominant species. The fishing is from Teddington downstream to Richmond Bridge.

SPECIES Dace, roach, chub, bream and barbel.

TECHNIQUES AND BAITS Float fishing with a stick float will catch the smaller species such as dace, roach and skimmer bream. Maggots or casters should be used as bait and loose feeding on the 'little and often' principle to keep the shoal feeding. Leger with a feeder using maggots as bait for the larger fish.

SEASON 16th June to 14th March.

ACCESS At Teddington the river is reached from Ferry Road on the north bank and by footpath from Riverside Drive, Richmond, on the south bank. The river can also be reached from Ham Car Park, near Ham House; River Lane, Petersham; and Richmond town centre – all on the south bank.

The fishing is free.

River Thames – Richmond (Surrey) T 37

This section of the Thames runs past Kew Gardens on the south bank and Syon Park on the north bank, and is more picturesque than stretches further downstream. The fishery is from Richmond Bridge downstream to Kew Bridge. Roach and dace are the predominant species but, especially on the top section of the length, a few chub, bream and barbel are caught.

SPECIES Roach, dace, chub, bream, barbel, eels and flounders.

TECHNIQUES AND BAITS Stick float fishing with casters and maggots is best for the dace and roach. Larger fish are taken on swim feeder tactics with maggots as bait.

SEASON 16th June to 14th March.

ACCESS Access is from Kew Green, Kew; or Water Lane or Chalmondeley Walk, Richmond. The fishing is free.

River Thames – Chiswick (Greater London) T 38

Some excellent dace and roach catches are taken from this length of the

Thames, which stretches from Chiswick Bridge to Putney Bridge. A few carp have even turned up in catches occasionally. Most fish are caught fairly close to the bank.

SPECIES Dace – catches up to 15 lb (6.8 kg), roach, eels and flounders.

TECHNIQUES AND BAITS Mainly stick float fishing with a light line and small hooks. Maggots and casters are the usual baits but hemp is also worth trying.

SEASON 16th June to 14th March.

ACCESS Access points include Ship Lane and Dukes Field at Mortlake, Chiswick Mall, Hammersmith Bridge, and the embankment near Putney Bridge.

The fishing is free.

Roughgrounds Farm Lake (near Lechlade, Gloucestershire) T 39

This is a specialist carp water comprising 3 acres (1.2 ha), and containing shallows and reed margins. This lake has been exclusively stocked with specimen carp up to 20 lb (9.1 kg). The lake has yielded 196 lb (89 kg) of carp to one angler during a six-hour period, including ten double figure carp, the best being 19 lb (8.6 kg). The fishing is restricted to 15 anglers on any one day, and keepnets are not allowed.

SPECIES Carp (mirror, leather and common).

TECHNIQUES AND BAITS This is a specialist water requiring a specialist approach. As it is only a small lake, the carp very quickly get 'educated' to certain baits. Most fish fall to high-protein baits but particle baits, such as corn, tic beans and maple peas are always worth a try.

SEASON 16th June to 14th March.

ACCESS This lake is situated off the A361 Lechlade to Burford road just north of Lechlade.

Day tickets are obtained from Mr A Chase, The Paper Shop, Burford Road, Lechlade.

Queenford Lagoon (Dorchester, Oxfordshire) T 40

This 70 acre (28 ha) gravel-pit controlled by Amey Anglers Association was, without doubt, the most famous water in the country in 1984. Within the space of a few weeks, an Oxford angler smashed the bream record twice. The first fish weighed 13 lb 14 oz (6.3 kg) and the second fish a staggering 15 lb 6 oz (7 kg). However, before rushing to Queenford to try your luck for bream, it must be stressed that the water holds very few. In fact, only a handful have ever been caught there. Although this lake has great potential as a big fish water, it is not easy to fish, and the angler simply fishing for pleasure and wanting lots of bites might be a little disappointed. The average depth of the water is 12 ft (3.7 m) and there is a prolific growth of Canadian pondweed in the margins. Part of the fishery is bordered by trees, and the busy Dorchester by-pass runs behind the southern bank.

SPECIES Specimen carp, pike and bream. The lake also has a fair number of tench and roach.

TECHNIQUES AND BAITS Long-range legering is best for the large fish. Protein baits should be used for the carp, and lobworms for the bream. Deadbaiting in winter yields the best pike.

SEASON 16th June to 14th March.

ACCESS Queenford Lagoon is situated off the Dorchester by-pass. Access is via Burcot Lane only.

Permits are obtained from Mr R Lacey, 8 The Glebe, Culham, Abingdon, Oxford.

Dorchester Gravel Pit Complex (Dorchester, Oxfordshire) T 41

This is a fishery complex of three gravel-pits and a short stretch of the River Thames, all of which are covered by a single permit.

Dorchester Lagoon

This is a 40 acre (16 ha) gravel-pit, containing specimen carp, pike, tench and bream. The depth of the pit varies greatly, with plenty of shallows and sand-bars. The deepest area is about 8–10 ft (2.4–3.0 m). The fishing potential of this lake is tremendous, and some of the local specimen hunters are tipping this water to produce double figure bream in the future. At present, tench to 6 lb (2.7 kg), pike to 20 lb (9.1 kg) and carp to 30 lb (13.6 kg) have been recorded. The water fishes best in summer and autumn. Sailing also takes place on this lake.

River Thames

The permit covers a 300 ft (91 m) length of the River Thames on the opposite side of the A415 Dorchester to Abingdon road, as far as Dorchester Lagoon. The river, at this point, is noted for its chub and barbel.

Orchid Lake

Orchid Lake is an extremely interesting water with many features such as shallows, reed beds and sand-banks. The water covers 20 acres (8 ha), and the maximum depth is 10 ft (3 m). This is a good summer and autumn fishery. This water contains a good number of crucian carp and rudd.

The Creek

This is a small lake of 2 acres (0.8 ha), situated next to Orchid Lake. The water is very shallow with an average depth of only 3 ft (0.9 m).

SPECIES *Dorchester Lagoon*: carp, pike, tench, chub, perch and roach. *Orchid Lake*: mirror and common carp, tench, bream, roach, perch, crucian carp and rudd. *The Creek*: small roach and tench, and carp. *River Thames*: barbel, chub, bream, roach, perch and pike.

TECHNIQUES AND BAITS The larger fish in the Dorchester Lagoon and Orchid Lake need to be tackled using specimen methods: legering at long range with baits such as lobworm, corn and high-protein pastes. The ledges and sand-bars are obvious fish-holding areas. The small fish in Orchid Lake and The Creek can be tackled on simple float rigs using maggots or casters. In the Thames, legering is best for catching the bigger chub and barbel. Luncheon meat is a good bait here, too. Float fishing, with casters as bait, will take the roach and the shoal chub.

SEASON 16th June to 14th March.

ACCESS The lakes are sandwiched between the A415 Dorchester to Abingdon road and the A423(T) Dorchester to Oxford road. The River Thames is on the opposite side of the A415 to Dorchester Lagoon.

Information and permits from Mr R Lacey, 8 The Glebe, Culham, Abingdon, Oxford.

Theale Complex (near Reading, Berkshire) T 42

This is a large gravel-pit complex comprising three lakes. The largest is Theale Lagoon, and this water covers 100 acres (40 ha) and $1\frac{1}{2}$ miles (2.4 km) of bank. The lake is also used for sailing. Moatland Pond is connected to Theale Lagoon and is a small water of only 3 acres (1.2 ha). Nearby Wellmans Water cover 80 acres (32 ha). This is a relatively new water, and is also used for water-skiing which has priority over fishing.

SPECIES *Theale Lagoon and Moatland Pond*: roach, bream, tench, carp, pike and perch. *Wellmans Water*: roach, bream, tench and perch.

TECHNIQUES AND BAITS Float fishing close to the bank will catch the smaller species. The larger fish are taken by long-range legering tactics.

SEASON 16th June to 14th March.

SEASON Theale Complex is situated between Theale and Reading, close to Junction 12 of the M4 motorway. Four car parks are located near the lakes.

Permits are obtained from Tulls Tackle, Tilehurst, Reading, Berkshire; and the tackle shop called 'Two Guys', in Basingstoke, Hampshire. Details are available from the Head Bailiff, Mr P Howes.

River Kennet – Manton Fishery (near Marlborough, Wiltshire) T 43

The upper Kennet is a chalk stream with gin-clear water, vigorous weed growth and plenty of fly life. Fishing on the Manton Fishery is available for 1 mile (1.6 km), mostly on both banks. The riverside is variable with open banks, wooded copses and deep holes with overhanging vegetation. The river is regularly stocked with brown trout. On the side of the fishery there is a fishing shelter with cooking facilities. Fishing tuition is available if required from Malcolm Hassam (NAC Grade 1 instructor). The number of rods fishing on any one day is restricted to ensure good sport for all. The limit is four fish.

SPECIES Brown trout.

TECHNIQUES AND BAITS Fly fishing only: traditional dry fly and nymph.

SEASON 15th April to 30th September.

ACCESS Manton is just west of Marlborough on the A4 road.

Permits must be booked in advance from Mr M Hassam, 4 Kingsbury Street, Marlborough.

Trilakes (Sandhurst, Berkshire) T 44

This is a beautiful 18 acre (7 ha) landscaped lake stocked with a wide variety of coarse fish and a supplement of trout. The water ranges in depth from 5 to 9 ft (1.5 to 2.7 m). The main species are carp, tench and bream. The facilities at Trilakes are excellent, with good car parking, toilets, and a shop for snacks and confectionery.

SPECIES Carp, tench, roach, perch, bream, rudd, pike and trout.

TECHNIQUES AND BAITS Float fishing using a waggler float set to fish over depth is most effective. The best baits are maggots, sweetcorn, bread and casters. Bait is available at the site shop.

SEASON Mid April to the end of February.

ACCESS The fishery is reached by taking the Yateley road out of Sandhurst.

Permits are obtained from the fishery office on site. Information is available from Mr C Homewood, Trilakes Limited, Yateley Road, Sandhurst.

Holly Bush Lane Fishery (Farnborough, Hampshire) T 45

The fishery comprises three lakes totalling 20 acres (8 ha), only one of which (the car park lake) may be fished with a day ticket. All three lakes are well stocked with coarse fish, including carp and pike to specimen size. The middle lake is a carp fishery, and may only be fished with a special carp season ticket. An ordinary season ticket holder may fish both the remaining two lakes.

SPECIES Carp, bream, tench, roach, perch and pike.

TECHNIQUES AND BAITS All recognised coarse fish tactics for lake fishing will take fish.

SEASON 16th June to 14th March inclusive. No night fishing.

ACCESS Leave the M3 motorway at Junction 4 and travel south on the A325 Farnborough road, for 3 miles (4.8 km) and then turn left at the Queen's Hotel roundabout on to the A3011 Lynchford road. The entrance to the fishery is 1 mile (1.6 km) along this road opposite the Fir Tree public house.

The car park is 330 yards (300 m) down the lane on the left.

Permits are obtained from J & A Newsagents, 300 yards (300 m) before the fishery turn-off. Fishery Manager: Mr G Rowles, Lakeview Farm, Old Bury Hill, Westcott, near Dorking, Surrey.

Basingstoke Canal – Odiham to Byfleet (Hampshire – Surrey) T 46

This fishery covers 34 miles (54.7 km) of the Basingstoke Canal, but only 15 miles (24.1 km) are fishable, as several stretches are badly overgrown and weeded up. The best stretches to fish are around Odiham, and also between Fleet and Aldershot. In general, the Hampshire end of the canal is better fishing than the Surrey end.

SPECIES Tench, bream, roach, carp and pike.

TECHNIQUES AND BAITS The usual canal tactics of a very slim waggler float fished in conjunction with fine lines and small hooks are usually employed. If some good sizeable tench or carp are encountered in weedy sections of the canal, it would be wise to increase the breaking strain of the line.

SEASON 16th June to 14th March.

ACCESS Access is off the A287 road near Odiham and off the B3011 road between Fleet and Aldershot.

Permits are obtained from bailiffs who patrol the banks.

Old Bury Hill Lake (near Dorking, Surrey) T 47

This is a very attractive 12½ acre (5 ha) fishery with well-established bankside vegetation. The water is interesting to both the specimen hunter and the general angler. This is also one of the few stillwaters in the country to have an established stock of zander. This species, which is so feared by some authorities, has fitted into the ecosystem perfectly and offers good sport. Boats are available and they are especially useful for pike fishing in the winter. The carp and tench fishing at Old Bury Hill is excellent, with specimen fish caught every year.

SPECIES Carp, tench, roach, rudd, bream, perch, pike and zander.

TECHNIQUES AND BAITS All general coarse fishing methods and baits work at Old Bury Hill. The carp may become rather wary as the season progresses, so most serious carp anglers now use hair rigs and bolt rigs. The zander are usually taken on small fish bait especially at dawn and dusk.

SEASON 16th June to 14th March.

ACCESS The lake is situated just off the A25 Dorking to Guildford road, less than 1 mile (1.6 km) from Dorking. The entrance is signposted, and is almost opposite Sondes Place Research Institute, Milton Heath. Parking is close to the lake. Toilets and a small refreshment hut are provided.

Permits and enquiries from Mr G Rowles, Lakeview Farm, Old Bury Hill, Westcott, near Dorking, Surrey.

South West Water Authority

The South West Water Authority covers Devon and Cornwall. Although the area is not noted for its fishing, particularly its coarse fishing, there are a surprisingly large number of stillwater coarse fisheries in the region which offer some very good carp fishing. Some of these fisheries, such as College Reservoir near Penryn, are quite large. In addition there are hordes of small pond fisheries owned by farms which issue inexpensive day tickets to visitors.

There are also many reservoirs in the area available for trout fishing. Some of these are fished only for wild brown trout, whereas some are stocked with very big rainbow trout. Devon and Cornwall are very popular holiday areas during the summer, but most of the tourists head for the coast and anglers fishing the reservoirs on the fringe of, say, Dartmoor can find tranquility and very pleasant surroundings.

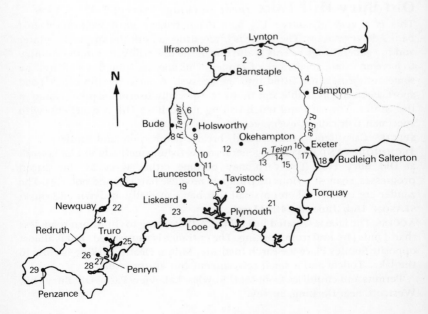

Key	Page
1 Lower Slade Reservoir	173
2 Wistlandpound	173
3 East Lyn River – Glenthorne and Watersmeet Fisheries	174
4 Wimbleball	174
5 Darracott Reservoir	175
6 Upper Tamar	175
7 Lower Tamar	176
8 Bude Canal	176
9 Tinney Waters	177
10 Dutson Water	177
11 River Tamar – Lifton	178
12 Stone Lake	178
13 Fernworthy Reservoir	179
14 River Teign – Drewsteignton	179
15 Kennick and Tottiford Reservoirs	180
16 River Exe – Exeter	180
17 Exeter Canal – Exeter	181
18 Squabmoor	181
19 Siblyback Reservoir	181
20 Burrator	182
21 Avon Dam	182
22 Porth Reservoir	183
23 Shillamill Lakes	183
24 Bolingey Lake	184
25 Trenestrall Lake	184
26 Stithians Reservoir	185
27 College Reservoir	185
28 Argal Reservoir	186
29 Drift Reservoir	186

The rivers in the area are also dominated by game fishing. There are salmon and sea trout, and plenty of brown trout fishing. The tiny rivers which flow off Dartmoor are enjoyable to fish but the available fishing is very fragmentary. Local tackle dealers will advise on the best trout fishing on the rivers. Very often the salmon fishing is controlled by hotels who issue permits only to paying guests.

Lower Slade Reservoir (near Ilfracombe, Devon) SW 1

This reservoir is managed as a coarse fishery, although the water authority do stock a few brown trout occasionally. The predominant species are roach and skimmer bream, but there are a few good carp in the lake. All coarse fish must be returned. The bag limit for trout is three fish.

SPECIES Roach, bream, tench, carp, perch and brown trout.

TECHNIQUES AND BAITS All methods are allowed on the reservoir but cereal-based groundbaits are banned. Loose feeding with samples of the hookbait is allowed. All carp must be returned immediately to the water and not retained in keepnets. Waggler float fishing with maggots, casters and sweetcorn will catch most species.

SEASON No close season for the coarse fish. 15th March to 12th October for the brown trout.

ACCESS The fishery is reached via the minor road (signposted Lee) just south of Ilfracombe off the A361 road.

Permits are restricted to 12 a day and can be obtained from Slade Post Office, Slade, near Ilfracombe.

Wistlandpound (Blackmoor Gate, near Ilfracombe, Devon) SW 2

This is a very productive trout fishery on the fringe of Exmoor Forest and has, in the past, yielded double figure rainbow trout. The fishing is from the bank only and the fishery extends to 41 acres (17 ha). The water produces nearly 4000 trout every season and the catch rate is around two fish per rod per day.

SPECIES Rainbow trout to 10 lb (4.5 kg) and brown trout to 2 lb (0.9 kg).

SEASON Fly fishing only. Lure fishing is best early and late in the season. During the late spring and early summer, dry fly fishing is worth trying.

SEASON 1st April to 31st October. Fishing from 1 hour before sunrise to 1 hour after sunset.

ACCESS The reservoir is reached by taking the minor road south at Blackmoor Gate off the main A39 Barnstaple to Lynton road.

Day permits are obtained from a self-service unit at the reservoir. The Warden is Mr G Rogers.

East Lyn River – Glenthorne and Watersmeet Fisheries (Lynmouth, Devon) SW 3

The East Lyn river rises in Exmoor Forest and flows west to enter the sea at Lynmouth. The river is a game fishery with the main species being brown trout. There is also a fair run of salmon and sea trout. The fishery is in two parts. The Watersmeet Fishery is leased from the National Trust and is downstream of Rockford. This part of the river is the better salmon fishery. Salmon and sea trout enter the river from March onwards. The Glenthorne fishery is upstream to Brendon Bridge and offers very good trout fishing. In total there are 6 miles (9.7 km) of fishing which includes 17 named salmon pools.

SPECIES Brown trout, salmon and sea trout.

TECHNIQUES AND BAITS The trout fishery is fly only and standard wet fly fishing tactics are best employed, although dry fly can be good at times during the summer. For the salmon no shrimp or prawn fishing is allowed and worm fishing is not allowed until 1st June.

SEASON 15th March to 30th September (brown and sea trout). 1st March to 31st October (salmon – Watersmeet) and 1st March to 30th September (salmon – Glenthorne).

ACCESS The fishery is reached via the A39 road outside Lynmouth.

The fishery is managed by the South West Water Authority and permits are obtained from The Warden, Combe Park Lodge, Hillsford Bridge, Lynton, Devon; The Ironmongers, High Street, Porlock, Somerset; Angler's Corner, Imperial Buildings, Castle Hill, Lynton; or by post from the Information Office, Fisheries and Recreation Dept, South West Water Authority, 3–5 Barnfield Road, Exeter.

Wimbleball (near Bampton, Devon) SW 4

Wimbleball covers 374 acres (151 ha) and is possibly the most productive trout fishery in the South West Water Authority region. The reservoir is a very irregular shape with several elongated arms of water reaching out from the main lake. The fishing is very good with big rainbow trout and, in the past, this has been one of the very few waters to stock with the hybrid tiger trout, though whether this stocking with tiger trout will continue is undecided. For the angler's family there is a picnic area and a children's adventure playground. A nature trail leads through the nearby Hurscombe nature reserve.

SPECIES Rainbow trout to 8 lb (3.6 kg) and brown trout to 3 lb (1.4 kg).

TECHNIQUES AND BAITS Fly fishing only. Lure fishing works well early in the season. Later in the year, nymph and buzzer fishing catches a lot of fish.

SEASON 1st May to 31st October. Fishing from 1 hour before sunrise to 1 hour after sunset.

ACCESS The reservoir is reached by taking the A396 road north from Bampton for 5 miles (8 km) and then turning off to the village of Brompton Regis. The reservoir is near the village.

Permits are obtained by self-service at the recreation area at the reservoir. The Warden is Mr B Poole.

Darracott Reservoir (Great Torrington, Devon) SW 5

This small reservoir on the outskirts of Great Torrington is run as a mixed coarse fishery. The water holds plenty of roach and small bream, with a few big carp.

SPECIES Roach, bream, tench, perch and carp.

TECHNIQUES AND BAITS Spinning is banned. The most successful method is float fishing with a waggler float and using maggots, casters or bread as bait. Sweetcorn is good for the tench and carp. No cereal-based groundbait should be used but loose feeding is allowed. Carp must not be kept in nets.

SEASON Open all year round. Fishing from 8 am to 6 pm.

ACCESS The water is to the north of Great Torrington and is reached by taking the minor road opposite Great Torrington church and then heading towards the village of Huntshaw.

Permits must be obtained in advance from Mr D Ives, Town Mills Hotel, Great Torrington.

Upper Tamar (Kilkhampton, near Bude, Cornwall) SW 6

Upper Tamar is a trout fishery covering 81 acres (33 ha). Some sizeable rainbow trout are stocked in the reservoir and there are also some big brown trout. Adjoining the car park there is a picnic and recreation area, which overlooks the reservoir. The land surrounding the reservoir is rich in wild flowers and, on the path to Lower Tamar Reservoir, there are extensive reed beds with some interesting bird life. For these reasons this is an excellent reservoir for a family outing. The catch rate is two fish per rod, per day and the bag limit is five fish.

SPECIES Brown trout to 4 lb (1.8 kg) and rainbow trout to 5 lb (2.3 kg).

TECHNIQUES AND BAITS Fly fishing only. Lures work best early in the season on slow sinking lines. During the summer, nymphs, buzzers and dry flies work well.

SEASON 1st April to 31st October. Fishing from 1 hour before sunrise to 1 hour after sunset.

ACCESS From Bude take the A39(T) road north for 5 miles (8 km) to the village of Kilkhampton and then turn right on to the minor road to the reservoir.

Permits are obtained from the upper car park at the reservoir. Tackle can also be hired for the day. The Warden is Mr K Spalding, Sparrapark, Upper Tamar Lake, Kilkhampton, Bude.

Lower Tamar (Kilkhampton, near Bude, Cornwall) SW 7

This 40 acre (16 ha) lake is managed as a coarse fishery and is also an interesting lake for bird life. There is an extensive reed bed in the top part of the lake. The predominant species is rudd, but there are some big carp.

SPECIES Rudd, carp, tench, bream and dace.

TECHNIQUES AND BAITS Legering, using a swing tip and a small feeder packed with maggots, is a good technique for the bream. Waggler fishing, using maggots, casters or bread is best for the rudd, tench and smaller bream. Carp must not be kept in keepnets and the use of cereal-based groundbait is banned, but loose feeding with samples of hookbait is permitted.

SEASON The fishery is open all year round. Fishing from 1 hour before sunrise to 1 hour after sunset.

ACCESS From Bude take the A39(T) road north for 5 miles (8 km) to the village of Kilkhampton and then turn right on to the minor road to the reservoir.

Permits are obtained on site. The Warden is Mr K Spalding, Sparrapark, Upper Tamar Lake, Kilkhampton, Bude.

Bude Canal (near Bude, Cornwall) SW 8

Bude Canal runs from the sea to Marhamchurch, a distance of 1¼ miles (2 km). The canal was never completed, and its depth at the inland end is only 2 ft (0.6 m). At the seaward end, towards the lock gates, the depth averages 10 ft (3 m). The bed of the canal is stony and the weed growth is quite prolific in summer, although the controlling Bude Canal Angling Association do undertake a lot of weed clearance at this time of year. The canal is exceptionally well stocked with sizeable coarse fish. The tench average 3 lb (1.4 kg), and carp to 22 lb 6 oz (10.1 kg) have been recorded.

SPECIES Carp, tench, roach, perch, dace and eels to 6½ lb (2.9 kg).

Fly fishing at Bayham Abbey, a medium-sized 'put and take' trout fishery.

The author with a big haul of early season tench from a shallow lake.

TECHNIQUES AND BAITS In the clear waters of a canal, fine tackle and small hooks are the order of the day. In this case, it would be wise to step up the line strength if seriously seeking carp or tench. A compromise must be achieved between getting bites and avoiding a broken line. Corn, maggots, casters and bread are all good baits.

SEASON The water is open all year except from 1st April to 31st May inclusive. This short close season is imposed by the controlling club.

ACCESS Permits can be obtained from the bailiff on the canal bank; the information bureau, near the castle (on the canal side); and also from tackle shops in the town of Bude.

Tinney Waters (near Holsworthy, Devon) SW 9

These are three small lakes covering a total of 2 acres (0.8 ha). The depths vary between 4 and 12 ft (1.2 and 3.7 m). The lakes are in a secluded location, surrounded by woodland in the upper Tamar Valley. The lakes are very well stocked, especially with carp. Tench are also present but these have proved difficult to catch. Carp must not be kept in a net and barbless hooks must be used for carp fishing. There are wildfowl on the lakes and the owners have ruled that non-toxic weights must be used. Accommodation and a licensed restaurant are available.

SPECIES Carp to 18 lb (8.2 kg), rudd – average $\frac{1}{2}$ lb (0.2 kg), tench and eels.

TECHNIQUES AND BAITS Specimen tactics are recommended for the carp. Free-lined bread crust is effective here and is an exciting way of fishing. The rudd and tench are taken on float-fished bread, redworm or maggots. Groundbaiting is not allowed but loose feeding is permitted.

SEASON There is no close season in this region for coarse fish.

ACCESS Tinney Waters are located on a minor road 3 miles (4.8 km) south-west of Holsworthy at the village of Pyworthy.

Advance booking is essential. Contact Mr J E Greenaway, Tinney Waters, Pyworthy, near Holsworthy.

Dutson Water (near Launceston, Cornwall) SW 10

This is a $\frac{3}{4}$ acre (0.3 ha) disused clay-pit. The lake is very picturesque, with lush surroundings set in farmland. The deepest area of the lake is around 12 ft (3.7 m). The banks on one side of the lake are too far from the water, so fishing spots have been cut out. On the other side of the lake, the banking is lower and fishing is comfortable. There are a few weed beds but not enough to cause problems when fishing. The fishing is good, with several species of coarse fish, notably carp to 17 lb (7.7 kg). A self-catering cottage is also available. Advance booking is not necessary for the fishing.

SPECIES Carp, tench, rudd, perch and crucian carp.

TECHNIQUES AND BAITS Float fishing with a waggler float using maggots or casters as hookbait is best. Bread and corn will also catch the carp and tench. There is no need to fish very heavy, and a 3 lb (1.4 kg) breaking strain line should land most fish. Groundbaiting is not allowed.

SEASON There is no close season for coarse fish in the region.

ACCESS Dutson Water is at Lower Dutson Farm on the A388 road, 1½ miles (2.4 km) north of Launceston. Parking and toilet facilities are adjacent to the lake.

Permits are obtained from Mr and Mrs E J Broad, Lower Dutson Farm, Launceston.

River Tamar – Lifton (near Launceston, Cornwall) SW 11

The Tamar is a major game river and has some good runs of salmon and sea trout. The river rises above the Tamar Reservoirs north of Bude and then flows south-east to enter the sea through a large estuary at Plymouth. Centred on Lifton, there are 20 miles (32.2 km) of fishing available on the Tamar and its tributaries. The fishing is controlled by the Arundell Arms Hotel. Hotel residents have priority for the fishing but some day tickets are usually available for visitors. The hotel also offers fishing tuition and there is also a 3 acre (1.2 ha) lake, stocked with rainbow trout.

SPECIES Brown trout, salmon and sea trout. (Rainbow Trout in the lake.)

TECHNIQUES AND BAITS Fly fishing for the brown trout and standard wet fly tactics are best used.

SEASON 1st March to 14th October (salmon), 3rd March to 30th September (sea trout) and 15th March to 30th September (brown trout).

ACCESS Lifton is on the A30(T) road east of Launceston.

Permits are obtained from the Arundell Arms Hotel, Lifton. Information regarding the fishing and details of the courses is available from Mrs A Voss-Bark at the Arundell Arms Hotel.

Stone Lake (near Okehampton, Devon) SW 12

Stone Lake covers 4½ acres (1.8 ha) and is an old lime quarry. The water is very deep in places – as much as 60 ft (18.3 m). Only about half of the bank around the lake is accessible for fishing as there is a steep drop to very deep water. The vegetation is sparse, with a few iris growing in the margins. Being such a deep lake, most of the food supply is in the margins so fish can be caught fishing under the rod tip. The lake holds some good coarse fish, notably carp. Farmhouse accommodation is available and a brochure can be obtained on request.

SPECIES Carp to 16 lb (7.3 kg), roach, rudd, perch, tench and bream.

TECHNIQUES AND BAITS Leger for the larger specimens on the edge of the 'drop offs'. Margin fishing is worthwhile with a waggler float set so that the bait just trips bottom. Bulk the shot under the float so that the bait fishes on the 'drop' to search the water for rudd.

SEASON There is no close season for coarse fish. Night fishing is not allowed at Stone Lake.

ACCESS Stone Lake is at Bridestowe, 11 miles (17.7 km) east of Launceston on the A30 road to Okehampton.

Permits are obtained from Mr W P Ponsford, Stone Farm, Bridestowe, Okehampton, Devon.

Fernworthy Reservoir (Chagford, Devon) SW 13

This 76 acre (31 ha) reservoir is a good venue for a family outing. As well as excellent fishing for rainbow trout, the lake offers picnic areas on the banks, forest walks and nature trails. The water is well stocked throughout the season with some big rainbow trout.

SPECIES Rainbow trout to 6 lb (2.7 kg) and brown trout to 3 lb (1.4 kg).

TECHNIQUES AND BAITS Standard reservoir fly fishing tactics are best. Nymphs and buzzers should be used during the summer.

SEASON 1st May to 31st October. Fishing from 1 hour before sunrise to 1 hour after sunset.

ACCESS The reservoir lies on the north of Dartmoor and is approached by a minor road south-west of Chagford.

Permits are obtained from the self-service unit at the reservoir. The Warden is Mr P Hatton.

River Teign– Drewsteignton (Devon) SW 14

The River Teign rises on Whitehorse Hill on Dartmoor and flows east then south to enter the sea at Teignmouth. The river is a game fishery and, while trout are the predominant species, there is a fair run of salmon and sea trout. The fishery, around Drewsteignton, covers 12 miles (19.3 km) of the upper Teign. The fishing on the left bank is from Chagford Bridge to Upperton Weir. On the right bank, fishing is allowed from the three fields above Rushford Bridge and then from one field below Rushford Bridge to the fence above Doggemarsh Weir. Also on the right bank is a stretch from the east end of Whiddon Wood to the noticeboard $\frac{3}{4}$ mile (1.2 km) above Steps Bridge.

SPECIES Brown trout, salmon and sea trout.

TECHNIQUES AND BAITS Fly fishing only is allowed for the trout. Standard wet fly tactics work well, especially early in the season in fast broken water. On the Teign, no worm fishing is allowed for salmon before 1st June.

SEASON 15th March to 30th September (brown trout), 1st February to 30th September (salmon) and 15th March to 12th October (sea trout).

ACCESS The number of permits issued to visitors fishing for salmon and sea trout is limited to three rods per day and are obtained from The Anglers Rest, Fingle Bridge, Drewsteignton. Permits for brown trout fishing are not restricted and can be obtained from the same address and also from the following: Bowdens, The Square, Chagford; Drum Sports, Courtenay Street,

Newton Abbot; Mill End Hotel, Sandypark; Clifford Bridge Caravan Park; or The Exeter Angling Centre, Smythen Street, off City Arcade, Fore Street, Exeter. Information can be obtained from the Upper Teign Fishing Association whose Secretary is Mr A J Price, The Anglers Rest, Fingle Bridge, Drewsteignton.

Kennick and Tottiford Reservoirs (near Moretonhampstead, Devon) SW 15

These two reservoirs lie in a scenic setting on the very north-eastern edge of Dartmoor, and are separated by a causeway. Kennick covers 45 acres (18 ha) and Tottiford covers 35 acres (14 ha). (There is a third reservoir – Trenchford – in the group that cannot be fished.) Both the reservoirs are well stocked with sizeable trout throughout the season.

SPECIES Rainbow trout to 6 lb (2.7 kg) and brown trout to 3 lb (1.4 kg).

TECHNIQUES AND BAITS Fly fishing only on both reservoirs. Standard reservoir fly fishing tactics work with nymph and buzzer fishing in the summer.

SEASON 1st April to 31st October. Fishing from 1 hour before sunrise to 1 hour after sunset.

ACCESS From Moretonhampstead, take the B3212 road east for 2 miles (3.2 km); at Five Crossways turn right towards the reservoirs.

Permits are obtained from the self-service machine at Kennick. The Warden is Mr R Davison.

River Exe – Exeter (Devon) SW 16

The River Exe is Devon's longest river, rising on Exmoor and then flowing south to enter the sea at Exmouth south of Exeter. The middle and upper reaches of the river offer some good game fishing. In the lower reaches, around Exeter, there are some good coarse fishing stretches on the river. Exeter and District Angling Association control a lot of fishing near the town and visitors may purchase tickets to fish these waters. The stretches are too fragmented to list individually but a permit gives the exact details and covers much of the river around Exeter. In this area bream are the predominant species and some good catches can be taken. Upstream of the town, roach are more numerous and run to a good size. Along the entire stretch there are a lot of dace and perch. The depth of the river varies between 3 and 12 ft (0.9 and 3.7 m).

SPECIES Roach, perch, dace, bream, carp and eels.

TECHNIQUES AND BAITS Float fishing using a waggler float is the most successful method, although trotting through with a stick float is a better method in the faster swims. The best baits are maggots, casters and bread.

SEASON 16th June to February (the exact closing date can vary).

ACCESS The fishing is centred around Exeter.

Permits are obtained from The Exeter Angling Centre, City Arcade, Fore Street, Exeter.

Exeter Canal – Exeter (Devon) SW 17

The Exeter Canal is 6 miles (9.7 km) long and runs south-east from Exeter to the River Exe estuary. The fishing is for coarse fish, with bream being the predominant species. The canal also holds some fair sized tench and carp.

SPECIES Bream, roach, rudd, perch, tench, carp, pike, dace and eels.

TECHNIQUES AND BAITS Standard canal tactics work best with a light waggler float and fine tackle. Hooks need to be small, and the best baits are maggots and casters. Bread flake will attract the larger roach and bream.

SEASON 16th June to 14th March.

ACCESS South of Exeter there are several access points off the B3182 road and the A377 road.

Permits are obtained from The Exeter Angling Centre, City Arcade, Fore Street, Exeter.

Squabmoor (Budleigh Salterton, near Exmouth, Devon) SW18

This is a 4 acre (1.6 ha) coarse fishery reservoir near to the south coast of Devon. The fishery is attractive and easily accessible all round, as it is located on a common. Roach and rudd are the predominant species but some double figure carp are present. Night fishing is allowed on this reservoir but, as a permit is only valid for one calendar day, a second permit is required for a night fishing session.

SPECIES Roach, rudd, carp, tench and bream.

TECHNIQUES AND BAITS For the smaller species, try float fishing with a waggler float using maggots, casters or bread as hookbait. Light leger for the bream in the deeper areas. Freelined protein baits are best for the carp.

SEASON All the year round.

ACCESS From Budleigh Salterton, take the A376 road towards Exmouth and, at the village of Knowle, turn right on to the B3179. At the first major crossroads, turn right again and the reservoir is on your right.

Permits are obtained from Knowle Post Office; The Tackle Shop, 20 The Strand Exmouth (open Sunday mornings); or The Exeter Angling Centre, City Arcade, Fore Street, Exeter (all in Devon). The Warden is Mr A Davies.

Siblyback Reservoir (near Liskeard, Cornwall) SW 19

Siblyback Reservoir covers 140 acres (57 ha) and is an excellent fishery for rainbow trout, with a rod average of over two fish per visit. For the angler's family there is a play and picnic area with excellent views across the reservoir. The water is well stocked throughout the season.

SPECIES Brown trout to 4 lb (1.8 kg) and rainbow trout to 5 lb (2.3 kg).

TECHNIQUES AND BAITS Fly fishing only. Standard reservoir tactics are effective.

SEASON 1st April to 31st October. Fishing from 1 hour before sunrise to 1 hour after sunset.

ACCESS Take the B3254 road north from Liskeard and turn left at the village of Upton Cross. Take this minor road through Minions and then turn right to the reservoir.

Permits are obtained from a self-service unit at the reservoir. The Warden is Mr R England.

Burrator (Yelverton, near Tavistock, Devon) SW 20

This moorland reservoir covers 150 acres (60 ha). Part of the reservoir is surrounded by forest and the fishery lies on the very western edge of Dartmoor. The fishing is for both brown and rainbow trout, stocked as fingerlings. Access to the reservoir banks is restricted to permit holders for fishing and birdwatching only, so this is not a family water.

SPECIES Brown trout and rainbow trout.

TECHNIQUES AND BAITS Fly fishing and spinning for the trout is allowed in zoned areas.

SEASON 15th March to 30th September. Fishing from sunrise to midnight.

ACCESS The reservoir is reached via the B3212 road from Yelverton. Turn off at the Burrator Inn.

Permits are obtained from the self-service unit on site. The resident warden is Mr R Armstrong.

Avon Dam (South Brent, Devon) SW 21

Avon Dam covers 50 acres (20 ha) and is set in open moorland on the southern edge of Dartmoor. The fishing is for trout, which are released into the reservoir as fingerlings. The scenery is superb but a walk is needed to reach the fishery.

SPECIES Brown trout and brook trout.

TECHNIQUES AND BAITS Fly fishing, spinning and worm fishing are all allowed on the reservoir in zoned areas. No floats are allowed for the worm fishing.

SEASON 15th March to 12th October. Fishing from 1 hour before sunrise to 1 hour after sunset.

ACCESS The reservoir is reached by travelling through South Brent, past Didworthy Hospital to Shipley Bridge car park. Access is then on foot along a hard track for $1\frac{1}{2}$ miles (2.4 km). The walk is not difficult and is through pleasant scenery alongside the tiny River Avon.

The fishing is free to holders of a South West Water Authority trout rod licence. The Warden is Mr G Strickland.

Porth Reservoir (near Newquay, Cornwall) SW 22

Porth is a beautiful 40 acre (16 ha) reservoir only a short distance away from the bustling seaside resort of Newquay. The crystal-clear water is unusual in that it is slightly alkaline, whereas most of the reservoirs in the south-west are slightly acid. There are coarse fish in Porth but the fishing is mostly for the rainbow trout. The reservoir has some attractive wooded areas coming right down to the water's edge. Boats are available at the reservoir but not on Tuesdays or Wednesdays. The average catch at Porth is two fish per rod per day.

SPECIES Rainbow trout.

TECHNIQUES AND BAITS Fly fishing only. The fish respond well to nymph fishing. Teams of traditional wet flies on floating or slow sinking lines work best. Mallard and Claret, Invicta and Damsel Nymph are all recommended flies.

SEASON 1st April to 31st October. Fishing from 1 hour before sunrise to 1 hour after sunset.

ACCESS Turn off the A3059 road between Newquay and St Columb Major at the water tower, and take the minor road to the reservoir.

Permits are obtained from a self-service unit. The Warden at Porth is Mr D Parkyn, Porth Reservoir, Newquay.

Shillamill Lakes (near Looe, Cornwall) SW 23

Shillamill comprises four lakes, three of which contain coarse fish to specimen size. The fourth lake is used for fly fishing for trout in the evening only. The largest lake is 2 acres (0.8 ha), and is stocked with specimen carp to 33 lb 2 oz (15 kg). This lake has depths up to 12 ft (3.7 m). The other two coarse fishing lakes are each of 1½ acre (0.6 ha) area. One contains carp and tench; the other holds some carp and tench, but also some massive roach and perch. Crucian carp are present to specimen size in all three lakes. The fourth lake is the Old Mill Pool and is stocked with rainbow trout. The banks are firm and easily accessible on all the lakes, and some fishing spots have been created where banks are steep. Carp must not be retained in keepnets.

SPECIES *Lake 1*: carp to 33 lb 2 oz (15 kg) and crucian carp. *Lake 2*: tench to 6 lb 1 oz (2.7 kg), carp and crucian carp. *Lake 3*: tench, carp, roach to 2 lb 6 oz (1 kg), perch to 4 lb 6 oz (1.9 kg) and crucian carp to 2 lb 8 oz (1.1 kg). *Old Mill Pool*: rainbow trout to 2 lb 8 oz (1.1 kg).

TECHNIQUES AND BAITS Specimen carp tactics are required on the carp lake. On the other lakes, waggler fishing is best but, because of the size of the fish, do not fish too fine. Worms, maggots, bread and corn are all good baits here.

SEASON There is no close season for the coarse fish. Night fishing is allowed by arrangement with the owner.

ACCESS Shillamill Lakes are at Lanreath, 6 miles (9.7 km) north-west of Looe on the B3359 road.

Permits are obtained from the owner, Mr John Facey, on site.

Bolingey Lake (near Perranporth, Cornwall) SW 24

Bolingey Lake is a spring-fed coarse fishery in the middle of the village of Bolingey. The area of the lake is $4\frac{1}{2}$ acres (1.8 ha) and the depth drops away to 10 ft (3 m). The owner has planted extensive vegetation around the lake, including bog iris, wild mint and rushes, to create a very pleasant environment. There is an island in the lake and one bank juts out to form a peninsula. Carp are the predominant fish but smaller species, such as roach and perch, are also present.

SPECIES Common, leather and mirror carp to 20 lb (9.1 kg), crucian carp, tench to 5 lb (2.3 kg), roach to $1\frac{1}{2}$ lb (0.7 kg), and perch.

TECHNIQUES AND BAITS For general fishing, a waggler float set so the hook is just tripping the lake bed is best. Maggots, casters, corn and bread are all good baits. For larger carp, float tackle can still be used but step up the strength of the tackle. There is a ban on the use of groundbait but loose feeding is allowed.

SEASON There is no close season in Cornwall for coarse fish. Fishing is from dawn to 1 hour after sunset. Night fishing is not allowed.

ACCESS Bolingey Lake is at the village of Bolingey, 1 mile (1.6 km) from Perranporth and 7 miles (11.3 km) from Newquay.

Permits are available on the banks of the lake. For further details contact Mr W Phillips.

Trenestrall Lake (near St Mawes, Cornwall) SW 25

Trenestrall Lake is a man-made lake of 2 acres (0.8 ha). The lake was formed 16 years ago and has now matured so that it looks completely natural. The average depth is 3 ft (0.9 m), with deeper holes down to 6 ft (1.8 m). The bottom of the lake is hard mud, and there is an abundance of weed. The banks are lined with reedmace and rushes, affording plenty of cover. The lake lies in the bottom of a secluded valley but anglers may take their cars down to the water's edge. The fishing is for mixed coarse fish and, although specimens are unlikely, the water is very well stocked. Night fishing for the carp is allowed.

SPECIES Carp, tench and small roach.

TECHNIQUES AND BAITS Waggler fishing with maggots is best for the small roach. The same tackle with a slightly heavier line will also catch the tench and carp, using corn as bait. Floating bread crust is well worth trying in the gaps between weed beds for the carp.

SEASON There is no close season for coarse fish in the region, but please check with the owner to ascertain that the fishery is open.

ACCESS Trenestrall Lake is at Trenestrall Farm, Philleigh, Ruan High Lanes. The farm is reached by taking the B3289 road from St Mawes to King Harry Ferry, and then the minor road to Philleigh.

For further details or bookings contact the owner Mr W Palmer.

Stithians Reservoir (near Redruth, Cornwall) SW 26

This is a long, narrow and irregularly shaped trout fishery, covering 274 acres (111 ha). Fishing is from the banks only for trout, which are stocked as fingerlings. The size limit for the trout is 7 in (18 cm) and the bag limit is four fish. Big trout are unlikely on this reservoir.

SPECIES Brown trout, rainbow trout and brook trout.

TECHNIQUES AND BAITS Fly fishing only. Because big fish are unlikely to be caught, it is pointless using heavy reservoir tackle. Light wet fly tactics in the many bays and from the peninsulas will give more pleasure.

SEASON 15th March to 12th October. Fishing from 1 hour before sunrise to 1 hour after sunset.

ACCESS Stithians is reached by taking the B3297 road south from Redruth and then turning left along the minor road at Four Lanes.

Day permits are obtained from the self-service unit by the reservoir dam. The Warden is Mr N Vogwill.

College Reservoir (Penryn, Cornwall) SW 27

This is a 38 acre (15 ha) reservoir managed as a coarse fishery. The fishing is mainly for roach, but the water also holds some sizeable carp and tench. College Reservoir is surrounded by attractive woodland and is well sheltered.

SPECIES Roach, perch, bream, carp and tench.

TECHNIQUES AND BAITS Float fishing close in, using a waggler float and maggot, caster or sweetcorn bait, is best for the smaller fish. Legering with a swing tip or quiver tip will lure the better bream. No cereal-based groundbait may be used, and carp must not be retained in keepnets.

SEASON Open all year round.

ACCESS College Reservoir is located across the road from Argal Reservoir near Penryn, Cornwall. Cars should be parked in Argal car park and the reservoir approached by a footpath.

Permits are available on site. The resident warden is Mr R Evans, Little Argal Farm, Budock, Penryn.

Argal Reservoir (Penryn, Cornwall) SW 28

This is a very pleasant 65 acre (26 ha) trout fishery with attractive woodlands nearby. For anglers' families a picnic area with tables adjoins the car park, giving panoramic views over the reservoir. Toilets and facilities for disabled persons are provided next to the car park. The reservoir is regularly stocked with rainbow trout and the average catch is 1.7 fish per rod per day.

SPECIES Rainbow trout to 5 lb 2 oz (2.3 kg), brown trout to 2 lb 12 oz (1.2 kg) and brook trout.

TECHNIQUES AND BAITS Fly fishing only. All the usual reservoir methods are effective.

SEASON 1st April to 31st October. Fishing from 1 hour before sunrise to 1 hour after sunset.

ACCESS The reservoir is located 3 miles (4.8 km) south of Penryn and is approached via the B3291 road.

Permits are obtained on site. The resident warden is Mr R Evans, Little Argal Farm, Budock, Penryn.

Drift Reservoir (near Penzance, Cornwall) SW 29

This is a lovely 65 acre (26 ha) trout fishery on the tip of Cornwall. The water has extensive shallow areas with weed beds, old tree trunks and clumps of rushes, so waders really are a necessity to fish at Drift. The shallow areas are rich in feed and the trout at Drift are very free rising. The water has a natural head of brown trout, and a lot of good rainbow trout are stocked.

SPECIES Brown trout to 6 lb (2.7 kg) and rainbow trout to 5 lb (2.3 kg).

TECHNIQUES AND BAITS Fly fishing only. The dry fly fishing can be excellent. In the deeper areas small black lures fished on slow sinking lines work well.

SEASON 1st April to 12th October.

ACCESS Drift Reservoir is close to the A30 Penzance to Land's End road, 3 miles (4.8 km) west of Penzance.

Permits to fish and information are obtained from Mr T B Shorland, Driftways, Drift, Penzance.

Wessex Water Authority

Wessex is one of the smallest water authority regions in the country. It covers an area from the Somerset coast, near Minehead and Weston-super-Mare, across country to the Dorset coast from Weymouth to Bournemouth. Although small, the Wessex area takes in such famous rivers as the Hampshire Avon and the Dorset Stour.

Key	Page
1 Chew Valley Lake	188
2 Blagdon Reservoir	188
3 Clatworthy Reservoir	189
4 Sutton Bingham	189
5 River Stour – White Hartwater	190
6 River Avon – Downton	190
7 River Avon – Breamore	191
8 River Avon – Severals Fishery	191
9 River Avon – Royalty Fishery	192
10 Lapsley's Trout Fishery	192
11 Hucklesbrook Trout Lake	193
12 White Sheet Farm Trout Fishery	194
13 River Stour – Throop Fishery	194

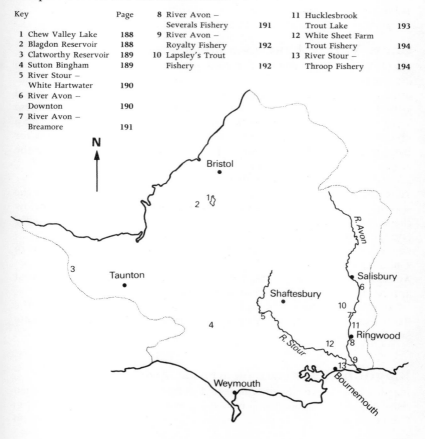

The Bristol Avon is another major river in the area but, for the visiting angler, there is very little day ticket fishing available on this river. Bournemouth and Christchurch are popular centres for visiting anglers, with the Royalty Fishery on the Hampshire Avon and the magnificent Throop Fishery on the Dorset Stour nearby. Double figure barbel can be caught on both these stretches of river. Of the two, the Royalty receives more fishing pressure than the nearby Throop water, but Throop is arguably a slightly better fishery.

Reservoir trout fishing is not over-abundant in the region, with the exception of the reservoirs of Chew Valley and Blagdon which are managed by the Bristol Waterworks Company. The Kings Sedgemoor Drain and the Huntspill were once famous for the big bream and roach catches but, at the moment, they are not fishing particularly well. Not many of the gravel-pits in the area are available on day tickets.

For visitors to the region, day ticket waters are not very numerous, although some clubs do issue weekly permits.

Chew Valley Lake (near Bristol, Avon) W 1

Chew Valley Lake covers a massive 1200 acres (480 ha) and is an outstanding trout fishery. The reservoir has extensive shallow areas and, during the late spring when the water warms up, there is a prolific weed growth. The weed supports a lot of natural life and consequently these areas are very productive for the trout. The bank fishing is good and a favourite spot for brown trout is Moreton Bank. Another good area for bank fishing is at Nunnery Point. Boats are available and these give the angler the chance to cover more water.

SPECIES Brown trout and rainbow trout.

TECHNIQUES AND BAITS Fly fishing only. Lures will catch fish early in the season at Chew. As the water warms up the fish feed avidly at or just below the surface, and nymph fishing brings better results. Buzzers, Damselfly Nymphs and Corixa are good patterns.

SEASON 5th April to 15th October. Fishing is from 1 hour before sunrise to 1 hour after sunset.

ACCESS The reservoir is located at Chew Stoke, south of Bristol, and is best approached on the A37 road and then the A368 road.

Permits are obtained on site. Information can be obtained from the Recreations Officer, Bristol Waterworks Company, Woodford Lodge, Chew Stoke, Bristol.

Blagdon Reservoir (near Bristol, Avon) W 2

Blagdon is really where reservoir trout fishing began. This long-established fishery held the rainbow trout record for many years with an $8\frac{1}{2}$ lb (3.9 kg) fish taken in 1924 by Lt Col Creagh Scott. This was a wild fish grown on from a fingerling. Today the water is still excellent and capable of producing large fish. Blagdon is an extremely attractive reservoir and can be fished from either a boat or the bank. The trout are handsomely marked and grow fat on the rich feed.

SPECIES Brown trout and rainbow trout.

TECHNIQUES AND BAITS Fly fishing only. Lures will catch fish at Blagdon and early in the season they produce the best results. During the summer, the best sport is enjoyed using small nymphs and buzzers, especially during the evening.

SEASON 5th April to 15th October. Fishing from 1 hour before sunrise to 1 hour after sunset.

ACCESS From Bristol take the A38 road to Churchill and then the A368 road east to Blagdon village.

Permits are obtained on site. Information can be obtained from the Recreations Officer, Bristol Waterworks Company, Woodford Lodge, Chew Stoke, Bristol.

Clatworthy Reservoir (Wiveliscombe, Somerset) W 3

Clatworthy is a 130 acre (53 ha) trout fishery on the edge of Exmoor. The reservoir is long and narrow with bays and long inlets, and is surrounded by trees and gently rolling hills. The water is deep, even close to the shore in many places, and both boat and bank fishing are available. The reservoir is regularly stocked with both brown and rainbow trout and there is also a natural head of brown trout. The River Tone inlet and the Thripp end are 'hot spots'.

SPECIES Brown trout and rainbow trout.

TECHNIQUES AND BAITS Fly fishing only. Black lures, such as Sweeny Todd, Undertaker and Black Muddler, are popular flies at Clatworthy. During the summer, dry fly fishing for the brown trout can be very rewarding.

SEASON 31st March to 15th October.

ACCESS The water is reached via the town of Wiveliscombe, which lies on the A361(T) Taunton to Bampton road.

Permits are obtained at the reservoir. Information can be obtained from Mr R Deer.

Sutton Bingham (near Yeovil, Somerset) W 4

Sutton Bingham trout fishery is a hammer-shaped reservoir, covering 145 acres (59 ha). The lake is a lowland water set in gently rolling hills on the Somerset/Devon border. The fishing lodge and car park are located at the head of the reservoir near the dam. Special facilities are available at Sutton Bingham for disabled anglers. Both bank and boat fishing are available. The catch limit is six fish.

SPECIES Brown trout and rainbow trout.

TECHNIQUES AND BAITS Fly fishing only. All reservoir methods will prove effective at Sutton Bingham.

SEASON 24th March to 15th October.

ACCESS The reservoir is best approached by taking the A37 road for about 4 miles (6.4 km) south of Yeovil and then the minor road on the right to the reservoir.

Permits are available at the reservoir. For information contact Mr P Hill.

River Stour – White Hartwater (Sturminster Newton, Dorset) W 5

This is an attractive stretch of river from 2 miles (3.2 km) north of the village of Hinton St Mary running downstream for 7 miles (11.2 km) on both banks to Fiddleford Mill. This takes in three good mill pools on the river. The water is clear but weedy, and the river banks are lush and natural. The fishing is mainly for chub and roach. The controlling club is Sturminster and Hinton Angling Association.

SPECIES Chub, roach, bream, pike and eels.

TECHNIQUES AND BAITS Small river tactics are required. Keep well hidden and trot down with float tackle using bread, maggots or casters as bait. Legering in the mill pools, using bread and cheese as bait, will lure the bigger chub.

SEASON 16th June to 14th March.

ACCESS Hinton St Mary is just north of Sturminster Newton on the B3092 road. The lower reaches of the fishery can be reached off the A357 road.

Permits should be obtained before fishing from the White Hart Hotel, Sturminster Newton.

Introduction to the River Avon

The Hampshire Avon has produced more specimen fish than any other English river. In the 1950s and 1960s the Avon produced hundreds of specimen chub, barbel, roach and dace. The upper river above Salisbury is a trout river running fast and clear over a gravel bed with masses of streamer weed. From Downton downstream to Christchurch the river's coarse fish begin to predominate. The best area for coarse fish is between Ringwood and Christchurch, where every year many big barbel are caught.

River Avon – Downton (near Salisbury, Wiltshire) W 6

The fishing on the left bank of the river is controlled by the Black Bull Hotel. The river is swift flowing with deeper pools. The fishing for roach and chub can be excellent during the winter. In the summer, the main species are chub and barbel. This stretch of river also holds some very big dace. The river near the island is a productive area.

SPECIES Chub, barbel, dace, roach and pike.

TECHNIQUES AND BAITS Leger with an open-ended feeder for the chub and barbel. During the winter float fishing with a heavy Avon-type float in the deeper glides is best for roach, chub and dace. The best baits are bread flake, bread crust, cheese, luncheon meat and maggots.

SEASON 16th June to 14th March.

ACCESS Downton is 6 miles (9.7 km) south of Salisbury and is reached by taking the A338(T) road to Long Close and then turning left on to the B3080 road.

Permits are obtained from the Black Bull Hotel, Downton.

River Avon – Breamore (near Fordingbridge, Hampshire) W 7

This stretch is known as the Bat and Ball Water and covers both banks of the river for 1 mile (1.6 km) downstream from the mill at Breamore. The river is fairly wide and streamy with a few deeper holes. Chub are the predominant species with some large dace and roach, especially during the winter.

SPECIES Chub, roach, dace, barbel and pike.

TECHNIQUES AND BAITS Float fish with a big Avon-type float. Bulk the shot towards the hook to keep the bait down near the river bed. The best baits are bread, maggots and casters. Leger for the larger species, using big baits, such as cheese, bread crust and luncheon meat.

SEASON 16th June to 14th March.

ACCESS Breamore is on the A338(T) road just north of Fordingbridge.

Permits are obtained from the Bat and Ball Hotel, Breamore.

River Avon – Severals Fishery (Ringwood, Hampshire) W 8

This fishery covers $1\frac{1}{2}$ miles (2.4 km) of the east bank of the Avon between Ringwood and Moortown. The Avon at this point is deep, wide and fast flowing. At the start of the season it can be very weedy but the weed is mostly cut back by the water authority. The main species are chub and barbel. During the summer most anglers concentrate on the barbel and it is a good water to try for a double figure fish. The chub are the predominant species in the winter.

SPECIES Chub, barbel, roach, dace and pike.

TECHNIQUES AND BAITS Legering is best for the barbel and chub. During the summer the bait must be placed in the clear areas between the weed beds. A swimfeeder full of maggots is best to draw the barbel out from under the weed. Strong tackle is needed to keep a hooked fish out of the weed. During the winter, trotting using a big Avon-type float with bread, maggots or casters is effective for the dace, chub and roach.

SEASON 16th June to 14th March.

ACCESS Access is via Hampshire Hatches lane, Moortown, Ringwood.

Permits are obtained from the Corner House Store, Moortown; or the Tackle Shop, West Street, Ringwood.

River Avon – Royalty Fishery (Christchurch, Dorset) W 9

This is probably the most famous stretch of coarse fishing in the country. The fast-flowing water of the Avon has produced huge barbel, chub, roach and pike. In recent years, the Avon at Christchurch has also produced many bream, even in the faster stretches. The Royalty Fishery stretches from near the confluence with the Stour, upstream for 4 miles (6.4 km), mostly on both banks. It is really the barbel fishing that attracts anglers to the Royalty, and no other stretch of river has produced as many double figure specimens. The present record barbel of 13 lb 12 oz (6.2 kg) was taken from the Royalty Fishery in 1961 by Joe Day. The stretch is also good for game fish, with both salmon and sea trout being caught.

SPECIES Barbel, chub, roach, bream, pike, dace, salmon and sea trout.

TECHNIQUES AND BAITS Legering in between the weed beds is the best way of catching the barbel and chub on the Avon. Bread, cheese, luncheon meat and maggots are the best baits. Long trotting will take the dace, chub, roach and barbel.

SEASON 1st February to 30th September (salmon) and 16th June to 14th March (coarse fish).

ACCESS The fishery is at Christchurch near Bournemouth.

Permits can be obtained from Davis Fishing Tackle, 75 Bargates, Christchurch. A separate permit operates for game fish. Information regarding the fishery is available from The Fishery Manager, West Hampshire Water Company, Mill Road, Christchurch.

Lapsley's Trout Fishery (near Fordingbridge, Hampshire) W 10

This is a complex of six spring-fed lakes covering a total of 8 acres (3.2 ha), plus ¾ mile (1.2 km) of stream fishing. The trout in these lakes have a very high average weight, and the record for the fishery is held by a 13 lb 4 oz (6 kg) rainbow trout. The lakes are extremely rich, with plenty of weed growing in the clear water. The average catch rate per day over a season is nearly three fish per rod, and the average depth of the lakes is 6 ft (1.8 m). Twenty-four rods are allowed each day and the catch limit is five fish for a full-day permit. Half-day, evening and junior day permits are also available.

SPECIES Rainbow trout.

TECHNIQUES AND BAITS Fly fishing only. Because the lakes are gin clear, the trout can readily be seen, and this is one water where you can carefully stalk individual fish with the aid of polarised sunglasses. The most successful method is to cast a leaded nymph to the trout and then tweak the lure back in front of the fish.

SEASON 17th March to 26th October. Fishing is from 8.30 am to half an hour after sunset.

ACCESS The fishery is at Rockbourne Road, Sandleheath, near Fordingbridge, Hampshire.

Apply in advance for permits at the address above.

Hucklesbrook Trout Lake (near Fordingbridge, Hampshire) W 11

Hucklesbrook is a recently created gravel-pit fishery covering 32 acres (13 ha). Up to 40 anglers can be accommodated and there are four boats available. The average depth of the water is 8 ft (2.4 m). Two anglers are allowed in each boat and to save conflict with bank anglers the boats must be moored to the buoys when fishing. Two day tickets are available: a 4-hour ticket with a two fish limit and a full-day permit with a four fish limit. A very large selection of fly-dressing materials is available on site and tuition for beginners can be arranged. Tackle can be bought or hired and family accommodation can be arranged for visitors.

SPECIES Rainbow trout to $10\frac{1}{2}$ lb (4.8 kg), brown trout to $4\frac{3}{4}$ lb (2.2 kg), brook trout (when available). The average weight per trout is $1\frac{1}{4}$ lb (0.8 kg).

TECHNIQUES AND BAITS Fly fishing only is allowed. The trout at Hucklesbrook respond to most methods of fly fishing. During the summer months, when the water temperature is high, a lure fished on a slow sinkline is effective. Once the limit has been taken, fishing must stop and no fish can be returned.

SEASON 1st April to 30th September inclusive. Fishing is allowed from 9 am; the finishing time depends on the time of year. Ask for details when obtaining permit.

NB Day ticket price includes Wessex Authority rod licence.

ACCESS Hucklesbrook is on the A338 road between Fordingbridge and Ringwood.

For further details and permits contact Mr S Hare, Hucklesbrook Angling, Fordingbridge.

White Sheet Farm Trout Fishery (near Wimborne Minster, Dorset) W 12

This fishery consists of three beautiful lakes, covering 7 acres (2.8 ha). The average depth of the lakes is 10 ft (3 m). They are extremely rich and abound in aquatic life. Alder flies are especially numerous during the late spring. The average weight of the trout in these well-stocked lakes is over 2 lb (0.9 kg) with rainbow and brown trout up to nearly 10 lb (4.5 kg). The number of rods is restricted to 20 a day.

SPECIES Rainbow trout to 9 lb 4 oz (4.2 kg), brown trout to 7 lb 14 oz (3.6 kg).

TECHNIQUES AND BAITS Fly fishing only. Lures will catch fish, but these crystal clear lakes are ideal for nymph and buzzer fishing. Mayfly Nymphs, tied to Richard Walker's famous dressing, are especially successful. Damsel Nymphs and Black Buzzers are also productive. When the fish are feeding near the bottom try a leaded shrimp. The limit is four fish a day.

SEASON Fishing is from 8 am to sunset (not later than 9 pm).

ACCESS White Sheet is reached by taking the A31 Ringwood to Wimborne Minster road and turning off at the Old Thatch Inn.

Advance booking from Mr P Cook, White Sheet Farm Trout Lakes, White Sheet, Wimborne Minster, Dorset.

River Stour – Throop Fishery (Holdenhirst, Dorset) W 13

This stretch of the Dorset Stour is well known for its big barbel and chub. In 1961 an angler fishing for salmon caught an out-of-season barbel weighing 16¼ lb (7.4 kg). During the 1984 season barbel up to 12 lb (5.4 kg) were caught. The Throop Fishery covers 5½ miles (8.8 km) of the river on both banks from 100 yards above Iford bridge to Muscliffe. Also included in the fishery is the mill pool at Throop, which holds some good carp, tench and bream. The river is fast flowing and deep, with plenty of bankside vegetation. Some huge chub and barbel are taken at Throop every season and the roach fishing is also superb, with plenty of 2 lb (0.9 kg) fish caught. The river also has a run of salmon, and permits are available to fish for them.

SPECIES Barbel, chub to 6½ lb (2.9 kg), roach, dace, pike, tench, salmon and trout. In the mill pool there are also carp to 12 lb (5.4 kg) and bream to 7 lb (3.2 kg).

TECHNIQUES AND BAITS Legering is the best tactic for the big barbel and chub. Bread, cheese, sweetcorn, luncheon meat and maggots are the best baits. Hemp seed is banned, and barbel must be returned straight to the river. Standard float fishing tactics will catch the other species.

SEASON 16th June to 14th March (coarse fish) and 1st February to 30th September (salmon).

ACCESS Permits and information are obtained from Mr G Sutcliffe, School House, Holdenhirst village, Bournemouth, Dorset.

Southern Water Authority

The Southern Water Authority covers an area which includes Kent, Sussex and part of Hampshire, as well as the Southampton area. The area includes the River Test, which is world famous for its trout fishing. There is little day ticket fishing available on this river and what there is, is very expensive.

The major river in Kent is the Medway. This river suffered very serious pollution during the late sixties and, although it has now largely recovered, the sport can be a rather patchy. An interesting water is the Royal Military Canal, which is now used as a land drain for Romney Marsh. During the winter the sluices are opened to allow water to run off the land, and this means that the level of the canal drops. During the summer, the canal is worthy of attention from specimen hunters as it holds some big tench, carp and bream. It must be one of the few canals you can seriously fish with a carp rod.

Bewl Bridge is the best trout fishing reservoir in the area and as well as

Key	Page
1 River Medway – Maidstone	196
2 Chiddingstone Castle Lake	196
3 Weir Wood Coarse Fishery	197
4 Ardingly Reservoir	197
5 Bewl Bridge Trout Fishery	198
6 Pooh Corner Trout Fishery	198
7 Tenterden Trout Waters	199
8 Royal Military Canal	199
9 Farthings Lake	200
10 River Rother – near Rye	200
11 Lakedown	201
12 Fishers Pond	201
13 Black Dike Fishers	201
14 Broadlands Lake	202
15 Kingfisher Lake	202
16 Leominstead Trout Fishery	203
17 Sway Lakes	203

producing good fishing, it is scenically attractive. There are a fair number of good gravel-pit fisheries in the region, notably Old Bury Hill Lake in Surrey and Broadlands Lake in Hampshire. There are also a number of shallow landscaped lakes associated with stately homes and historic buildings. Chiddingstone Castle is such a lake, and this water once produced the national record bream.

River Medway – Maidstone (Kent) S 1

The River Medway rises near Forest Row in Sussex and flows north-east through Tonbridge and Maidstone to enter the Thames Estuary at Rochester. At Maidstone there are nearly 5 miles (8 km) of free fishing on the river. The fishing is on the north bank from East Farleigh Bridge downstream to Maidstone Bridge and then on the south bank from Maidstone Bridge to Allington Lock near the M20 motorway bridge. Anglers should note that a few short lengths along this stretch are not accessible. The weir pool area at East Farleigh is a good spot for dace, roach and bream. Towards Maidstone, some sizeable chub can be caught, especially where the river is lined by trees. From Maidstone to Allington Lock the water is deeper with many swims over 10 ft (3 m) deep and the predominant species on this length is roach. An interesting feature of the entire water is that carp are starting to show and some very big fish have been reported. During the summer, the river is plagued by pleasure craft and undoubtedly the fishing suffers as a result. The best time to fish during the summer is early and late in the day.

SPECIES Bream, roach, chub, dace, pike, bleak and some carp.

TECHNIQUES AND BAITS In the streamier sections, try float fishing, using a stick float, and in the slower lengths a waggler float. Maggots, casters, hemp and bread flake are the best baits. In the known bream swims legering with bread, in conjunction with an open-ended feeder, is a successful method.

SEASON 16th June to 14th March.

ACCESS Access is from various roads around Maidstone. At East Farleigh the approach is via the A26 road.

The fishing is free but anglers must hold a Southern Water Authority Rod Licence.

Chiddingstone Castle Lake (near Tonbridge, Kent) S 2

This small 3 acre (1.2 ha) lake is situated in the grounds of Chiddingstone Castle. It was here, in 1945, that Ted Costin caught a 13 lb 8 oz (6.1 kg) bream, which held the British record for the species for over 20 years. The bream are still present at Chiddingstone but are not of any great size. The dominant species now is carp, and it is in order to catch these that most anglers visit the lake. Most of the carp are small, but a few over 10 lb (4.5 kg) are caught. The lake is extremely tranquil with tree-lined banks and beds of lilies growing in the water. The depth varies from only 2 ft (0.6 m) at one end to 7 ft (2.1 m) near the dam wall. This is not a specialist carp water, and good mixed catches of carp, roach, 'skimmer' bream, rudd and gudgeon can be taken by casual float fishing. The carp can readily be caught in mild spells during the winter.

SPECIES Carp, roach, perch, bream, gudgeon and rudd.

TECHNIQUES AND BAITS Float-fished maggots and casters will take many small fish of all species during the summer. The large specimens of carp and roach are taken on bread. Corn, high-protein paste and other particles will all catch carp.

SEASON 16th June to 14th March.

ACCESS Chiddingstone is between Tonbridge and Edenbridge off the B2027 road. Park in the car park and the bailiff will collect the permit fee on the bankside.

Weir Wood Coarse Fishery (near East Grinstead, Sussex) S3

This reservoir covers 280 acres (113 ha) and was formerly a good trout fishery. Since being converted to a coarse fishery, Weir Wood has become one of the premier roach waters in the country. The roach fishing is superb with big catches of fish averaging over 1 lb (0.5 kg). Roach weighing 2 lb (0.9 kg) are not at all rare on this reservoir. Because of the massive size of the reservoir they are sometimes a little difficult to locate but the size and condition of these fish make this water worth exploring. The perch in the reservoir also run to over 2 lb (0.9 kg) and there is always the chance of a big brown trout left in the reservoir when it was a trout fishery.

SPECIES Roach, perch and pike.

TECHNIQUES AND BAITS Legering with an open-ended feeder using maggots or casters as bait is the best technique. Float fishing at long range with a big driftbeater float and the same baits will also yield results. Bread is another bait worth trying for the larger roach.

SEASON 16th June to 14th March.

ACCESS Weir Wood is located 1 mile (1.6 km) west of Forest Row, which is on the A22 London to Eastbourne road.

Permits are obtained on site from the Recreation Office at the south-east corner of the reservoir.

Ardingly Reservoir (Hayward's Heath, West Sussex) S 4

This reservoir, managed as a trout fishery, covers 180 acres (73 ha). The long northern arm of the reservoir is a nature reserve, and no fishing is allowed in this section. The western bank is also in private hands so the bank fishing is restricted to the eastern bank from Ardingly Dam, past West Hill embankment to Balcombe Mill Dam. The reservoir is very attractive, set in gently rolling grassland with wooded areas, notably near Balcombe Mill. The fishery is well stocked with both brown and rainbow trout. The limit is six fish.

SPECIES Brown trout and rainbow trout.

TECHNIQUES AND BAITS Fly fishing only. Popular flies are Dunkeld, Black and Peacock Spider and Black Muddler.

SEASON 3rd April to 31st October.

ACCESS The reservoir is located 3 miles (4.8 km) north of Hayward's Heath, approached via College Road, Ardingly.

Permits are available on site at the lodge at the southern end of the reservoir.

Bewl Bridge Trout Fishery (near Lamberhurst, Kent) S 5

This is a massive 770 acre (310 ha) reservoir very irregularly shaped with lots of bays and peninsulas. Boats are available but the bank fishing on this reservoir is very good indeed. Weed growth is prolific and can be a bit of a problem in some areas during the summer. The fishing for rainbow trout is excellent.

SPECIES Brown trout, rainbow trout and brook trout.

TECHNIQUES AND BAITS Lure fishing is best early in the season, but good catches are taken on nymph and buzzer during the summer. Fly fishing only is allowed.

SEASON 3rd April to 31st October.

ACCESS The reservoir is located 1½ miles (2.4 km) south of Lamberhurst on the A21(T) London to Hastings road.

Permits are available on site from the Recreation Office at the north-west end of the reservoir.

Pooh Corner Trout Fishery (near Rolvenden, Kent) S 6

This fishery is set in peaceful and beautiful countryside in the Weald of Kent, and has three spring-fed pools with a total area of 3 acres (1.2 ha). The pools vary in depth from 3 to 18 ft (0.9 to 5.5 m), and are stocked every week with fish weighing over 1 lb (0.5 kg). There are plenty of large trout over 3 lb (1.4 kg) in the water. Eight rods a day are permitted on the lake. The fishery incorporates the South-east England School of Fly Casting, run by Mr Ian Thomson, and arrangements for individual tuition or group instruction can be made.

SPECIES Rainbow trout and brown trout.

TECHNIQUES AND BAITS Fly fishing only is allowed, and once the limit of four fish (two on an evening permit) has been caught the angler must stop fishing or purchase a second ticket. Large lures are not allowed and this is a

fishery where skilful nymph fishing in the clear water pays dividends.
Delicate dry fly fishing will also catch plenty of trout.

SEASON 3rd April to 29th October. Fishing times from 8.30 am to 1 hour
after sunset.

ACCESS The fishery is located on the B2086 road to Benenden just outside
Rolvenden. For booking details and information contact Mr I Thomson,
Pooh Corner, Rolvenden, Cranbrook, Kent.

Tenterden Trout Waters (Tenterden, Kent) S 7

Tenterden Trout Waters consists of three lakes totalling 5 acres (2 ha). The
average depth of the lakes is 15 ft (4.6 m), and the fishery is located in
pleasant surroundings. This water is managed as a trout fishery, and is
regularly restocked throughout the season. There is a unique catch-and-
return system operating at Tenterden. All fish caught are placed in retainer
baskets, located around the fishery. At the end of the day the angler can
then select his two best fish and the remainder are returned to the lake to
fight another day. The average catch rate is an impressive six fish per rod,
and the average size is 2 lb (0.9 kg).

SPECIES Brown trout to 5 lb 10 oz (2.6 kg), rainbow trout to 8 lb 4 oz (3.7 kg).

TECHNIQUES AND BAITS Fly fishing only. This is an excellent water for
using dry flies and nymphs. Sedges, Stick Fly, Pheasant Tail Nymph and
Gold Ribbed Hare's Ear are all good flies to try at Tenterden.

SEASON 3rd April to 31st October. Fishing from 9 am to 1 hour after sunset.

ACCESS Tenterden is on the A28 Canterbury to Hastings road, 12 miles
(19.3 km) south-west of Ashford. Permits and enquiries to Mr and Mrs B
Evans, Coombe Farm, Tenterden, Kent.

Advance booking is advisable.

Royal Military Canal (Kenardington, near Rye, Kent) S 8

The Royal Military Canal is now disused and is a superb tench fishery. The
water is very weedy as there are no boats to churn the water up, and very
much stronger tackle needs to be used than is normal for canal fishing. The
water around Kenardington produces many tench over 3 lb (1.4 kg), and
5 lb (2.3 kg) fish are not uncommon. The canal is in an attractive setting on
the edge of Romney Marsh.

SPECIES Tench, roach, carp and bream.

TECHNIQUES AND BAITS Float fishing, using a small waggler float and
fishing against the weed beds or in the gaps in the weed beds. Best baits are
maggots, casters, sweetcorn and bread. Lobworm is also worth trying for
the larger tench.

SEASON 16th June to 14th March.

ACCESS Kenardington is reached via the minor road north-east from

Appledore.

Permits are obtained from the Swan Inn at Appledore. Appledore is located on the B2080 road, south-east of Tenterden.

Farthings Lake (Battle, East Sussex) S 9

This is a beautiful 3 acre (1.2 ha) lake set in a picturesque wooded valley. The number of day tickets is limited so advance booking is necessary. The fishing for carp and tench is good.

SPECIES Carp, tench, roach, rudd and bream.

TECHNIQUES AND BAITS Float fish using a waggler float and maggots, casters or corn as bait. Leger for the bigger carp using high-protein paste baits or 'boilies'.

SEASON 16th June to 14th March. Fishing from 8 am to sunset.

ACCESS Take the B2095 road from Battle in a westerly direction (signposted Catsfield and Bexhill). The entrance to the fishery is on the right-hand side of this road $1\frac{1}{2}$ miles (2.4 km) from Battle, opposite a track marked Millers Farm. The car park to Farthings Lake can be found approximately a further 100 yards on the right.

Permits can be obtained from Stiles Garage or Surridge Newsagents, both in Battle High Street, after 9 am. For further information contact Mr G Rowles, Lakeview Farm, Old Bury Hill, Westcott, near Dorking, Surrey.

River Rother (near Rye, East Sussex) S 10

This fishery, on the River Rother, is between Wittersham Bridge and Iden Lock. The fishing is on both banks for $3\frac{1}{2}$ miles (5.6 km). The river is wide and slow and the average depth is between 8 and 10 ft (2.4 and 3 m). The banks are open and access is easy. The stretch is permanently pegged for matches and day ticket applicants would be wise to check whether matches are taking place, especially at weekends. Two spots with wheelchair access are available free of charge for disabled anglers at Newbridge. The main species are roach and bream.

SPECIES Roach, bream and chub.

TECHNIQUES AND BAITS Float fish using a waggler float with maggots and casters as bait. Set the depth so that the bait is just tripping bottom. Bread flake is sometimes worth trying for the bream and chub.

SEASON 16th June to 14th March.

ACCESS The river is reached from minor roads leading off the B2082 road just north of Rye.

Permits are obtained from 'Shoot a Line' Tackle Shop, Rye; Miss Catt, Lock Cottage, Iden Lock; or Mr Eccles, Tyson Farm, Newbridge, East Sussex.

Lakedown (Burwash, East Sussex) S 11

Lakedown trout fishery comprises four lakes totalling 16 acres (6 ha). This fishery has deservedly earned a fine reputation for producing very big rainbow trout and for consistent high catches. A considerable number of double figure trout are caught every year with the average size of the trout being over 2 lb (0.9 kg). The lakes are in a beautiful setting, with some special fishing jetties. Anglers are limited to four fish a day, and fishing is from the bank only with no wading. Forty-five anglers a day can fish.

SPECIES Rainbow trout to over 10 lb (4.5 kg); brown trout.

TECHNIQUES AND BAITS Fly fishing only. One of the lakes is reserved exclusively for dry fly fishing. On another lake anglers are only allowed to use a floating line. On the remaining two lakes all types of fly fishing are allowed. Early in the season black flies and lures work well, and later on good catches are taken on green and white flies.

SEASON 1st April to end of October. Fishing is from 9 am to sunset.

ACCESS Advance booking is advisable. Contact Mr K Hooker, Oaken Wood Cottage, Holmshurst, Burwash Common, East Sussex.

Fishers Pond (Colden Common, near Winchester, Hampshire) S 12

This 10 acre (4 ha) lake is part of an old monastery fish pond (over 1000 years old). The site is still used for fish rearing (mainly carp). The lake is shallow, being 3 ft (0.9 m) on average, with the deepest area being 6 ft (1.8 m), and is surrounded by woodland. The fishing is predominantly for carp and tench.

SPECIES Carp, tench, roach, bream and eels.

TECHNIQUES AND BAITS Float fishing with waggler float and maggots, casters, bread or sweetcorn baits. Use bread crust and high-protein paste baits specifically for the carp.

SEASON 16th June to 14th March.

ACCESS The fishery is at the junction of the B3051 road and the A333 road south of Colden Common, 6 miles (9.7 km) south of Winchester.

Permits are obtained at the house on the fishery. For details contact Mr Paton, Fishers Pond Fishery.

Black Dike Fishery (Eastleigh, Hampshire) S 13

This was an old drainage channel which has been dug out to form a canal-like fishery. The water is $\frac{3}{4}$ mile (1.2 km) long and 33 ft (10 m) wide. The water is not very deep, averaging 3 ft (0.9 m) and is a good summer fishery, especially for sizeable tench.

SPECIES Tench to $7\frac{1}{2}$ lb (3.4 kg), carp, crucian carp, roach, rudd, perch and bream.

TECHNIQUES AND BAITS Float fishing with a waggler float using maggots, casters, bread and sweetcorn as bait is best.

SEASON 16th June to 14th March. Night fishing is allowed.

ACCESS The lake is located at Eastleigh, off Twyford Road. Permits are obtained from Mr R Drew, Eastleigh Bait and Tackle, 44 Twyford Road, Eastleigh, Hampshire.

Broadlands Lake (near Southampton, Hampshire) S 14

This is a 26 acre (11 ha) coarse fishery fed by extremely rich chalk water. The lake varies in depth from 3 to 13 ft (0.9 to 4 m) and was created several years ago by excavation of gravel for the M27 motorway. The lake fishes well for tench and carp during the summer, and during the winter some excellent grayling are caught. This is one of the few stillwaters in the country containing this species. The bankings are accessible all the way round the lake.

SPECIES Carp, tench, bream, roach, perch, pike, chub, dace, grayling and eels.

TECHNIQUES AND BAITS Float fishing with a waggler float using maggots, casters, bread or corn is the best tactic for most species. Legering is best for the carp and tench.

SEASON 16th June to 14th March. Fishing from 7 am to 8 pm. Night fishing only by special arrangement.

ACCESS Broadlands is located between Totton and Ower just west of Southampton and is close to the M27 motorway.

Permits are obtained on the bank.

Kingfisher Lake (Testwood, near Southampton, Hampshire) S 15

This is a well-matured 3 acre (1.2 ha) gravel-pit fishery, containing some very big carp. The lake is not very deep, ranging from 2 to 6 ft (0.6 to 1.8 m). The area is wooded around part of the lake and is a good birdwatching area, rich in wildlife. The best carp to date weighed 31 lb (14.1 kg).

SPECIES Carp, tench to 5 lb (2.3 kg), roach, perch, pike and chub.

TECHNIQUES AND BAITS Specimen tactics, using high-protein baits, are needed for the larger carp. Float fishing with a waggler float and using maggots, casters, bread or sweetcorn will give sport with the smaller species.

SEASON 16th June to 14th March.

ACCESS From Southampton, take the Millbrook road to Bournemouth and at the Elephant and Castle roundabout, take the Totton Road. This is Testwood Lane, and it leads to the Salmon Leap pub. A dirt track leads from the pub to the Kingfisher Lake.

Day permits are obtained from Mr E Hoskins, 40 Aldermoor Avenue, Aldermoor, Southampton.

Leominstead Trout Fishery (Emery Down, Lyndhurst, Hampshire) S 16

This is an excellent 8 acre (3.2 ha) trout fishery in the New Forest. The lake is in a lovely setting amid trees and rhododendrons. The lake is very roughly triangular in shape with the base of the triangle at the dam end. Also at the dam end are the owner's house, the fishing hut and the car park. The inlet stream flows into the lake at the opposite end. The lake is regularly stocked with prime rainbow trout and there are also some wild brown trout present, which spawn in the feeder stream. The water is deep, especially at the dam end, where it drops off to 20 ft (6.1 m). The bag limit is four fish and once this is achieved the angler has to stop fishing or buy a second permit. The rods are limited to 26 a day.

SPECIES Rainbow trout – record 12 lb 14 oz (5.8 kg) and brown trout – record 6 lb 9 oz (3 kg).

TECHNIQUES AND BAITS Fly fishing only. The maximum hook size allowed is a size 10 long shank. A slow sinking line is useful with small lures and nymphs. Recommended patterns are Black and Silver, White or Black Marabou, Dambuster, Coachman, Damsel Nymph, Black Buzzer and Corixa.

SEASON 3rd April to 31st October.

ACCESS Leominstead is reached via the minor road from Lyndhurst to Stoney Cross, just north of Emery Down Village.

Permits are obtained from Mr L Jarmal, Leominstead Trout Fishery, Emery Down, Lyndhurst.

Sway Lakes (near Lymington, Hampshire) S 17

Coarse fishing is available here on two lakes each covering $1\frac{1}{2}$ acres (0.6 ha). The average depth of the lakes is 5 ft (1.5 m) with a few areas down to 8 ft (2.4 m). The lakes are man-made, and situated in open, marshy land. The main species are carp and tench, which grow to a large size.

SPECIES Tench, carp, roach, rudd and perch.

TECHNIQUES AND BAITS Float fishing with a waggler float using maggots, casters, bread and sweetcorn is best for most species. Free-lined paste baits are best for the carp. No groundbaiting is allowed.

SEASON 16th June to 14th March. Fishing from dawn to dusk. Night fishing is allowed only by prior arrangement.

ACCESS Sway Lakes are located between Lymington and the village of New Milton, Hampshire.

Permits are obtained on site from Mr T Clark, Barrows Lane, Sway.

Northern Ireland

The fishing in Northern Ireland is, without any doubt, the best in the British Isles. The coarse fishing potential is tremendous, and the waters of the River Erne and its tributaries (the major system for anglers) are full of bream and roach. The fishing in the six counties of Tyrone, Fermanagh, Down, Antrim, Armagh and Londonderry is controlled by the Department of Agriculture, which has done a splendid job in developing some of the areas for fishing. Access to remote waters by way of roads and car parks has been made and, in waters where the margins are shallow and swampy, fishing platforms have been constructed and stiles and footsticks have been erected around waters to give ease of access on foot. The Department of Agriculture has also created a number of areas suitable for disabled anglers to gain access.

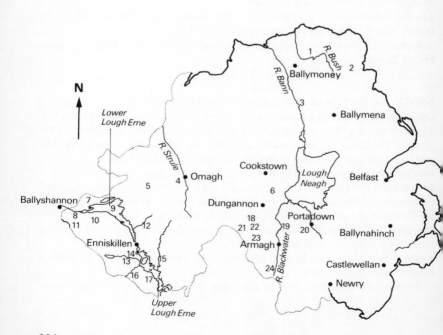

Key	Page				
		10 Navar Forest Lakes	211	22 Lough Creeve	218
		11 Lough Melvin	211	23 Enagh Lough	219
1 River Bush	205	12 Ballinamallard River	212	24 Clay Lake	219
2 Dungonnell Reservoir	206	13 Arney River	213		
3 Lower Bann		14 Mill Lough	213		
Navigational Canal	206	15 Colebrook River	214		
4 River Strule	207	16 Cam or Cladagh River	214		
5 Lough Lee	207	17 Upper Lough Erne	215		
6 Roughan Lough	208	18 Brantry Lough	216		
7 Lough Scolban	209	19 River Blackwater	216		
8 River Erne	209	20 Upper Bann River	217		
9 Lower Lough Erne	210	21 White Lough	217		

Apart from the fishing which is controlled directly by the Department of Agriculture, there is also a wealth of coarse fishing on the rivers and lakes where visitors can fish simply by gaining permission from the landowner, with no fees involved (apart from the usual rod licence). The game fishing in the area is also very good, and the trout fishing on Lough Melvin and Lower Lough Erne is first class – particularly for big brown trout. Most anglers who travel to Northern Ireland do so for the huge hauls of roach and bream that can be taken, but it is worth pointing out that the pike fishing in Lough Erne is also potentially as good, if not better, than anywhere else in the British Isles.

River Bush (County Antrim) NI 1

The unrestricted stretch of the River Bush covers 24 miles (38.6 km) from near Bushmills to Armoy. This is a salmon, sea trout and brown trout river with a good run of summer grilse. The downstream limit is near Walkmill, and from here to Stroan Bridge the river is mainly slow flowing and fairly deep with just a few isolated shallows. The banks on this length are fairly high. From Stroan Bridge to Magherahony, the river is faster flowing over a gravel bed. There are a few deeper pools which hold salmon. The brown trout fishing on this section is good. Above Magherahony the river is more of a mountain stream with rocks, boulders and cascades. There are a few deep pools that hold salmon, and the banks are well lined with bushes for cover. Sport on these upper reaches can be fast and furious with small to medium-sized brown trout.

SPECIES Salmon, sea trout and brown trout.

TECHNIQUES AND BAITS Fly fishing, with worm fishing allowed from 1st July. Spinning is allowed on the length between Bellisle Bridge and Conagher Bridge from 1st July.

SEASON 1st March to 30th September.

ACCESS Access to the river is best gained from one of the many bridges or official car parks. These are signposted, and anglers should have no difficulty in locating them. Access along the river banks has been made easier by the construction of stiles and footsticks over most of the stretch.

A Fisheries Conservancy Board Game Fishing Rod Licence and a

Department of Agriculture Game Fishing Permit are required. Permits can be obtained from A Truss, 116 Main Street, Bushmills; Smyth's Tackle, 17 Enagh Road, Ballymoney; or Messrs F and A Cusick, Post Office, Armoy, Ballymoney (all in County Antrim).

Dungonnell Reservoir (near Ballymena, County Antrim)
NI 2

Dungonnell is a long, narrow water covering 70 acres (28 ha). It is a public supply reservoir with a large population of brown trout. The reservoir lies on moorland and the shores near the dam are rocky. The south shore is fairly firm but the west shore is very marshy in places. The peninsula on the north side, just above the dam, creates a sheltered bay on the lee side and this is a good place to fish.

SPECIES Wild brown trout to 2 lb (0.9 kg). The reservoir holds a lot of smaller trout, and measures have been taken to reduce spawning success and increase the size ratio.

TECHNIQUES AND BAITS All legal methods, except groundbaiting and maggots, are allowed. Worm bait will catch trout but to enjoy the fishing, light fly tackle is best used with a team of wet flies.

SEASON 1st March to 31st October.

ACCESS The reservoir is situated near the village of Cargan on the Waterfoot road (A43) out of Ballymena. At the crossroads as you approach Cargan, about 10 miles (16 km) out of Ballymena, turn right. The road to the reservoir, the first on the left, $\frac{1}{2}$ mile (0.8 km) from Cargan is signposted.

A Fisheries Conservancy Board Game Fishing Rod Licence and a Department of Agriculture Game Fishing Permit are required. Permits can be obtained from Fyfe's Stores, 194–196 Glenravel Road, Cargan, County Antrim.

Lower Bann Navigational Canal (County Antrim) NI 3

Three sections of the canal can be fished: $\frac{1}{2}$ mile (0.8 km) at Toome; $\frac{1}{4}$ mile (0.4 km) at Portna; and 1 mile (1.6 km) at Movanagher. All three are readily accessible and are popular coarse fisheries. The lower part of the Toome stretch is noted for its perch. Fishing at Portna is restricted to the stretch below the locks as the stretch upstream of the locks is inaccessible and dangerous, due to the steep nature of the rocky banks. On the Movanagher stretch three fishing stands specially designed for disabled anglers have been erected. These stands are adjacent to car parks, one of which is the Fish Farm car park. There are plenty of big bream in the canal, and roach have appeared which are rapidly spreading along the stretch.

SPECIES Pike, perch, roach, bream and eels.

TECHNIQUES AND BAITS Waggler fishing with maggot or worm bait is best. Legering with a quiver tip rod is effective for the bream. The pike fishing is good and deadbaiting or spinning will both work well. Some big perch are taken on spinners.

SEASON All year.

ACCESS *Toome*: Travelling from Belast on the A6 towards Londonderry, take the first street to the left in Toom village. *Portna* Off the Kilrea to Portglenone A54 road, $\frac{1}{4}$ mile (0.4 km) out of Kilrea, turn left for a short distance and left again to the canal area. *Movanagher*: From Kilrea take the B62 road, signposted towards Ballymoney, for $1\frac{1}{2}$ miles (2.4 km) crossing over the Bann Bridge to McLaughlins Corner. Here turn left and immediately left again by the B64 for $2\frac{1}{4}$ miles (3.6 km) to the approach road to Movanagher Fish Farm which is on the left.

A Fisheries Conservancy Board Coarse Fishing Rod Licence and a Department of Agriculture Coarse Fishing Permit are required. These can be obtained from Curtis Spence Garage, New Street, Ronaldstown; Mr J Matthews, 72 Ballymoney Street, Ballymena, County Antrim; or Mr P McGroggan, 34 Broughshane Street, Ballymena.

River Strule (Cappagh stretch, near Omagh, County Tyrone) NI 4

The Strule is a fine game river and is reputed to contain the biggest brown trout in the entire Foyle system. It is for the roach, however, that anglers are allowed to fish at Cappagh; any game fish accidentally caught must be returned gently to the water. The Strule is a small river with a steady flow. This stretch is just over $1\frac{1}{2}$ miles (2.4 km) long, extending downstream on the right (east) bank only from the junction with the famous Fairywater. The river is teeming with roach up to specimen size. A reputed 4 lb (1.8 kg) roach from the Strule was once fed to a cinema cat before it could be officially verified.

SPECIES Roach to 2 lb (0.9 kg) and eels.

TECHNIQUES AND BAITS Stick float maggot, or pole fishing, will take the most fish. One regulation on this water stipulates a maximum breaking strain of $4\frac{1}{2}$ lb (2 kg) and maximum hook size 12. This is to prevent illegal game fishing and will not affect the roach fishing.

SEASON All year round except the period between 1st July and 20th October.

ACCESS The entrance to the fishery is near Cappagh Church which is indicated by a road sign $1\frac{1}{2}$ miles (2.4 km) out on the Omagh to Gortin B48 road.

A Department of Agriculture Coarse Fishing Permit is required and can be obtained from Tyrone Angling Supplies, Bridge Street, Omagh.

Lough Lee (near Castlederg, County Tyrone) NI 5

This is an isolated lough in a wild and beautiful setting among the mountains of West Tyrone. The lough covers 37 acres (15 ha) and is well stocked with brown trout. Two pound (0.9 kg) fish are regularly taken and, in the crystal-clear waters of the lough, the trout have evolved a bright coloration and are vividly marked. Cars must be parked 1 mile (1.6 km) away from the lough but a special path has been marked out for anglers. Please remember that this is sheep country and dogs are not welcome.

SPECIES Brown trout.

TECHNIQUES AND BAITS All legal methods of angling are permitted but fly fishing is most rewarding. Early season worm fishing is effective when the water is cold.

SEASON 1st March to 20th October.

ACCESS From the B50 Omagh to Castlederg road, turn west at the signpost 5 miles (8 km) north of Drumquin (3 miles (4.8 km) south of Castlederg) and continue for $1\frac{3}{4}$ miles (2.8 km) to the sign at the copse at Clare Lodge. Turn south for $1\frac{1}{2}$ miles (2.4 km) to the limit of the surfaced country road. From there it is a 20 minute walk to the lough.

A Foyle Fisheries Commission Game Fishing Rod Licence and a Department of Agriculture Game Fishing Permit are required. Permits can be obtained locally from Tyrone Angling Supplies, Bridge House, Bridge Street, Omagh, County Tyrone.

Roughan Lough (near Coalisland, County Tyrone) NI 6

Roughan Lough is one of the few waters in Northern Ireland to bes stocked with big rainbow trout. The fishing is for rainbow trout only and fish to over 10 lb (4.5 kg) have been taken in recent years. The lough covers 48 acres (19 ha) and part of the southern shore is out of bounds to anglers. The Department of Agriculture have created footpaths and stiles around the shore, and where the bank is difficult fishing platforms have been constructed. Anglers should note that water-skiing is allowed on the lough occasionally.

SPECIES Rainbow trout to 10 lb 5 oz (4.7 kg).

TECHNIQUES AND BAITS All legal methods, except maggots and groundbait, are allowed. Fly fishing only is allowed from the boats. Lure fishing works well with sinking lines, especially early in the season.

SEASON 1st May to 31st December.

ACCESS The lough is reached by driving north-west from Coalisland to the village of Newmills. Continue through the village, keeping right at the fork in the road. The lough is on the right, 1 mile (1.6 km) further on. A car park is provided at the lough.

A Fisheries Conservancy Board Game Fishing Rod Licence and a Department of Agriculture Game Fishing Permit are required. Permits can be obtained locally from Mr S Quinn, Main Street, Coalisland; Dungannon Sports Centre, 19 Thomas Street, Dungannon; or Hamilton's, James Street, Cookstown (all in County Tyrone).

Lough Scolban (near Belleek, County Fermanagh) NI 7

This lough covers 171 acres (69 ha) and was only opened up for fishing in 1976. Initially it was designated a brown trout fishery but it holds far more coarse fish and is now a recognised coarse fishery. Most species of coarse fish are present, including bream and roach, but the lough's potential is not really known as few anglers are willing to pass Lough Erne to fish Scolban. Anglers are allowed to fish from their own boats but caution is advised as there are a lot of unmarked shallows in the lough. This is one of those waters where anglers could well discover some outstanding, unexploited coarse fishing.

SPECIES Rudd, pike, perch, bream, roach and brown trout.

TECHNIQUES AND BAITS There are no restrictions on methods or baits, and most stillwater tactics will work.

SEASON All year round.

ACCESS The lough is signposted from the main Kesh to Belleek road.

A Fisheries Conservancy Board Coarse Fishing Rod Licence and a Department of Agriculture Coarse Fishing Permit are required. Permits can be obtained from the Hotel Carlton, Belleek; Lough Erne Hotel, Kesh; Thomas Flynn, The Bridge, Kesh; or the Post Office, Kesh (all in County Fermanagh).

River Erne (near Belleek, County Fermanagh) NI 8

At Belleek, $3\frac{3}{4}$ miles (6 km) of the River Erne can be fished as it flows out of Lough Erne. The lower lough is rated as a game fishery and there are many large trout to be caught in the river. The mayfly hatch lasts for about six weeks and the trout fishing during this period is very good, with plenty of fish in the 4–6 lb (1.8–2.7 kg) range caught. The coarse fishing is also excellent, with some huge bream and roach shoals roaming the river. The pike fishing is largely unexploited, but the potential would appear to be very high. The river is very wide and boats can be hired, although only fly fishing is allowed from the boats. There is a short area near to Roscor Viaduct which is private but this stretch is well signposted. The Department of Agriculture fishery is on the south side of the river but the opposite bank can be fished free of charge if the landowner's permission is obtained.

SPECIES Brown trout, roach, pike, perch, rudd, bream, eels and the occasional salmon.

TECHNIQUES AND BAITS Fly fishing only is allowed from boats, otherwise there are no restrictions. The usual coarse fishing tactics will produce bumper catches of bream and roach. Anglers who use deadbaiting or livebaiting will catch some of the large pike which live in these waters. The larger trout are usually caught on spinners but sedge fishing and standard loch fishing work well.

SEASON 1st March to 30th September for salmon and trout but all year for coarse fish.

ACCESS The fishing area is off the Belleek to Enniskillen shore road. Several car parks are available. A Fisheries Conservancy Board Game Fishing Rod Licence and a Department of Agriculture Game Fishing Permit are required. Permits are obtained locally from the Hotel Carlton, Belleek; Lough Erne Hotel, Kesh; or the Post Office, Kesh (all in County Fermanagh). Boats can be hired from the Hotel Carlton, Belleek.

Lower Lough Erne (Enniskillen, County Fermanagh) NI 9

Lower Lough Erne is of a more regular shape than the upper lough and, although there are still plenty of coarse fish present, it is managed as a game fishery. The brown trout fishing is superb, with double figure specimens caught every year – the largest brown trout in recent years tipped the scales at 17 lb (7.7 kg). The best trout fishing is in the north-western end of the lough between Owl Island and Roscor Bridge. Plenty of trout are caught in the 2–3 lb (0.9–1.4 kg) size range, especially during the mayfly hatch which can be spectacular.

From July onwards, there is a run of grilse, and the best areas for these are from Roscor Bridge up to Heron Island and across to the Garvary River. The bag limit for trout is six fish and the size limit is 12 in (30 cm). The corner of the lough nearest to Enniskillen is designated a coarse fishery area, with the usual bream and roach fishing. The extent of the coarse fishing is to an imaginary line across the lough from the mouth of the Ballinamallard River to the nearest point on the shore opposite Castlehume. South and east of this line a coarse permit is required, and north and west a game permit is required. As with the upper lough, the Department of Agriculture has developed many sites around the lough and constructed anglers' car parks.

SPECIES Brown trout to 20 lb (9.1 kg), salmon, sea trout, pike, bream, roach, rudd, perch and eels.

TECHNIQUES AND BAITS Fly fishing is usually employed for the trout and, during the mayfly hatch, virtually any big, bushy dry fly will be taken. Drift fishing from a boat, with a team of three wet flies, works well. During late summer, dapping with a cranefly ('daddy long legs') catches some sizeable trout and is very enjoyable. In the designated coarse fishing areas, there are no restrictions on bait or methods and the usual coarse fish tactics are successful.

SEASON 1st March to 30th September for salmon, sea trout and brown trout. All year round for coarse fishing in designated areas.

ACCESS The Department of Agriculture has created a great many angling centres mostly along the northern shore of the lough. The coarse fishing areas include Cornagrade, Round 'O' Quay and Trory, which are all at the Enniskillen end of the lough. The other areas are: Acheson's Quay; Blaney (picnic area); Boa Island (east end); Boa Island (west end); Carrickreagh;

Castle Archdale Forest; Castle Caldwell Forest; Clonelly; Curraghmore; Goblusk Landing Stage; Leggs; Lowery; Muckross; Rossharbour; Rossigh (picnic area); Sandy Bay; Tonagorm.

A Fisheries Conservancy Board Game Fishing Rod Licence and a Department of Agriculture Game Fishing Permit are required except for the designated coarse fishing areas where the less expensive coarse licence and permit only are needed. Permits and boats can be obtained from the Hotel Carlton, Belleek; Lakeland Tackle, Henry Street, Enniskillen; or Lough Erne Hotel, Kesh (all in County Fermanagh).

Navar Forest Lakes (Derrygonnelly, County Fermanagh) NI 10

There are three good trout lakes in the Navar Forest, namely Achork, Glencreawan and Meenameen. This is a beautiful scenic area and there is a cliff-top viewpoint in the forest. This is the ideal venue for a family fishing trip, being complete with forest walks and picnic areas. Achork is the smallest lake at 10 acres (4 ha), and lies alongside the forest drive. The northern shore is in the shelter of rocks. Paths and picnic tables are provided and there are plenty of good perch as well as trout – which makes good fishing for children. The deepest water is along the rocky shore. Meenameen and Glencreawan are roughly the same size, about 46 acres (19 ha). Glencreawan fishes better from mid-July onwards. Meenameen holds plenty of trout to 1 lb (0.5 kg), with a few fish up to 3 lb (1.4 kg). This lough fishes well from May to the end of June, during the excellent mayfly hatch on the water. The bag limit is four fish and the size limit is 10 in (25 cm).

SPECIES Brown trout and perch. A few rainbow trout are sometimes stocked in Glencreawan.

TECHNIQUES AND BAITS All legal methods are allowed but maggots and groundbait are banned. Fly fishing only is allowed from the boats.

SEASON 1st March to 30th September.

ACCESS From nearby Belleek, follow the forest drive signs.

A Fisheries Conservancy Board Game Fishing Rod Licence and a Department of Agriculture Game Fishing Permit are required. Permits can be obtained locally from the Lough Navar Forest Office (when open); or from the Hotel Carlton, Belleek; or Derrygonnelly Autos, Main Street, Derrygonnelly (all in County Fermanagh).

Lough Melvin (near Garrison, County Fermanagh) NI 11

Lough Melvin is renowned for its salmon and trout fishing. The border with the Irish Republic straddles Lough Melvin and is marked by a line of buoys. Melvin provides the Northern Ireland angler with his or her only opportunity to catch salmon from the early spring run, with fish up to 20 lb (9.1 kg). The salmon grilse average 5 lb (2.3 kg) and the trout average 1 lb

(0.5 kg). Gillaroo and sonaghan trout (variations of brown trout) are present in the lough. The gillaroo trout has developed a special stomach equipped to deal with a diet of snails, and the sonaghan looks very similar to a sea trout. The lough covers 1050 acres (425 ha), and the Northern Ireland portion of the water is centred on the town of Garrison with a shoreline of $3\frac{1}{2}$ miles (5.6 km) extending from Blair's Bridge in the south-east to Inniskeen in the north with an offshore peninsula in the region of $\frac{1}{2}$ mile (0.8 km).

SPECIES Spring salmon, grilse, brown trout (including gillaroo and sonaghan), perch and char.

TECHNIQUES AND BAITS All legal methods are allowed on Lough Melvin, except maggots and groundbaiting. Traditional fly fishing with a team of three wet flies on the drift is used for the trout, and trolling from a boat for the larger salmon. Worm bait will take trout and perch.

SEASON 1st February to 30th September.

ACCESS From Enniskillen take the A4 road to Belcoo, turning right by the B52 to Garrison.

A Fisheries Conservancy Board Game Fishing Rod Licence and a Department of Agriculture Game Fishing Permit are required. (NB These permits are only valid in the Northern Ireland area of the lough.) Permits are obtained from the Lake Hotel, Garrison; or the Hotel Carlton, Belleek, County Fermanagh. Boats can be hired from the Hotel Carlton, Belleek.

Ballinamallard River (Ballinamallard, County Fermanagh) NI 12

This is a very attractive little river which flows into the northern side of Lower Lough Erne. The stretch controlled by the Department of Agriculture is known as the Riversdale length, and covers 1 mile (1.6 km) of fishing. The river at this point flows through a woodland setting. The river is classed as a game fishery with some good trout but there are also lots of roach. (The roach are not quite as numerous as they are in some of the other Erne tributaries but they are of a good size.) Pike are also present in good numbers with a lot of double figure specimens. An electro-fishing survey carried out a few years ago revealed many trout of around 2 lb (0.9 kg). A few salmon are also caught occasionally.

SPECIES Roach, brown trout, salmon, pike and eels.

TECHNIQUES AND BAITS All legal methods including groundbait and maggots are allowed for coarse fish. The trout will take a dry fly, especially in late spring at mayfly time. The roach are best tackled with a stick float and maggots.

SEASON 1st March to 30th September.

ACCESS The entrance to the fishery is off the A35 Enniskillen to Irvinestown Road at Kilgortnaleague Bridge.

A Fisheries Conservancy Board Game Fishing Rod Licence and a

Department of Agriculture Game Fishing Permit are required. Permits can be obtained locally from the Brooklands Hotel, Ballinamallard; or Mr J A Knaggs, Ballinamallard.

Arney River (near Enniskillen, County Fermanagh) NI 13

The Arney flows in an easterly direction from Lower Lough Macnean to Upper Lough Erne. The river is slow flowing and extremely rich as it drains the limestone uplands of the Macnean catchment. The coarse fishing is excellent, especially in the lower reaches near Lough Erne. Roach predominate and enormous catches are possible, including some very large individual specimens. Some big bream shoals are also to be found. The Department of Agriculture has developed 5 miles (8 km) of the river from the A32 Enniskillen road to Lough Erne. Trout are plentiful in the upstream reaches and there is often a late season salmon run.

SPECIES Roach, perch, bream, brown trout and salmon.

TECHNIQUES AND BAITS Waggler fishing is best for the roach and bream, using plenty of groundbait to hold the shoals. The roach can be located all along the river but the bream shoals tend to be more nomadic. Legering with a quiver tip will also take the bream. Maggots and bread are the best baits.

SEASON 1st March to 30th September for the trout and salmon. All year round for coarse fish.

ACCESS About 5 miles (8 km) south of Enniskillen on the A32 turn east at the Five Points to Arney village, then turn south towards Old Arney Bridge. The entrance is to the west of the bridge, by Sessiagh Lane and is signposted. Car parks are located along the river.

A Fisheries Conservancy Board Coarse Rod Licence and a Department of Agriculture Coarse Fishing Permit are required. Permits can be obtained locally from the Lakeland Hotel, Bellanaleck; G A Cathcart, Bellanaleck Post Office; or Mrs Bracken, Letterbreen Post Office (all in County Fermanagh).

Mill Lough (Bellanaleck, County Fermanagh) NI 14

This lough has been regularly stocked with both brown trout and rainbow trout but, because the perch population remains high despite constant trapping, the future of the fishery is under review. As no more rainbow trout are to be stocked, these will die out leaving perch and brown trout. There are reputedly some really massive brown trout in this lough. The water covers 100 acres (40 ha) and the shoreline is basically stony. A pathway has been created along the north shore. Ten fishing platforms have been erected where access is difficult. There are a lot of interesting bays and inlets around the shoreline. The bag limit for trout is four fish and the size limit is 10 in (25 cm).

SPECIES Mainly perch and brown trout.

TECHNIQUES AND BAITS Fly fishing only from the boats is allowed, otherwise all methods are permitted, except for the use of maggots or groundbait. Float-fished worm will catch a large number of perch.

SEASON 1st March to 30th September.

ACCESS The lough is near Bellanaleck village, 4 miles (6.4 km) from Enniskillen. The lough is signposted from the outskirts of the village.

A Fisheries Conservancy Board Game Fishing Rod Licence and a Department of Agriculture Game Fishing Permit are required. Permits can be obtained locally from the Lakeland Hotel, Bellanaleck or the Post Office, Bellanaleck. Boats may be hired from Mr G A Cathcart, Post Office, Bellanaleck; Mr J Foster, Toneyloman, Bellanaleck; Mr G L Stephenson, Tully, Bellanaleck; or Mr R C Keys, Ardtonagh, Bellanaleck.

Colebrook River (near Lisnaskea, County Fermanagh) NI 15

This river is another famous tributary of the Erne system. Rising north of Creagh the river flows west and then south to enter Upper Lough Erne. The lower reaches of the river are full of coarse fish, mainly roach and bream. The stretch of river opened to the public by the Department of Agriculture covers 2 miles (3.2 km) of the best coarse fishing around Lisnaskea. The roach fishing is exceptional and, if the shoals are concentrated, it is possible to catch a fish every cast. Some big fishing matches have been held on this length and in one 5-hour contest the 160 competitors landed nearly $1\frac{1}{2}$ tonnes of fish.

SPECIES Roach, bream, perch, rudd, eels and pike.

TECHNIQUES AND BAITS Float fishing with a waggler float and maggots will catch plenty of fish. Plenty of feed is needed to keep the shoals concentrated. Pole fishing is probably faster for fishing competitions.

SEASON All year round for coarse fish.

ACCESS From Lisnaskea proceed a few hundred yards along the A34 towards Maguiresbridge, turn left and drive along the B514 to the first road junction. Turn left again to the river which is signposted. Car parks are provided.

A Fisheries Conservancy Board Coarse Fishing Rod Licence and a Department of Agriculture Coarse Fishing Permit are required. Permits can be obtained locally from Erne Tackle, Main Street, Lisnaskea; or J Meldrum, Main Street, Lisnaskea.

Cam or Cladagh River (near Enniskillen, County Fermanagh) NI 16

This is a tributary of the River Erne, and offers excellent coarse fishing for bream and roach. The water is fairly deep and slow flowing, and the banks are clean and easily fished. The stretch known as McHugh's Bank is controlled by the Department of Agriculture and is 240 ft (73 m) long.

However, the banks upstream, downstream and opposite to this stretch can be fished upon asking the riparian owner's permission, which is usually readily given. Access to these banks is excellent. The water is teeming with fish but, on average, they are slightly smaller than in the main lough.

SPECIES Roach, bream, rudd, perch, pike and eels.

TECHNIQUES AND BAITS Float fishing with a waggler float is mostly used for the roach and bream. Maggot is the easiest bait, although worm and bread will also catch plenty of fish. Plenty of groundbait is needed to hold the fish in the swim.

SEASON All year for coarse fish.

ACCESS Travel 8 miles (12.9 km) along the A4 road and then take the A509 from Enniskillen. The fishery is along the first road on the left before Carrs Bridge and the road is now signposted 'Cam River'. A car park is provided at the riverside.

A Fisheries Conservancy Board Coarse Fishing Rod Licence and a Department of Agriculture Coarse Fishing Permit are required. Permits are obtained locally from the Lakeland Hotel, Bellanaleck, County Fermanagh; or G A Cathcart, Bellanaleck Post Office.

Upper Lough Erne (Enniskillen, County Fermanagh) NI 17

It is not really possible to do justice to the coarse fishing potential of Lough Erne. The lough and its many tributary rivers are simply teeming with roach, rudd and bream. This is possibly one of the finest coarse fishing venues in Europe and, in recent years, the Department of Agriculture has made more of the banks accessible to anglers. Car parking areas, footpaths, stiles, footbridges and fishing platforms have all been created, and signs and noticeboards erected to aid anglers.

The lough between Enniskillen and Newtown Butler has a very irregular shoreline riddled with bays, inlets and islands. An angler could spend a lifetime fishing Lough Erne and still not explore it thoroughly. Roach are to be found everywhere, and huge shoals of bream roam the lough and the tributaries. The pike tend to be forgotten with so many roach and bream about, but the potential for catching this species is great.

SPECIES Bream, roach, pike, perch, rudd and eels, plus hybrids of roach/bream and rudd/bream.

TECHNIQUES AND BAITS Every conceivable method of coarse fishing will catch fish. On the main lough itself, legering will probably take more bream using a swing tip, but waggler fishing will take the roach. Maggots are the bait to use simply for speed. The bream are partial to worm, and lots of groundbait is required.

SEASON All year for coarse fish.

ACCESS Virtually the whole of the shoreline can be fished but the Department of Agriculture have created the following areas: Belle Isle Bridge; Broadmeadow; Carry Bridge; Cleenish Viaduct, Corradilar;

Corrigans; Derryad Quay; Derryvore; Galloon Bridge; Inishmore Bridge; Irvine's Island; Killmore Quay; Knockinny Quay; Lady Brooke Bridge; Lady Craigavon Bridge; Ring; Rossdoney; Schools; Scotch Store; Wattle Bridge; Weirs Bridge.

A Fisheries Conservancy Board Coarse Fishing Rod Licence and a Department of Agriculture Coarse Fishing Permit are required. Permits can be obtained from the Hotel Carlton, Belleek; Lakeland Tackle, Henry Street, Enniskillen; or Lough Erne Hotel, Kesh (all in County Fermanagh). Boats can also be hired from these centres.

Brantry Lough (near Benburb, County Tyrone) NI 18

This is a very productive fishery covering 60 acres (24 ha). The lough is situated in a forestry amenity area and, at one time, was managed as a rainbow trout fishery but is now stocked only with brown trout. A surfaced path has been built around the shore, and several angling stands have been constructed. There is a very soft boggy area in the bay at the south-east corner of the lough and anglers should take great care when wading in this part of the lake. The bag limit is four fish and the size limit is 10 in (25 cm).

SPECIES Brown trout.

TECHNIQUES AND BAITS All legal methods except groundbait and maggots may be used. Fly fishing only is allowed from the boats.

SEASON 1st March to 31st October.

ACCESS From Belfast take the M1 to Dungannon and then head south on the B45 road to Caledon for 6 miles (9.7 km). Fork right at the bridge over the Oona River and turn right at the crossroads, $\frac{1}{2}$ mile (0.8 km) further on. Proceed for 2 miles (3.2 km) until the lake (which is signposted) is reached. A car park is located near the lakeside.

A Fisheries Conservancy Board Game Fishing Rod Licence and a Department of Agriculture Game Fishing Permit are required. Permits can be obtained locally from Hamilton's, James Street, Cookstown, County Tyrone; or John F Devlin, The Deerpark Inn, 18 Main Street, Caledon, County Tyrone.

River Blackwater (Blackwatertown, County Tyrone) NI 19

The River Blackwater rises south of Caledon and flows north to enter Lough Neagh near Moy. The stretch at Blackwatertown covers $1\frac{1}{2}$ miles (2.4 km). Downstream of the town bridge the river is classed as a coarse fishery with good roach fishing and some bream. Above the bridge the fishing is for salmon and trout. A few dollaghan (a variety of trout unique to Lough Neagh) run at times.

SPECIES Salmon, brown trout (dollaghan), pike, perch, roach, bream and eels.

TECHNIQUES AND BAITS All legal methods are allowed, including groundbait and maggots for coarse fishing. Spinning and fly fishing only for the salmon and trout. Stick float fishing with maggot bait works well for the coarse fish. A pole is an effective way of taking a lot of roach quickly. SEASON 1st March to 31st October for salmon and trout. All year for coarse fish.

ACCESS The fishery can be approached from the centre of Blackwatertown.

A Fisheries Conservancy Board Game Fishing Rod Licence and a Department of Agriculture Game Fishing Permit are required if fishing above the town bridge. Anglers fishing downstream of the bridge need only the coarse permit equivalents. Permits can be obtained locally from James Beggs, 54–56 Scotch Street, Dungannon; K Cahoon, 2 Irish Street, Dungannon; Dungannon Sports Centre, 19 Thomas Street, Dungannon; or Hamilton's, James Street, Cookstown, (all in County Tyrone).

Upper Bann River (Portadown, County Armagh) NI 20

This stretch of the River Bann, which covers 10 miles (16 km) from Portadown to Lough Neagh, needs no introduction to regular readers of the angling press. The fishing is simply superb for roach and bream, and is rated as one of the best coarse fisheries in Europe. Five-hour match catches regularly top 100 lb (45.4 kg) individually, and for the pleasure angler who catches the river in form, only his stamina will limit his catches. The pike fishing on this stretch is also worthwhile as with all the foodfish available they grow very large. The Department of Agriculture has improved access to the river, and five fishing areas have been developed by arrangement with local landowners. The five areas are: Boulevard; Hoy's Meadows; Portadown Park; Irwin's Quay; and Milk Quay.

SPECIES Pike, roach, bream, perch and trout.

TECHNIQUES AND BAITS Float fishing with a waggler, and maggot as hookbait, will catch all the roach and bream desired. Plenty of groundbait is needed to hold a big bream shoal.

SEASON All year for coarse fish.

ACCESS From Portadown the fishery is alongside the B2 road to Lough Neagh.

A Fisheries Conservancy Board Coarse Fishing Rod Licence and a Department of Agriculture Coarse Fishing Permit are required. These can be obtained from The Fisheries Conservancy Board, 21 Church Street, Portadown; or Telford Stores, 17 Woodhouse Street, Portadown.

White Lough (near Aughnacloy, County Tyrone) NI 21

This 23 acre (9 ha) lough was, at one time, completely inaccessible but there is now a surfaced path from the adjoining country road around the entire shoreline. The Department of Agriculture have also built numerous fishing platforms around the lough. There is an abundance of pike and perch in the lough, with pike to over 20 lb (9.1 kg) recorded. The lough is extremely rich in natural food, and an indication of this is that periodically there is an algal bloom which can hamper fishing. The lough is in a pleasant setting near Rehaghy Mountain.

SPECIES Pike, perch and eels.

TECHNIQUES AND BAITS Spinning, livebaiting and deadbaiting will all catch pike. The perch can be taken on worm or maggot bait.

SEASON All year round.

ACCESS From Aughnacloy take the B128 road to Benburb and turn right at the second (Rehaghy) crossroads, 2 miles (3.2 km) out.

A Fisheries Conservancy Board Coarse Fishing Rod Licence and a Department of Agriculture Coarse Fishing Permit are required. Permits can be obtained from Hamilton's, James Street, Cookstown or Mr J F Devlin, The Deerpark Inn, 18 Main Street, Caledon (both of these are in County Tyrone).

Lough Creeve (near Benburb, County Tyrone) NI 22

This 45 acre (18 ha) lough is first and foremost a pike fishery. Some huge pike have been taken from Creeve, the best being a 35 lb (15.9 kg) fish. Several other pike between 25 and 29 lb (11.3 and 13.2 kg) have been taken in recent seasons. The lough is extremely productive, and scientific examination has shown that the growth rate of the lough's perch exceeds all other Irish waters. Fishing stands have been built around the lough and a specially constructed hardcore path gives easy access. Deciduous woodland surrounds the lake and provide shade for both the lake and the car parks. The area has been developed for forest recreation and includes a touring caravan site.

SPECIES Pike to 35 lb (15.9 kg), perch to 2 lb (0.9 kg) and eels.

TECHNIQUES AND BAITS Large numbers of pike are caught on spinners but perch deadbaits and livebait take the larger fish. Seabaits, such as sprat and herring, are well worth trying. Do not fish too light as the pike here fight a lot harder than their English counterparts. The perch can be caught on worm, spinner or maggots. All legitimate methods are allowed at Creeve.

SEASON All year round.

ACCESS From Caledon turn left for Minterburn off the Dungannon B45 road. A short distance from Caledon, turn right at Minterburn towards Lough Cleeve. When travelling from Aughnacloy take the Benburb road for $4\frac{1}{2}$ miles (7.2 km) and turn right at Holland's Cross, where the lough is indicated by a sign.

A Fisheries Conservancy Board Coarse Fishing Rod Licence and a Department of Agriculture Coarse Fishing Permit are needed. Permits are obtained locally from Mr J F Devlin, The Deerpark Inn, 18 Main Street, Caledon; or Hamilton's, James Street, Cookstown (both in County Tyrone).

Enagh Lough (near Caledon, County Tyrone) NI 23

A small lough of 13 acres (5 ha), Enagh is located alongside the main Caledon to Dungannon road. This water is an excellent pike fishery and has plenty of fish in the 15–20 lb (6.8–9.1 kg) size range. There is also a good head of bream to medium size. It is suspected that this water also holds tench but, like a lot of waters in Ireland, it has not been subjected to very much serious fishing. The side of the lough nearest the road has been developed for angling and a small car park, hardcore path and fishing platforms have been constructed.

SPECIES Pike to 20 lb (9.1 kg), bream to 5 lb (2.3 kg), perch and eels.

TECHNIQUES AND BAITS Spinning with a large mepps, or plug fishing, will give much sport with the perch and small to medium-sized pike. The big pike are best tackled with small bream deadbaits or sea fish baits, such as herring. Swing tipped maggot is best for the bream, using light groundbaiting.

SEASON All year round.

ACCESS The lake is 1 mile (1.6 km) from Caledon on the Dungannon road.

A Fisheries Conservancy Board Coarse Fishing Rod Licence and a Department of Agriculture Coarse Fishing Permit are required. Permits are obtained from Mr J F Devlin, The Deerpark Inn, 18 Main Street, Caledon; or Hamilton's, James Street, Cookstown, County Tyrone.

Clay Lake (near Keady, County Armagh) NI 24

This is a 120 acre (49 ha) supply reservoir. It is full of pike and perch, although many of the pike are small. However, some big pike are caught, and the largest recorded is 24 lb (10.9 kg). The perch fishing is very good with plenty of fish to 1 lb (0.5 kg). Stiles have been erected all round the reservoir to give easy access to the shoreline which, for the most part, is stony.

SPECIES Pike to 24 lb (10.9 kg), perch to 1½ lb (0.7 kg), rudd and a few brown trout.

TECHNIQUES AND BAITS As the lake is a supply reservoir, maggots and groundbaiting are not permitted. The usual deadbaiting and spinning will take the pike, and worm bait will catch plenty of perch. The rudd can be caught on worm or breadpaste but the groundbait ban hampers the catching of this species.

SEASON All year round.

ACCESS From Armagh travel south by the A29 to Keady then continue towards Castleblayney on the B3 for 1¼ miles (2 km).

A Fisheries Conservancy Board Coarse Fishing Rod Licence and a Department of Agriculture Coarse Fishing Permit are required. Permits are obtained from Mr H McGinnity, 70 Victoria Street, Keady; or Mr J McKeever, Hardware Shop, Bridge Street, Keady.

Useful information

Water Authority Addresses

Scotland
Orkney Tourist Board
Kirkwall
Orkney

Orkney Trout Fishing Association
17 Hermaness
Kirkwall

North West Water Authority
New Town House
Buttermarket Street
Warrington
Cheshire

Northumbrian Water Authority
Northumbria House
Regent Centre
Gosforth
Newcastle upon Tyne
Tyne and Wear

Yorkshire Water Authority
21 Park Square South
Leeds

Welsh Water Authority
Cambrian Way
Brecon
Powys

Severn Trent Water Authority
Abelson House
2297 Coventry Road
Sheldon
Birmingham

Anglian Water Authority
Ambury Road
Huntingdon
Cambridgeshire

Thames Water Authority
Nugent House
Vastern Road
Reading
Berkshire

South West Water Authority
Peninsular House
Rydon Lane
Exeter
Devon

Wessex Water Authority
Regional Operations Centre
Wessex House
Passage Street
Bristol
Avon

Southern Water Authority

Guildbourne House
Chatsworth Road
Worthing
West Sussex

Northern Ireland

Department of Agriculture
Fisheries Division
Castle Grounds
Stormont
Belfast

Fisheries Conservancy Board
21 Church Street
Portadown
Co Armagh

Publications

Anglers Mail
Kings Reach Tower
Stamford Street
London
Telephone: 01-261 5980/6025/5998

Angling Times
Bretton Court
Bretton Centre
Peterborough
Cambridgeshire
Telephone: Peterborough 266222

Coarse Angler
281 Ecclesall Road
Sheffield
Yorkshire
Telephone: Sheffield 686132

The Coarse Fishing Handbook
– address as *Angling Times*.
Telephone: Peterborough 264666

Trout and Salmon and *Trout Fisherman*
– address and telephone number as
The Coarse Fishing Handbook.

Angling organisations

Anglers' Co-operative Association
Midland Bank Chambers
Westgate, Grantham
Lincolnshire
Telephone: Grantham 61008

Gives advice and financial support to
litigants taking proceedings against
polluters.

National Anglers' Council
5 Cowgate
Peterborough
Cambridgeshire
Telephone: Peterborough 54084

Promotes and protects the interests of
all angers – coarse, sea and game.
Free advisory service dealing with
legal and other matters.

National Federation of Anglers
Halliday House, 2 Wilson Street
Derby
Telephone: Derby 362000

Founded to protect, improve and
promote coarse fishing in Britain.

National anglers' council record weights

barbel 13 lb 12 oz (6.2 kg)
bleak 4 oz 4 dr (0.1 kg)
bream 13 lb 12 oz (6.2 kg)
carp (common) 44 lb (20 kg)
carp (crucian) 5 lb 10 oz 8 dr (2.6 kg)
chub 7 lb 6 oz (3.3 kg)
dace 1 lb 4 oz 4 dr (0.6 kg)
eel 11 lb 2 oz (5.0 kg)
grayling 3 lb 10 oz (1.6 kg)
gudgeon 4 oz 4 dr (0.1 kg)
perch 4 lb 14 oz 12 dr (2.2 kg)
pike 40 lb (18.1 kg)
roach 4 lb 1 oz (1.8 kg)
rudd 4 lb 8 oz (2.0 kg)
salmon 64 lb (29 kg)
tench 10 lb 1 oz 4 dr (4.6 kg)
trout (brown) 19 lb 9 oz 4 dr (8.9 kg)
trout (rainbow) 19 lb 8 oz (8.8 kg)
trout (sea) 20 lb (9.1 kg)
zander 17 lb 4 oz (7.8 kg)

Index

Subject index

barbel 7, 10, 12, 13, 14
bolt rig 20, *20*
bread crust 13
  paste 13
bream 8, 14, 16
buzzer 22

canal 15
carp 7, 14, 15, 16, 20
caster 12, 13, 14, 18
cheese paste 13
chub 10, 12, 13, 14
country code 8

dace 7
deadbait 15
disgorger 8

float 16
  antenna 18

Avon-type *12*
driftbeater *19*
sliding 17
stick 12, *12*
waggler 14, *14*, 15, 18, *19*
fly casting *21*
  fishing 10, 21–4
fly, dry 11, 22, 24
  wet 11

gravel-bed 12
gravel-pit 16–7, 18, 22
grayling 10, 11, 12
groundbait 15, 17, 18

hair rig 20, *20*
hook, barbless 8

keepnet 8
  knotless 7

lake 16
landing net, knotless 7
leger 13, *13*, 14, 17, 18
  river 13, *13*
  stillwater 18, *18*

maggot 11, 12, 14, 18

muddler 23, 24

nymph 22

pike 14
pond 16

quiver tip 13, 14, 17

redworm 11
reed bed 16
roach 7, 8, 13, 14, 17, 20
rudd 20

salmon 10
sink-and-draw method 15, *15*, 18
spate river 10, 12
sweetcorn 20
swimfeeder 12, 14

tarn 16
tench 7, 15, 16
trolling 24
trout 10, 11, 12, 21, 22, 23, 24
  brown 10

worm, gilt tail 11

Fishery index

C = coarse fishing;
G = game fishing

Abberton Reservoir (C) 146
Abbot Moss Lake (G) 47
Aled Isaf Reservoir (C) 88
Alwen Reservoir (C, G) 88
Ardingly Reservoir (G) 197
Argal Reservoir (G) 186
Arney River (C, G) 213
Attenborough South Lakes (C) 108
Avon Dam (G) 182

Bakethin Reservoir (C) 59
Bala Lake (C, G) 89
Balderhead Reservoir (G) 63
Ballinamallard River – Ballinamallard (C, G) 212
Bank House Fly Fishery (G) 54
Barton Broads (C) 123
Basingstoke Canal – Odiham to Byfleet (C) 171
Bassenthwaite Lake (C, G) 48
Beacon Tarn (C, G) 51
Bedfords Park Lake (C) 156
Bewl Bridge Trout Fishery (G) 198
Billing Aquadrome (C) 139

Black Dike Fishery (C) 201
Blackton Reservoir (G) 64
Blagdon Reservoir (G) 188
Blea Tarn (C, G) 51
Blea Water (C, G) 52
Blenheim Palace Lake (C) 149
Bolingey Lake (C) 184
Booton Clay Pit (C) 129
Bowyers Lake (C) 155
Brantry Lough (G) 216
Brenig Reservoir (G) 88
Broadlands Lake (C, G) 202
Bude Canal (C) 176
Burnhope Reservoir (G) 61
Burnmoor Tarn (C, G) 52
Burrator (G) 182

Cam or Cladagh River (C) 214
Castle Ashby Lakes (C) 139
Celyn Reservoir (G) 89
Chew Valley Lake (G) 188
Chiddingstone Castle Lake (C) 196
Chigborough (C) 147
Church Pool (C) 115
Clatworthy Reservoir (G) 189
Claverhambury Carp Lake (C) 155
Clay Lake (C, G) 219
Colebrook River (C) 214
College Reservoir (C) 185
Compton Verney Lake (C) 119

Coniston Water (C, G) 53
Coppermill Stream (C) 155
Cow Green Reservoir (G) 62
Crummock Water (C, G) 49
Cwmystradllyn Reservoir (G) 89

Damflask Reservoir (C, G) 85
Danebridge Fisheries (G) 57
Darracott Reservoir (C) 175
Deans Farm Fishery (C) 152
Derwent Water (C, G) 49
Dorchester Gravel Pit Complex (C) 168
Driffield Canal and Frodingham Beck (C, G) 82
Drift Reservoir (G) 186
Dungonnell Reservoir (G) 206
Dutson Water (C) 177

East Lyn River – Glenthorne and Watersmeet Fisheries (G) 174
Edgbaston Reservoir (C) 117
Edgefield Hall Lake (G) 128
Elan Valley Reservoirs (G) 91
Elliscales Ponds (C) 53
Elm Hag Lake (G) 81
Enagh Lough (C) 219
Esthwaite Water (C, G) 52
Exeter Canal – Exeter (C) 181

Eyebrook Reservoir (G) 132

Fairlop Lake (C) 157
Farmire Fishery (G) 78
Farthings Lake (C) 200
Fen Drayton Complex (C) 135
Fernworthy Reservoir (G) 179
Fishers Pond (C) 201
Folley River (C) 126
Fontburn Reservoir (G) 61
Fritton Decoy (C) 132

Gailey Trout Fishery (G) 116
Gladhouse Reservoir (G) 43
Grafham Water (G) 137
Grand Union Canal – Kings
    Langley (C) 151
Grand Union Canal – Tring (C)
    150
Grassholme Reservoir (G) 63
Great Pool (G) 116
Greenfield Lake/Beck (G) 74

Harrow Lodge Lake (C) 158
Hevingham Lakes (C) 129
Hay-A-Park (C) 79
Higham Farm Lakes (C) 100
High Dam (C, G) 52
Hill View Lakes (C, G) 124
Holly Bush Lane Fishery (C)
    170
Holwell Hyde Lake (C) 153
Hooks Marsh (C) 154
Hornsea Mere (C) 83
Hucklesbrook Trout Lake (G)
    193
Hury Reservoir (C, G) 64

Kennick Reservoir (G) 180
Kielder Water (G) 60
Kingfisher Lake (C) 202
Kings Weir Fishery (C) 154

Ladybower Reservoir (G) 99
Lakedown (G) 201
Lakeside Caravan Park (C) 145
Lake Vyrnwy (C) 109
Lapsley's Trout Fishery (G)
    192
Leighton Reservoir (G) 73
Leominstead Trout Fishery (G)
    203
Linford Lakes Complex (C, G)
    141
Little Paxton Fishery (C) 140
Llandegfedd Reservoir (G) 94
Llangorse Lake (C) 95
Llanllawddog Lake (G) 91
Llwyn-on Reservoir (G) 93
Llyn Alaw (G) 87
    Aled (C) 88
Llys-y-frân Reservoir (G) 91

Loch Ard (G) 40
    Arkaig (C, G) 34
    Avich (G) 38
    Awe (C, G) 39
    Bhac (G) 36
    Boardhouse (G) 28
    Borralie (G) 30
    Coldingham (G) 42
    Fitty (G) 42
    Harray (G) 28
    Hope (G) 30
    Hundland (G) 29
    Ken (C, G) 44
    Kirbister (G) 29
    Lanlish (G) 30
    Leven (G) 41
    Lindores (G) 41
    Lochindorb (G) 33
    Lochy (C, G) 34
    Lomond (C, G) 40
    Loyal (G) 31
    Lubnaig (C, G) 39
    Meadie (G) 32
    Naver (G) 31
    Ness (G) 33
    Quoich (G) 33
    Skeen (G) 43
    Staink (G) 31
    Stenness (G) 28
    Swannay (G) 29
    Tummel (C, G) 36
    Venachar (C, G) 40
    Woodhall (C, G) 43
Lockwood Beck Reservoir (G)
    64
Lough Creeve (C) 218
    Erne, Lower (C, G) 210
    Erne, Upper (C, G) 215
    Lee (G) 207
    Melvin (C, G) 211
    Scolban (C, G) 209
    Trout Fishery, The (G) 47
Loughton Lakes (C) 143
Lower Bann Canal (C) 206
Lower Slade Reservoir (C, G)
    173
Lower Tamar (C) 176

Malham Tarn (C, G) 74
Market Weighton Canal (C) 83
Mayesbrook Park Lakes (C)
    158
Mill Lough (C, G) 213

Nanpantan Reservoir (C) 109
Napton Reservoirs (C) 118
Navar Forest Lakes (C, G) 211
Nostell Priory Fisheries (C) 84

Old Bury Hill Lake (C) 171
Orkney Trout Lochs (G) 26
Overstone Solarium (C) 138

Packington Coarse Lakes (C,
    G) 118
Packington Trout Lakes (G)
    117
Pitsford Reservoir (G) 138
Pontsticill Reservoir (C, G) 93
Pooh Corner Trout Fishery (G)
    198
Poplars, The (C) 124
Porth Reservoir (G) 183

Queenford Lagoon (C) 167

Raphael Park Lake (C) 157
Red Tarn (G) 50
Ringstead Grange Trout
    Fishery (G) 137
River Ant – Ludham (C) 130
    Avon – Eckington (C) 119
    Avon – Evesham (C) 121
    Avon – Hampton Ferry (C)
    121
    Avon – Offenham (C) 120
    Avon – Stratford-on-Avon
    (C) 120
    Avon – Breamore (C) 191
    Avon – Downton (C) 190
    Avon – Royalty Fishery (C,
    G) 192
    Avon – Severals Fishery (C)
    191
    Blackwater –
    Blackwatertown (C, G)
    216
    Bure – South Walsham (C)
    131
    Bush – Bushmills to Armoy
    (G) 205
    Dane – near Middlewich (C)
    57
    Derwent – Belper (C, G) 101
    Derwent – Duffield (C, G) 101
    Don – Kintore (G) 35
    Eden – Carlisle (C, G) 47
    Erne – near Belleek (C, G)
    209
    Exe – Exeter (C) 180
    Frome – near Mordiford (C,
    G) 97
    Great Ouse – Buckingham
    (C) 143
    Great Ouse – Haversham (C)
    143
    Great Ouse – Littleport (C)
    127
    Great Ouse – Ten Mile Bank
    (C) 126
    Kennet – Manton Fishery
    (G) 169
    Lugg – Mordiford (C,G) 96
    Lugg – Moreton Water (C,
    G) 96

223

Medway – Maidstone (C) 196

Nene – Oundle (C) 133

Nidd – Knaresborough (C, G) 80

Nidd – Little Ribston (C, G) 81

Ribble – Great Mitton (C, G) 55

Ribble – Settle (G) 54

Roding – Buckhurst Hill (C) 156

Rother – near Rye (C) 200

Severn – Atcham (C) 113

Severn – Dinam Estate Fishery (C, G) 112

Severn – Hawbridge (C) 115

Severn – Llanidloes (C, G) 111

Severn – Penstrowed (C, G) 112

Severn – Ribbesford (C) 114

Severn – Ripple (C) 114

Spey – Aberlour (G) 32

Stour – Flatford Mill (C) 146

Stour – Throop Fishery (C) 194

Stour – White Hartwater (C) 190

Strule – near Omagh (C) 207

Swale – Richmond (C, G) 68

Tamar – Lifton (G) 178

Tay – Dalguise (G) 38

Teign – Drewsteignton (G) 179

Thames – Chiswick (C) 166

Thames – Dorchester (C) 162

Thames – Lechlade (C, G) 160

Thames – Maidenhead (C) 164

Thames – Marlow (C) 163

Thames – Molesey (C, G) 165

Thames – Newbridge (C) 161

Thames – Oxford (C) 161

Thames – Reading (C) 162

Thames – Richmond (C) 166

Thames – Tadpole Bridge (C) 160

Thames – Teddington (C) 166

Thames – Windsor (C) 164

Thames – weir pools, Lechlade to Benson (C) 160

Thames – weir pools, Benson to Henley (C) 162

Thames – weir pools, Henley to Windsor (C) 163

Thames – weir pools, Windsor to Molesey (C, G) 165

Thurne – Martham (C) 131

Tilt – Blair Atholl (G) 35

Trent – Attenborough (C) 103

Trent – Beeston Weir (G) 104

Trent – Clifton (C) 105

Trent – Clifton Grove (C) 104

Trent – Cromwell Weir (C) 108

Trent – Fiskerton (C) 106

Trent – Holme Pierrepont (C) 106

Trent – New Castle Fishery (C) 108

Trent – North Muskham (C) 107

Trent – Nottingham (C) 105

Trent – Stoke Bardolph (C) 106

Trent – Swarkestone (C) 103

Trent – Winthorpe (C) 107

Tummel – Pitlochry Dam (G) 37

Tummel – Pitlochry to Ballinluig (G) 37

Upper Bann – Portadown to Lough Neagh (C, G) 217

Ure – Bainbridge (G) 69

Ure – Boroughbridge (C) 72

Ure – Hawes (G) 69

Ure – Middleham (C, G) 70

Ure – Newby Hall (C, G) 71

Ure – Ripon (C, G) 71

Ure – Spennithorne (C) 70

Weaver – Church Minshull (C) 56

Welland – Market Deeping (C) 126

Wharfe – Bolton Abbey (G) 76

Wharfe – Grassington to Appletreewick (G) 75

Wharfe – Pool-in-Wharfedale (C, G) 76

Wharfe – Wetherby (C, G) 77

Wissey – Hilgay (C) 127

Wye – Hay-on-Wye (C) 95

Wye – Ross-on-Wye (C, G) 95

Roughan Lough (G) 208

Roughgrounds Farm Lake (C) 167

Royal Military Canal – Kenardington (C) 199

Rutland Water (G) 125

St Ives Complex (C) 133

Sankey to St Helens Canal (C) 56

Savay Lake (C) 151

Scaling Reservoir (G) 65

Selset Reservoir (G) 62

Semer Water (C, G) 73

Shillamill Lakes (C, G) 183

Siblyback Reservoir (G) 181

South Ockendon Carp Fishery (C) 147

Squabmoor (C) 181

Stithians Reservoir (G) 185

Stoneacres (C, G) 150

Stone Lake (C) 178

Sutton Bingham (G) 190

Swan Lake (C) 145

Swanton Morley Lakes (C) 128

Sway Lakes (C) 203

Talybont Reservoir (G) 92

Taverham Gravel Pits (C) 130

Teifi Pools (G) 90

Tenterden Trout Waters (G) 199

Theale Complex (C) 169

Thrapston Complex (C) 136

Three Lakes (C, G) 84

Tinney Waters (C) 177

Tittesworth Reservoir (G) 100

Tottiford Reservoir (G) 180

Trenestrall Lake (C) 184

Trilakes (C, G) 170

Tring Reservoirs (C) 150

Tunstall Reservoir (G) 61

Ullswater (C, G) 51

Ulverston Canal (C) 53

Upper Bann River (C, G) 217

Upper Tamar (G) 175

Usk Reservoir (G) 92

Vicarage Spinney Lake (G) 140

Washburn Valley Reservoirs (G) 77

Watendlath Tarn (G) 50

Waveney Valley Lakes (C) 144

Weir Wood Coarse Fishery (C) 197

Wentwood Reservoir (G) 94

Weybread Pits (C) 144

Whins Pond (G) 48

White Lough (C) 217

White Sheet Farm Trout Fishery (G) 194

Wimbleball (G) 174

Wistlandpound (G) 173

Wraysbury Gravel Pits (C) 152

Ynysyfro Reservoirs (G) 94